Techniques in
Computational Learning

CHAPMAN & HALL COMPUTING SERIES

Computer Operating Series
For micros, minis and mainframes
2nd edition
David Barron

Microcomputer Graphics
Michael Batty

The Pick Operating System
Malcolm Bull

ACCESS
The Pick enquiry language
Malcolm Bull

A Course of Programming in FORTRAN
3rd edition
V. J. Calderbank

Expert Systems
Principles and case studies
2nd edition
Edited by Richard Forsyth

Machine Learning
Principles and techniques
Edited by Richard Forsyth

Expert Systems
Knowledge, uncertainty and decision
Ian Graham and Peter Llewelyn Jones

Computer Graphics and Applications
Dennis Harris

Artificial Intelligence and Human Learning
Intelligent computer-aided instruction
Edited by John Self

Formal Concepts in Artificial Intelligence
Fundamentals
Rajjan Shinghal

Techniques in Computational Learning
An introduction
C.J. Thornton

Artificial Intelligence
Principles and applications
Edited by Masoud Yazdani

Techniques in Computational Learning

An introduction

C.J. Thornton
Lecturer
School of Cognitive and Computing Sciences
University of Sussex
Brighton

CHAPMAN & HALL COMPUTING
London · Glasgow · New York · Tokyo · Melbourne · Madras

Published by Chapman & Hall, 2–6 Boundary Row, London SE1 8HN

Chapman & Hall, 2–6 Boundary Row, London SE1 8HN, UK

Blackie Academic & Professional, Wester Cleddens Road, Bishopbriggs, Glasgow G64 2NZ, UK

Van Nostrand Reinhold Inc., 115 5th Avenue, New York NY10003, USA

Chapman & Hall Japan, Thomson Publishing Japan, Hirakawacho Nemoto Building, 6F, 1–7–11 Hirakawa-cho, Chiyoda-ku, Tokyo 102, Japan

Chapman & Hall Australia, Thomas Nelson Australia, 102 Dodds Street, South Melbourne, Victoria 3205, Australia

Chapman & Hall India, R. Seshadri, 32 Second Main Road, CIT East, Madras 600 035, India

First edition 1992

© 1992 C.J. Thornton

Printed in Great Britain by T.J. Press (Padstow) Ltd, Padstow, Cornwall

ISBN 0 412 40430 3   0 442 31574 0 (USA)

A catalogue record for this book is available from the British Library

Library of Congress Cataloging-in-Publication data available

Printed on permanent acid-free text paper, manufactured in accordance with the proposed ANSI/NISO Z 39.48-199X and ANSI Z 39.48-1984

Contents

13   Back–propagation   171

14   Learning to diagnose heart disease   192

15   Analysing internal representations   206

Preface

This book developed from notes for a course on Connectionist and Symbolic learning given at the School of Cognitive and Computing Sciences, University of Sussex (1986). It continued to evolve after I moved to Edinburgh and began to teach courses at the Department of Artificial Intelligence on Machine Learning and Connectionist Computing. It finally reached completion in the Autumn of 1991. The flavour of the book most strongly reflects the original audience: Sussex, Cognitive Science Students. In many cases these students are sophisticated programmers at ease with complex computational concepts but not particularly enthusiastic in learning new mathematical formalisms. My aim in writing this book was to find a way of presenting up-to-date material on computational learning in a manner that did not avoid the technicalities but confronted them from a computational viewpoint rather than a mathematical one. The book is, therefore, best suited to those who feel more at home with procedure definitions than they do with equations.

Aside from its emphasis on the computational approach, the book has a couple of other features worth mentioning. In particular, it has the unusual property of dealing with computational learning from both sides of the symbolic/connectionist divide. I had various reasons for choosing this hybrid approach. The main motivation however came out of me feeling that the two topics **rightly** go together. With the strong commonalities that exist between symbolic and connectionist learning algorithms I feel that the two areas should be treated as one. (This point is developed further in the final chapter.)

A second feature worth mentioning is the book's emphasis on the use of *examples* and *visualization*. In the majority of cases, I show the algorithms I introduce being put to work on 'real' learning problems, revealing the processing that takes place using pictures. Where I have found it impossible to use pictures I have tried to use plain English in preference to pseudo-code.

The book divides into its 'symbolic half' (chapters 2 to 8) and its 'connectionist half' (chapters 9 to 20). The first and last chapters are generic. Chapter 1 introduces the framework of ideas and concepts that I use throughout the book. Chapter 21 attempts to point out how many of the algorithms and models of learning explored in the body of the book effectively reduce to a single, statistical model of induction.

Within the core of the book there are clusters of chapters that should be read in sequence. Chapters 2, 3 and 4 all deal with the family of algorithms based on *candidate elimination*. Chapters 5 and 6 also form a sequence dealing with information theory, the classification algorithm and ID3. Chapters 7 and 8 are both fairly independent (dealing with conceptual clustering and explanation-based generalization) and might well be read out of sequence.

After Chapter 9 the book focusses on algorithms from the connectionist domain. Chapters 9 itself is essentially an introduction to connectionism. Chapters 10, 11 and 12 form a sequence and deal with simple, one-level nets.

Chapters 13, 14 and 15 extend this material in the obvious way . . . covering the back–propagation procedure and its applications. Chapter 16 is an exception and deals with the important but still relatively new topic of constructive induction. Chapter 17 is also something of an independent entity and deals with the WISARD net. Chapters 18 and 19 form a pair dealing with, respectively, the Hopfield net and the Boltzmann machine. Finally, Chapter 21 tries to bring together the connectionist and symbolic strands of the book to a single, not altogether optimistic, conclusion.

One of the attractions of computational learning as a subfield is its *accessibility*. Algorithms such as back–propagation and ID3 are not overly complex; most competent programmes should be able to run up implementations without losing sleep. I myself found the process of implementing, testing and analysing the algorithms that I was trying to describe in the book to be both helpful and *fun*. I doubt very much whether the book would ever have been finished had it not been for the involving properties of this hands-on activity. I therefore gratefully acknowledge the developers of the environment. Without Poplog, I doubt that I would have been able to develop the implementation packages, the graphics packages or the analysis packages on which the book depends. I would also like to thank the many students at Sussex and Edinburgh who have played a role in shaping the presented material.

I owe a huge debt to Peter Dayan who proof-read an earlier draft of the book and suggested many improvements. Lionel Moser also deserves thanks for turning out to be a copy editor at the eleventh hour. I am indebted to Randall Stark for discussions of abstruse topics (such as the binding problem) as well as help with more prosaic issues (such as C programming). I offer thanks for assistance and/or inspiration to Andy Clark, Guy Scott, Ben du Boulay, Harry Barrow, Jim Stone and Peter Ross. Finally I must thank Ruth who has never failed to deal effectively with any document that I cared to lay in front of her. All faults, errors and omissions that remain are entirely my own doing.

Diagrams reproduced with permission are as follows: Figure 2.1 – © 1986 Morgan Kaufmann Publishers. Reprinted with permission from R.S. Michalski, J.G. Carbonell, and T.M. Mitchell, *Machine Learning: An Artificial Intelligence Approach, Volume II*. Figure 10.7 reproduced with permission from *Machine Learning – Applications in expert systems and information retrieval* by Forsyth and Rada in 1986 by Ellis Horwood Limited, Chichester. Figure 2.1 from Patrick Henry Winston, *Artificial Intelligence*, © 1984, by Addison-Wesley Publishing Company, Inc., reprinted with permission of the publisher.

1

Introduction

1.1. How to avoid programming

As everyone who has ever programmed one will know, computers aren't all they are cracked up to be. Of course they are extremely useful but, all too often, the process of programming a computer to produce some particular type of behaviour turns out to be much harder than anticipated. This has been one of the great lessons of Artificial Intelligence (AI) research which is concerned with the writing of programs which produce 'intelligent' behaviour. Programming is hard! And in those cases where the behaviour we want does not have a clear, formal specification or theory, it may turn out to be beyond what can be achieved given available methods and resources.

Computational learning research provides a glimmer of a solution to this problem. Its primary concern is with the development of *learning algorithms*. These are programs which allow computers to acquire certain behaviours by learning learning rather than by being programmed. A computer running a learning program has a rudimentary ability to learn new behaviours. In some cases it may be a prerequisite of the learning that there is a 'teacher' or 'supervisor' who feeds in salient information. But in other cases, the learning may proceed in an entirely unsupervised way. The main point though is that in all cases no programming is required.

To get a flavour of how computational learning actually works let us look at an example. Imagine that we would like to have a computer capable of diagnosing whether or not someone has heart disease.[1] We might try to write the diagnosis program explicitly or, alternatively, we might try to use a computational learning algorithm to obtain the behaviour we want indirectly. There would be many ways of going about this. One possibility would be to use a learning algorithm that attempts to learn from

---

[1] There are obviously social and moral issues to be considered in connection with the construction of programs such as these. However, we will not consider these here.

examples. If we adopt this approach we have to obtain some examples of correct diagnoses.

Consider the data shown in Figure 1.1. These are taken from a survey of patients in Cleveland, USA.[2] Each line is divided up into two, bracketed parts. The first part is a list of symptoms or *attribute values* for a certain individual. The attribute values will not make much sense unless you happen to be familiar with the technicalities of of heart disease. However, it may be helpful to know that the attributes are — reading from left to right — sex, type of chest pain, blood pressure, low blood sugar, and resting ECG.[3] The second bracketed part contains either the word sick or healthy depending whether the individual turned out to have heart disease or not.

Each of these records forms an example of a correct diagnosis. Taken as a set they provide us with the examples that we need. Supplied to a suitable learning algorithm, these examples should enable the derivation of a general rule that allows correct diagnoses to be produced for *any* particular case, not just the ones explicitly shown. That is to say, it should enable the algorithm to make an *inductive leap* from the specific to

```
<[male asympt 160.0 false  hyp] [sick]>
<[male asympt 120.0 false  hyp] [sick]>
<[male notang 130.0 false norm] [healthy]>
<[fem  abnang 130.0 false  hyp] [healthy]>
<[male abnang 120.0 false norm] [healthy]>
<[fem  asympt 140.0 false  hyp] [sick]>
<[male asympt 130.0 false  hyp] [sick]>
<[male asympt 140.0 true   hyp] [sick]>
<[fem  abnang 140.0 false  hyp] [healthy]>
<[male notang 130.0 true   hyp] [sick]>
<[male abnang 120.0 false norm] [healthy]>
<[male angina 145.0 true   hyp] [healthy]>
```

Figure 1.1. Simple heart-disease training set.

---

[2] The data were derived from a survey carried out by Robert Detrano at the V.A. Medical Center, Long Beach and Cleveland Clinic Foundation. The pairs have been syntactically modified slightly for compatibility with other figures.

[3] Some of the attribute values are easily interpreted — e.g., male and fem — but others, such as asympt are more obscure. However, this is not a problem since, for present purposes, we do not need to know what the values mean.

the general case. The general rule should be able to take a totally novel case such as [male asympt 165.0 true hyp] and produce a correct diagnosis, i.e. [sick] or [healthy].

As it turns out, there are several learning algorithms we could apply. If we presented the examples to the *ID3* algorithm, for example (discussed in Chapter 6), then the algorithm would form a general rule which says that the individual is sick if the type of chest pain is asympt, but healthy provided that the type of chest pain is abnang, or if it is notang and the blood sugar is not low. This general rule yields correct diagnoses on all the examples in the set. If the general rule is a good one, then it will also yield correct diagnoses on other, novel cases.

Unfortunately, the fact that we can use computational learning quite successfully in this case does not mean that we can use it successfully in every case. In practice, learning algorithms are still limited to certain types of problems (such as diagnosis from attribute values). If we require the computer to produce some other type of behaviour then we will still have to use the traditional 'programming by hand' method.

1.2. Definitions of learning

Now that we have had a brief look at an example of computational learning, let us step back and approach the topic in a more systematic fashion. The convention, of course, is to begin with a definition. However, in the case of learning, this is not straightforward. Despite the best efforts of scientists in a variety of disciplines, our understanding of the process of learning is still fairly limited, and there is considerable disagreement over how the process should be defined. The following is a list of some of the definitions that have been suggested. Some refer to learning in biological organisms, some refer to learning in computers and some are generic.

*   Learning refers to the change in a subject's behaviour to a given situation brought about by his repeated experiences in that situation, provided that the behaviour change cannot be explained on the basis of native response tendencies, maturation, or temporary states of the subject (e.g., fatigue, drugs, etc.). (Hilgard and Bower, 1975)

*   Learning denotes the changes in [a] system that are adaptive in the sense that they enable the system to do the same task or tasks drawn from the same population more effectively the next time. (Simon, 1983)

- When a computer system improves its performance at a given task over time, without re-programming, it can be said to have learned something. (Forsyth and Rada, 1986)

- [Learning is] ... theory formation, hypothesis formation, and inductive inference. (Dietterich *et al.*, 1982)

- Learning is constructing or modifying representations of what is being experienced. (Michalski, 1986)

- Learning is making useful changes in our minds. (Minsky, 1988)

Quite a variety. Fortunately we are not concerned with learning in general but with *computational* learning in particular and this process is somewhat easier to pin down. Merely by virtue of the fact that computational learning is *computational* we know at least two things about it. We know that it is a computational process of some sort; and we know that whatever it creates (and we assume that any learning process produces something new) is some sort of computational representation or mechanism. As it turns out, in nearly all cases, computational learning aims to produce an implementation of a mapping between two sets of objects. This is called the *target mapping*. Although, since we can always regard a representation for a mapping as a definition of a mechanism which implements the mapping (i.e. takes certain objects as input and returns the objects they are associated with in the mapping), the target mapping is also sometimes called the *target mechanism*.

Adding to these comments the observation that the process which actually carries out the learning is called the *learner* we arrive at a basic model or definition of computational learning. This model says that computational learning is a process in which a *learner* produces a representation of a *target mapping* working from training information derived from some *environment*. This model is illustrated in Figure 1.2. Of course it is a very general model. But is it general enough? In particular, does it cover all the different varieties of computational learning? Let us move on to consider what these are.

1.3. Research paradigms in computational learning

At the present time computational learning research divides up roughly into three different areas. Firstly, there is the area known as *machine learning*. This investigates computational learning using symbolic algorithms and is often seen as originating with Patrick Winston's work on the *ARCH* program (Winston, 1975). Secondly, there

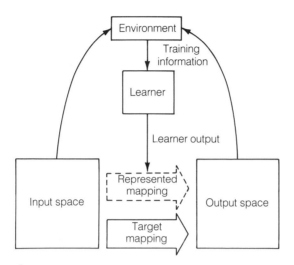

Figure 1.2. A basic model of computational learning.

is the area known as *connectionism*, sometimes called *parallel-distributed processing* or *neural networks*. This investigates computational learning using networks of simple, neuron-like units and originated with work by Rosenblatt and others carried out in the late 1950s and early 1960s. (Connectionism passed through a dark era in the 1970s but mushroomed in the 1980s following the popularization of algorithms such as *back-propagation*.) Finally, there is the area known as *genetic algorithms*. This investigates learning and other types of computation using processes akin to genetic mutation.

In this book we shall concentrate on techniques drawn from machine learning and connectionism. For clarity we will refer to the former as *symbolic learning techniques* and to the latter as *connectionist learning techniques*. For a good introduction to the related field of *genetic algorithms* see Goldberg (1989).

The basic model in which we view learning as the process by which a learner produces a representation of a target mapping covers learning in all three paradigms. It usually yields a better fit when dealing with symbolic learning since it is quite often the case in connectionist learning that the learner and the target mapping are inextricably bound together. Nevertheless, the basic model does provide us with a useful reference point from which to begin our investigations.

1.4. The target mapping

Let us consider the target mapping in more detail. As we have said, the learner's goal is to produce a representation of the target mapping. But how does the learner know what the target mapping is? The answer is that the learner is provided with information about it. In the simplest and most common case — exemplified above — the learner is given information about the target mapping in the form of examples. Each example shows a single association in the mapping. Putting it another way, each example shows what *output* should be returned by the target mechanism for a given *input*.

When the learner is presented with explicit input/output examples in this way, the learning process is said to be *supervised* and to involve *learning from examples*. The process is called supervised because it is reminiscent of the situation in which a teacher (or 'supervisor') helps a human being to learn a new concept by providing explicit examples of that concept.

In contrast to supervised learning we have *unsupervised learning*. In this approach, the learner does not receive explicit examples of desired input/output associations. Rather it has, embodied within it, some more general notion about the way in which inputs should be mapped on to outputs. Very often, this notion is simply the idea that inputs which are similar to one another should be grouped together and associated with the same output. Thus unsupervised learning is often used where we want to discover how some data divide up into similarity groups.

Although it is common to make a clean distinction between supervised and unsupervised learning, it is important to see that there is a continuum of possibilities between the two cases. An example of an intermediate case would be a situation in which the learner is not given explicit examples as such, but rather information that allows fairly accurate examples to be constructed or inferred. This would be a case of *near-supervised learning*. As a general rule, as the information (about the desired input/output associations) provided to the learner becomes relatively more explicit, so the learning becomes relatively more supervised.

1.5. Supervised learning

Consider a simple example in which we want a learner to produce a target mechanism which computes some kind of logical function. We will assume that the target mechanism should accept and return sequences of truth values where 1 = true, and 0 = false. If we are using a supervised learning algorithm then we have to provide examples. Let us assume that we give the learner three examples of desired input/output behaviour:

```
<[0  0]  [0]>
<[0  1]  [0]>
<[1  1]  [1]>
```

We have laid these examples out in the same way we laid out the examples for the heart-diagnosis problem. Each line shows one example formatted as a bracketed pair. The input for the example is the first component in the pair and the desired output (also called the *target output* or just *target*) is the second component. Each given example is called a *training pair* and the entire set is the *training set*. The training set forms a subset of the target mapping, i.e. it shows a subset of the input/output associations that are implemented by the target mechanism.

In some cases, we can provide a training set to a learner all in one go. In other cases, we have to provide it on a pair by pair basis. In the latter case, the passing in of a particular training pair is called a *presentation*. Whether we are presenting training pairs all in one go or pair by pair, a complete pass through the entire training set is called a *sweep* or an *epoch*. In the present case, a complete epoch would involve presenting the pair `<[0  0]  [0]>`, then the pair `<[0  1]  [0]>` and finally the pair `<[1  1] [1]>`.

1.5.1. Input and output spaces

There are a number of useful technical terms that allow us to talk about the structure and character of the training set and target mapping. First of all, the set of all possible training inputs is known as the *input space* (or in some cases *input language*) while the set of all possible training outputs is the *output space* (or *output language*).[4] In the present case we are thinking about a target mapping in which the inputs are 2-tuples[5] of truth values. There are four possible inputs corresponding to the four possible ways we can pair up truth values. These are:

---

[4] We use 'input language' and 'output language' in those cases where the objects are, or resemble, linguistic entities.

[5] An *n*–tuple is just a sequence of *n* items.

```
[0 0]
[0 1]
[1 0]
[1 1]
```

The output space is just the set of possible 1-tuples:

```
[1]
[0]
```

When inputs and outputs are simple sequences of values it is common to talk about *input vectors* and *output vectors*. We would then refer to a particular element in an input vector as a *component*. For example, we might say that the second component of the input vector [1 0] is 0. In connectionist work input and output vectors typically contain real numbers and can therefore be thought of as representing rays or points in an n-dimensional space (where n is the number of components in the relevant vectors). To keep the terminology simple, the word 'vector' tends to be used equivocally to refer to both the sequence of real numbers and the ray or line that it defines in the relevant space.

1.6. The behaviour of the learner

1.6.1. Hypothesis spaces

As we have said, in supervised learning (which is the most common form of computational learning) we present the learning algorithm with a training set of examples. Each example forms an input/output pair, i.e. it shows what output should be associated with (i.e. returned for) a given input. When the algorithm receives the examples, its task is to construct a representation of the target mapping. This representation should enable desired (correct) outputs to be returned for inputs which do not appear in the training set.

Of course, depending on the learning algorithm, the representation which is constructed will vary. As we will see, a connectionist learning algorithm may construct a representation which takes the form of a set of connection weights in a network. A symbolic learner on the other hand might construct a representation which takes the form of a symbolic data structure. However, from the conceptual point of view, we can think of the learner as trying to select a satisfactory representation from the set of all representations to which it has access. These candidate representations are called *hypotheses* and the entire set of possible hypotheses is called the *hypothesis space*. Using this terminology, we can describe supervised learning as a process in which the learner *searches* through a space of hypotheses for one which 'agrees' with all the examples in the training set.

What would this mean in the context of the example training set shown above? In a simple example we might have a learner that uses hypotheses based on simple patterns such as [# 1] and [0 #]. In these patterns the hash character is a wild-card that matches anything. Thus, a pattern such as [0 #] matches [0 0] and [0 1], while the pattern [# #] matches any 2-tuple at all. Patterns like these could be used to define hypotheses in a number of ways but a simple approach would be to say that a given hypothesis maps all inputs which match its underlying pattern on to 1 and all the rest on to 0. The pattern [1 #], then, 'defines' the mapping:

```
<[0 0] [0]>
<[0 1] [0]>
<[1 0] [1]>
<[1 1] [1]>
```

Supervised learning can now be achieved straightforwardly, by searching through the whole space of possible hypotheses (patterns), checking each one against the whole training set to see if it agrees on every example. If the training set is the one we used before, namely:

```
<[0 0] [0]>
<[0 1] [0]>
<[1 1] [1]>
```

then the search will reveal that only the patterns [1 1] and [1 #] define hypotheses which agree with the training set on all examples. If we add the training pair <[1 0] [1]> to the training set, then there is only one *satisfactory* hypothesis (i.e. one hypothesis which agrees with all the training pairs) and this is based on the pattern [1 #].

1.6.2. Bias

Carrying out supervised learning by blindly searching through the entire space of possible hypotheses is a feasible approach where the total number of hypotheses is small. But in practice the hypothesis space is rarely small. Typically it is rather large; in some cases, it is infinitely large. This means that blind hypothesis-space search is not generally effective and is hardly ever used in practice. But if blind search is infeasible, the only alternative is *guided* search; and if the learner is to carry out a guided search, then it must have some way of *knowing* where in the space it should look. In other words it must be guided by some knowledge about the problem being addressed.

A learner whose search of the hypothesis space is guided in this way is said to have a *bias*.[6] The effectiveness of the knowledge in leading the learner towards a satisfactory hypothesis is characterized in terms of its strength and its correctness. If the knowledge permits a relatively large number of hypotheses to be excluded from the search, the bias is said to be *strong*. Otherwise it is *weak*. If the knowledge causes only unsatisfactory hypotheses to be excluded then the bias is *correct*. Obviously, an effective bias is one which is both strong and correct since this will take the learner to a satisfactory hypothesis with a minimum amount of searching.

Bias is obtained by giving the learner some knowledge about the problem. There are various ways this can be done, as we will see later on. In general, the more knowledge the learner has, the more effective the bias. So the degree of bias is a measure of the amount of knowledge embodied in the learner. A simple way of measuring the *strength* of the bias involves looking at the number of hypotheses which are excluded by it. The more incorrect hypotheses that are excluded, the more effective the bias. In the extreme case, the knowledge allows *all* incorrect hypotheses to be excluded. In this case — if the bias is correct — the learner necessarily selects a correct hypothesis at its first attempt!

In the example described above, where we have a learner exhaustively searching the hypothesis space, we might try to strengthen the bias by exploiting any available background knowledge about the domain. If we have reason to believe that a satisfactory representation will always make some distinctions between different inputs we might want to exclude the cover-all pattern [# #] from the learner's repertoire. This would increase the strength of the learner's bias very slightly without making it any less correct. If we wanted to substantially increase the strength of the bias we would have to remove several patterns from the repertoire.

1.6.3. Error and error rate

In ideal situations, the learner will succeed in building a perfect representation of the target mapping. But usually the representation is imperfect and does not yield the target output for all possible inputs. In these cases we want to have some way of measuring the performance of the representation constructed. A common way of doing this involves measuring the *error rate* of the chosen hypothesis. This is just the proportion of inputs for which the mechanism produces the wrong output, typically expressed as a percentage. For example, if the training set is:

---

[6] From the statistical point of view we would say that the learner is affected by *Bayesian priors*.

```
<[0 0] [0]>
<[0 1] [0]>
<[1 0] [0]>
<[1 1] [1]>
```

and the selected hypothesis is [1 #], then the mechanism deals with all the inputs correctly except for [1 0] which it maps on to 1. The hypothesis yields one incorrect output out of four cases. Thus we can say that the error rate is 25%.

A more revealing way of testing the performance of the current hypothesis is to evaluate it on cases which are not included in the training set. A set of pairs which are used in this way is called the *testing set*. Usually, error-rate figures are quoted for performance on a testing set rather than on the training set.

In connectionist learning it often makes sense to compare the numeric difference between components of actual outputs and components of target outputs. In these cases the concept of *mean error* is of use. If the mechanism maps inputs on to outputs as follows:

```
[0 0] → [0.1]
[0 1] → [0]
[1 0] → [0.8]
[1 1] → [0.99]
```

then we can compute the mean error by working out the average difference between corresponding components of actual and desired outputs. The mean error in this case is:

$$\frac{0.1 + 0 + 0.8 + 0.01}{4} = 0.23$$

There are other ways of computing mean error. A commonly used variant in connectionism is the *root-mean-squared error* or RMSE. The formula for this is:

$$\sqrt{\sum_i (L_i - T_i)^2}$$

Here L_i is the *i*th component of the actual output and T_i is the *i*th component of the target output, and *i* iterates over all component positions.

1.6.4. Compression

Aside from the performance of hypotheses we are also interested in their complexity. More complex hypotheses are more costly to represent and use. They may also be very difficult to interpret. The problem is that complexity is hard to measure. The complexity of a given hypothesis seems to depend on how it is implemented, and on what we regard as its countable components. For example, imagine that we have a hypothesis that takes the form of a network structure. How should we measure the size of this hypothesis? Should we treat it as a genuine network of nodes? If so, should we estimate the size in terms of the number of nodes or the number of connections between them? Should we take account of the fact that the network is actually simulated inside a conventional computer? If so, should we count the number of procedures in the program that simulates the network? Or should we count the number of binary words in the compiled version of the program?

Ideally there would be a way of estimating the size of a given hypothesis in absolute terms. This would allow us to compare the absolute size of the hypothesis with the size of the training set (i.e. the number of training pairs) and find out how much *compression* is obtained as we pass from the training set to the covering hypothesis. But, as yet, there is no general agreement as to what such a measure would be. Therefore there is no absolutely satisfactory way of computing the complexity of a hypothesis.

1.7. Basic learning strategies

The question of how particular learning algorithms actually work is addressed in the main body of the book. However, it may be helpful at this point to take a brief look at some of the strategies and principles that underlie symbolic and connectionist learning. There is, of course, a vast range or *space* of connectionist and symbolic learning algorithms but there is a surprising amount of commonality between the two fields.

1.7.1. The classical algorithm

The evolution of ideas that has led, ultimately, to the development of effective computational learning began at least two thousand years ago in Greek philosophy and, in particular, in the writings of Aristotle. Aristotle was not particularly interested in the process of mechanical learning but he was interested in the mental representation of *concepts.* And his theory of concept representation[7] provides us with one of the simplest learning algorithms.

Aristotle suggested that the representation of a concept in the mind must be a *summary description* of the entire class of things covered by the concept. He thought that this representation might be made up from the set of attribute values which are shared between all members of the class. He said that these values must be *singly necessary* (i.e. compulsory in all valid members of the concept) and *jointly sufficient* (i.e. in combination, a valid way of defining the concept). What is the justification for this?

Consider the concept *chair*. We might say that for something to count as a chair it has to have a seat, some legs and a back. This gives us three, singly necessary attributes, namely 'has seat', 'has legs' and 'has back'. Because each of these values is singly necessary, the complete set is jointly sufficient to define the concept. The set defines the concept since we can very easily use it to decide whether an arbitrary object is a chair. All we have to do is go through the set checking off each attribute in turn.

The process of deriving a list of shared attribute values yields a concept definition. Thus it forms a rudimentary *learning algorithm*. As such, it goes under a variety of names. But is often called the *classical algorithm* due to its historical origins and this is the name that we will use here.

1.7.2. Similarity-based learning versus knowledge-based learning

Underlying the classical learning algorithm is the notion of *class similarity*, i.e. the idea that the members of a given class (concept) tend to be more similar to each other than to non-members of the class. The word 'similarity' might mean a number of different things. But in general it denotes the degree of attribute sharing. The more attributes two objects have in common the more similar they are.

This basic idea of class similarity has led to the development of a whole range of algorithms that all function in roughly the same, similarity exploiting manner. The general strategy is called *similarity-based learning* or SBL. It is essentially a two-step process. First we try to find out how the objects in a given class are similar to each other, or alternatively how they differ from objects in other classes. Then we construct a representation of that class by somehow capturing the central tendency of the similarities/differences.

The similarity-based approach has been very successful both in symbolic learning and in connectionist learning. An early case of SBL in symbolic learning is

---

[7] Which appears to be a descendant of an earlier theory associated with Socrates.

Winston's ARCH program which attempted to define a class using an extension of the classical algorithm. The definitions produced not only specified shared features but they also specified features which a valid member of the class *must not* have. An early case of SBL in connectionist learning was Rosenblatt's *perceptron*. This was a simple neural network architecture in which the definitions were essentially numerical formulae, i.e. discriminant functions (as such they summarized inter-class *differences* rather than intra-class similarities).

Since the focus in similarity-based learning is firmly on the similarities in the data, SBL is often referred to as *data-driven* or *empirical* learning. A complementary form of learning is *knowledge-driven* learning. Here, the learning algorithm embodies a rich store of knowledge about what has to be learned and so the learning process is perceived as driven by the knowledge rather than by the data. A well-known example of knowledge-driven learning is *explanation-based learning* or EBL (see Chapter 8). In EBL, the aim is to refine the internal knowledge by seeing in what respects it applies to new inputs.

Unfortunately, in knowledge-driven learning we face the very difficult problem of ensuring that the knowledge which is actually driving the learning process is correct. In data-driven or empirical learning we face the problem of how to proceed in the case where the concepts which must be learned are *not* evidenced in the similarities among the relevant objects. For example, imagine trying to learn the concept of *chair* from descriptions of chairs which list only attributes such as colour, year of manufacture and age. The similarities between chairs are simply not expressed in these attributes so any attempt to capture the *chair* concept in terms of these attributes must fail. At the end of the book we will note how techniques of *constructive induction* can be used to overcome — to some degree — the limitations of the similarity-based approach in empirical learning.

1.8. Basic learning scenarios: concept learning and sequence prediction

We have now fleshed out our basic model of learning in a number of ways. The three main components in this model are the *training set*, the *learner* and the *target mapping*. The training set is a set of examples taken from the target mapping while the learner is an algorithm that searches a space of hypotheses for one which agrees with the training set on all inputs. The model is totally general in the sense that it covers the supervised learning of any deterministic mapping. We have already looked at an example involving the learning of a mapping which associates descriptions of individuals with medical diagnoses and a mapping between sets of truth values. What other possibilities are there?

One of the simplest cases is that of *concept learning*. Given the model we have introduced, concept learning is learning which occurs when the target mapping implements the *membership function* for a particular concept. For example, consider the training set that is shown in Figure 1.3.[8] The inputs, here, are descriptions of weather conditions and the outputs are either [yes] or [no]. Various target mappings might underlie the training set. But a credible possibility is a mapping that associates inputs with [yes] only if they describe a set of weather conditions satisfactory for an outdoor activity, e.g., playing golf.[9] Under this interpretation, the target mapping is effectively just the membership function for the concept 'good-conditions-for-playing-golf'.[10] Thus, a learner that forms a representation of the target mapping is, in some sense, learning a concept.

A generalization of concept learning is *classification learning*. In classification learning we have an arbitrary number of possible outputs but each one is a label for a particular class. The heart-disease training set, in which the possible outputs are [sick] and [healthy] is a case in point. Here [sick] can be thought of as a label for the

OUTLOOK	TEMP	PRESSURE	WINDY	CLASS
<[sunny	hot	high	no]	[yes]>
<[sunny	hot	high	yes]	[yes]>
<[overcast	hot	high	no]	[no]>
<[rain	mild	high	no]	[no]>
<[rain	cool	normal	no]	[no]>
<[rain	cool	normal	yes]	[yes]>
<[overcast	cool	normal	yes]	[no]>
<[sunny	mild	high	no]	[yes]>
<[sunny	cool	normal	no]	[no]>
<[rain	mild	normal	no]	[no]>
<[sunny	mild	normal	yes]	[no]>
<[overcast	mild	high	yes]	[no]>
<[overcast	hot	normal	no]	[no]>
<[rain	mild	high	yes]	[yes]>

Figure 1.3. Good-conditions-for-golf training set.

---

[8] Adapted from Quinlan (1986).

[9] This interpretation of the training set was suggested to me by Ah Chung Tsoi.

[10] Technically, a concept membership function should return a truth value. But this is not an obstacle provided that we interpret [yes] as meaning true, and [no] as meaning false.

class of inputs which describe sick individuals while [healthy] is a label for the class of inputs which describe healthy individuals. Of course, since there are only two possible outputs we might just as well have used [yes] and [no] and treated the problem as a concept learning problem.

An example of a training set for a more realistic classification learning problem is shown in Figure 1.4.[11] The underlying target mapping here associates descriptions of animals with a label indicating their species. Any representation that allows outputs to be produced from inputs effectively permits animals (or at least descriptions of animals) to be classified according to their species membership. Thus a learner which learns a representation for the target mapping is, in some sense, learning a classification scheme.

Another variant of the generic learning problem is the *sequence prediction* task. Consider the training set in Figure 1.5. Here, the single component of each input vector specifies a value in the sequence while the target output is simply the next value in the sequence.[12] A hypothesis which returned the correct output for any input would, in this case, effectively allow us to predict the continuation of the sequence from any given starting position. Thus finding a satisfactory solution to this sort of learning problem is equivalent to solving a sequence prediction task.

Of course there are special properties of sequence prediction problems which appear

BEAK	COLOUR	LEGS	SIZE	TAIL	WINGS	HAIRY	TRUNK	CLASS
<[yes	black	2	undef	yes	yes	undef	undef]	[blackbird]>
<[undef	brown	2	undef	yes	no	yes	undef]	[chimp]>
<[yes	golden	2	undef	yes	yes	undef	undef]	[eagle]>
<[undef	grey	4	big	no	no	undef	yes]	[elephant]>
<[yes	brown	2	big	yes	yes	undef	undef]	[falcon]>
<[undef	black	2	undef	no	no	undef	undef]	[gorilla]>
<[undef	grey	2	undef	yes	no	undef	undef]	[lemur]>
<[undef	brown	2	small	no	no	undef	undef]	[man]>
<[yes	brown	2	small	yes	yes	undef	undef]	[sparrow]>

Figure 1.4. Animal-classification training set.

---

[11] The training set is adapted from Muggleton (1987).

[12] The rule underlying the sequence is $n_{i+1} = (n_i + 1) \times 2$.

```
<[1]    [4]>
<[4]    [10]>
<[10]   [22]>
<[22]   [46]>
<[46]   [94]>
```

Figure 1.5. Sequence-prediction training set.

to be particularly suited to certain types of learning mechanism. Thus a learning mechanism for sequence prediction problems may fail completely if presented with a straightforward concept learning problem. And a learning mechanism for concepts may do very badly if presented with a sequence prediction problem.

1.9. Theoretical issues

1.9.1. Learnability

One of the problems which has most exercised researchers interested in learning is the question of *learnability*, i.e. the question of deciding when a particular learning problem has a solution. The classic contribution in this area was provided by David Hume in the eighteenth century. Hume was not directly interested in the problem of learning; he was more interested in the process of *induction* and particularly in its use as a basic, scientific method. However, his conclusions apply equally well to learning.

Francis Bacon had noted that the process of *induction by enumeration* underpins scientific progress. Induction by enumeration is what happens when, after observing that something is the case a certain number of times, we conclude that it is *always* the case. We are using it, for example, when we conclude, after having observed a large number of white swans, that all swans are white. We are also using it, in some sense, when we apply the classical learning algorithm since in concluding that all swans are white, we are effectively saying that 'white' is a singly necessary attribute for something which is to count as a swan.

Hume pointed out that this, or any related method of induction, is essentially unsound. No matter how many times we observe that something is the case, it is always possible that the very next observation we make will refute the rule that it is always the case. The sun has always risen in the east but tomorrow it *may* not do so.

Every swan we have ever seen may be white but the very next one we see *may* be some other colour. (There are black swans in Australia.) In an infinite universe, anything is possible, including the refutation of all general rules. Thus, Hume concluded, scientific knowledge cannot have a secure foundation.

In the philosophical context this problem is known as the *problem of induction*. And it appears to have dire consequences for the validity of scientific knowledge. The fact that there can be no secure foundation for inductive generalizations in an infinite universe suggests that any scientific method which relies on this procedure is necessarily unsound. Many philosophers have attempted to produce a solution to this dilemma. Karl Popper, for example, suggested that to avoid it science should proceed by *falsifying* incorrect hypotheses rather than by accumulating inductive generalizations. The fact that incorrect theories can, in some cases, be falsified with absolute certainty means — for Popper — that any science which proceeds via a series of falsifications is on a secure foundation. However, this is more of an in-principle solution rather than an in-practice one. Once an incorrect theory has been falsified, science has to provide a new candidate; and the provision of this is generally guided by unsound, inductive generalization. So, rather than disposing of the problem of induction, Popper's falsificationist doctrine may simply sweep it under the carpet.

1.9.2. Identification in the limit and PAC learning

The problem of induction is a trying dilemma. However, its existence certainly does not imply that satisfactory computational learning is impossible. The fact that in an infinite input space we cannot be *certain* that a particular learner has produced the correct hypothesis does not imply that the learner can *never* produce the correct hypothesis. It may well do so. In fact, Gold (1967) has provided a framework in which a learner is viewed as having successfully solved a learning problem (in an infinite input space) if, after seeing a certain sequence of training pairs, it settles on a certain hypothesis and never changes its mind thereafter. The learner in this case is said to have identified the target concept *in the limit*. This notion of identification in the limit, in combination with the concept of *identification by enumeration* (Gold, 1967), plays a central role in formal studies of inductive inference.

More recently Valiant (1984, 1985) has presented a model which deals with the issue of learnability from the probabilistic perspective. In this model a mechanism is said to have learned a concept if the hypothesis it has settled on returns an output which is *probably approximately correct* for any given input. The model is called the *PAC-learning* model (after 'Probably Approximately Correct') and is also used extensively in theoretical studies of induction.

1.10. Summary and concluding comments

This chapter has introduced the framework that will be used throughout this book for the purposes of describing and analysing computational learning methods. Because the book aims to deal with both connectionist learning and machine learning, the framework is effectively a hybrid. Some of the concepts introduced belong more exclusively to one domain than to the other. For example the concept of bias is, perhaps, more common in symbolic learning than in connectionist learning, while the notion of target mapping has the opposite character. However, most terms and concepts are common to the two fields.

This chapter has also looked at the way in which a learning problem can be construed as a classification task, a concept learning task or a sequence prediction task depending on the interpretation of the training pairs. When we look at a task in a certain way (e.g., as a concept learning task) we are opening up the possibility of viewing learning algorithms as models of the way in which this type of learning takes place in biological organisms. This is, of course, an entirely optional extension. In saying that an algorithm solves a concept learning task, say, we are not committing ourselves to the view that the algorithm forms a plausible model of concept learning. But we do have the option to consider the algorithm in that light.

This optional, psychological dimension to the enterprise of computational learning has both an up side and a down side. On the up side we have the benefits that accrue as a result of there being a strong, cross-fertilization of ideas between those approaching computational learning from a purely engineering perspective and those approaching it from a psychological perspective. On the down side, there are the misunderstandings that arise when work of an engineering or theoretical character is wrongly interpreted as having some kind of psychological significance. Of course, with a little bit of care we can reap the benefits of the up side without running into the sand on the down side. All that is required is to keep firmly in mind the distinction between the formal notion of computational learning and the less well-defined notion of psychological learning.

1.11. Health warning

In the present chapter we have taken a few liberties with the exposition — adopting certain habits and practices which should, ideally, have been properly introduced first. In particular we have adopted the widespread practice of using the word 'concept' equivocally to mean at least three different things. First, we have used the word in a Platonic sense; e.g., we have talked about the concept of *chair*. When used this way, the word 'concept' refers to some purely abstract entity which is assumed to be separate and independent of any particular entity. Second, we have used the word to refer to the internal representation or definition of a concept; e.g., we have talked about objects being covered by a given concept. Finally, we have used the word to refer to the class of things which the concept covers; e.g., we have talked about things being 'in' a given concept. This level of abuse will be continued throughout the book and the reader should be on the lookout to see which of the three meanings is intended in a given case. The payoff is a small but important reduction in the laboriousness of the language.

1.12. Further reading

A number of textbooks provide good introductory material which could serve as background reading for this chapter. For example, see the first chapter of Forsyth (1989) or of Langley *et al.* (1987). The introductory chapter of Holland *et al.* (1986) approaches the topic of learning from a more psychological perspective, dealing with some of the behaviourist work which forms by far the largest body of research on the topic of learning. Those comfortable with the artificial intelligence perspective might prefer to look at the introductory section of Dietterich *et al.* (1982). This provides a particularly good introduction to symbolic approaches. On the question of the metaphysical nature of concepts, a good starting point is Russell's (1946, Chapter XV) discussion on Plato's Theory of Ideas. For further introductory material on Aristotle's theory of concept representation see Sowa (1984). There is of course a vast philosophical literature which bears on the topic of concepts. But Sowa's material has the advantage of being explicitly computational.

The framework introduced draws on a great number of texts. It borrows particularly from Rendell (1986), Mitchell (1980), McClelland *et al.* (1986), from Forsyth's (1989) 'framework' article, and from Utgoff's 'bias' model (Utgoff and Mitchell, 1982; Utgoff, 1986b). See also Utgoff (1986a), Langley and Carbonell (1986), and Thornton (1989). For more on inductive inference, the problem of sequence prediction and of rule induction see the excellent survey article by Angluin and Smith (1983). Another useful reference for the general problem of sequence prediction is Dietterich and Michalski (1986). For further details on the topic of measuring the effectiveness of inductive bias consult Haussler (1988).

1.13. Problems

(1) How might we define computational learning? What is the process useful for?

(2) By what names do we normally refer to the mechanisms involved in a computational learning scenario? How many mechanisms are involved?

(3) How should one decide whether a learning experiment involves supervised learning or unsupervised learning?

(4) What is the difference between an output and an output value?

(5) How long does an epoch last?

(6) What does it mean to say that a learning mechanism explores a 'space' of hypotheses?

(7) Imagine a computational learner that is tending to terminate before discovering a satisfactory hypothesis. In what way should we try to modify its bias?

(8) In what cases will it be important to ensure that the bias of a learner is strong?

(9) What is the difference between concept learning, classification learning and sequence prediction?

(10) What are the distinguishing features of the Aristotelian concept representation and what are the main steps in the classical learning algorithm?

(11) Imagine that a computational learner is given access to a function for evaluating the degree to which outputs approximate target outputs. The function takes an input and an actual output and returns a number between 0 and 1. Higher values indicate that the actual output is a better approximation of the target output for the given input. Is the learner supervised? If not, how should we describe it?

(12) Does similarity-based learning produce generalization effects? What are they and in what circumstances might they be of benefit?

(13) What problems are encountered when we try to measure the complexity of hypotheses? Suggest a method for deriving *estimates* of complexity.

(14) What is Hume's *problem of induction*? What significance does it have for computational learning?

(15) In what cases would we say that a learner identifies the target hypothesis 'in the limit'?

(16) Define a simple set of features for describing students and, using these features, provide a training set for the concept of 'college student'.

2

Candidate elimination and the version space

2.1. Historical background

It is difficult to identify the precise point at which machine learning came into being. However, the publication of Samuel's (1959, 1967) work on learning algorithms for the game of checkers was an important breakthrough as was the work by Patrick Winston (1975) on concept learning. Winston's work was concerned with the problem of vision and, like many early vision researchers, he concentrated primarily on developing mechanisms for recognizing blocksworld[1] configurations represented as line drawings. He was interested in the question of how certain classes of configuration (e.g., arches) could be recognized. This led him to consider the ways in which definitions of such classes could be derived automatically from sets of positive and negative examples, i.e. in how concept representations could be learned.

Winston described a mechanism that learned concepts by looking for relationships between semantic network representations of blocksworld configurations. Similarity-based processes were particularly important in his formulation. One such process involved finding and exploiting commonalities among structural descriptions for the same type of configuration. This enabled his system to discover the fact, for instance, that all positive examples of arches exhibit certain structural relationships between components, e.g., they have two columns supporting a lintel of some sort. Having extracted this commonality, the system could then use it in the representation of the arch concept.

The other major process involved finding significant differences between positive

---

[1] See Winston (1975) or Winston (1984) for more on the blocksworld.

and negative examples (see Figure 2.1). This procedure particularly exploited a type of example known as a *near miss*. It enabled the system to enhance the representation of a concept so as to enable certain examples to be definitely classified as negatives on the basis of single, 'giveaway' attributes. The two main processes in Winston's method are *generalization* and *specialization* of the underlying representation. The system effectively generalizes the representation so as to cover the positives and specializes it so as to exclude the negatives. If examples are presented incrementally, then a new positive example triggers generalization and a new negative example triggers specialization.[2]

The idea that we can decompose learning into two distinct but related processes — generalization and specialization — has become a fundamental principle in symbolic learning. Although, in Winston's formulation, the description of the two processes is fairly complex, subsequent formulations have provided simpler descriptions of the way in which generalization and specialization can work together to produce a satisfactory representation. In particular Young *et al.* (1977) have provided a rationalization of Winston's method in which the representation language is based on one or

Example Near-miss	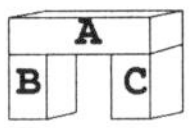	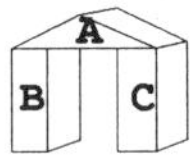
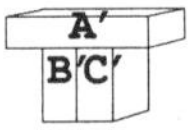	B′ and C′ touch	A is WEDGE A′ is BRICK B′ and C′ touch
	B and C support A	A is WEDGE A′ is BRICK B and C support A
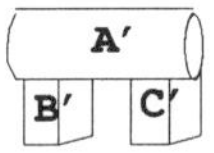	A is BRICK A′ is CYLINDER	A is WEDGE A′ is CYLINDER

Figure 2.1. The differences between two arches and three non-arches (after Winston, 19

[2] For the sake of brevity, positive examples of a concept are usually referred to just as *positives* while negative examples are simply *negatives*.

more generalization hierarchies (or lattices).

In the late 1970s, Mitchell (1977) described a method that is similar to Winston's in the sense that it is based on generalization and specialization but different in the way in which it explores the hypothesis space. Whereas in Winston's method, hypotheses are generated and tested one by one, in Mitchell's method, they are systematically eliminated from a representation of the entire hypothesis space. We will use the present chapter to look at the way in which this algorithm works. Later on (Chapter 3) we will see how it can be implemented and the sort of behaviour that can be obtained from it.

2.2. Classical concepts as region representations

We have seen that, in the Aristotelian model, mental concepts are assumed to be represented in terms of those attributes that are shared between all examples of the concept. This model leads us directly to an algorithm for learning concept definitions. Provided that each observation is labelled as either a positive or a negative example of the concept we wish to learn, the algorithm need only scan through all the positives and extract a list of all those attributes that are shared between all the examples.

Such a simplistic approach is bound to have limitations and we can see these most clearly by analysing the behaviour of the algorithm geometrically. Let us imagine that our training set is as follows:

```
<[blue    brick]      [yes]>
<[red     wedge]      [no]>
<[green   cylinder]   [no]>
<[blue    cylinder]   [yes]>
<[blue    sphere]     [yes]>
```

The inputs here are very simple, blocksworld descriptions. Each one specifies a colour attribute and a shape attribute for a given block. The target output is either **[yes]** or **[no]**, and these correspond to 'positive' and 'negative' in the obvious way. Thus the problem constitutes a concept learning problem.

The only attribute that is shared between all the positives is **blue**. Thus the definition produced by the classical learning algorithm will be the singleton set {**blue**}. In this case **blue** is being identified as the sole, singly necessary attribute for a member of the relevant concept — the set of jointly sufficient attributes is just {**blue**}.

What are the limitations of this sort of definition? Since they always contain just two attribute values, we can think of them as forming 'points' in a 2-dimensional instance space. The two dimensions of this space range over the possible values of the two attributes. And the attribute values of a given instance provide the 'coordinates' of the corresponding point in the space. Thus, to represent a given training set in the current input space, all we need do is draw out the 2-dimensional space and then label all the input descriptions in the training set with their target outputs — either **yes** or **no**.

In the diagram below we see our blocksworld training set represented in the described way. The colour values form the vertical dimension and the shape values form the horizontal dimension. The cells in the matrix corresponding to positives are labelled with **yes**. The cells that correspond to negatives are labelled with **no**.

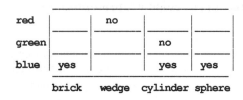

The hypothesis 'colour = **blue**' covers (i.e. generalizes) all descriptions that contain blue, i.e. **[blue brick]**, **[blue wedge]**, **[blue cylinder]** and **[blue sphere]**. The cells corresponding to these descriptions collectively form a rectangular region in the matrix, see below. Descriptions that are inside the region are covered by the concept definition. Descriptions that are outside the region are not covered.

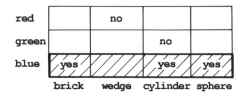

Looking at the situation geometrically brings out the fact that in forming the definition 'colour = **blue**', the classical algorithm has made an inductive leap. It has formed a definition that performs satisfactorily for all the examples in the training set. The training set shows that some examples are positive and some are negative. The definition formed does the same thing; but it also yields classifications of unseen instances. In particular, it classifies **[blue wedge]** as positive and all of **[red brick]**, **[green brick]**, **[green wedge]**, **[red cylinder]**, **[red sphere]** and **[green sphere]** as negative. It is the production of these extra classifications that is the inductive leap.

Unfortunately, inductive leaps can land you in hot water. Remember that the training set gives us just a *subset* of the target mapping. In forming a definition that covers the training set we are hoping to produce one that also covers the entire target mapping from which it is drawn. But it may turn out that the assumptions made in the inductive leap do not carry through to the target mapping. For example, imagine that the target mapping effectively labels cells in the matrix as shown in the diagram below.

Given this target mapping the instance [blue wedge] turns out to be an exception,[3] i.e. a negative instance that happens to share the colour attribute blue with all the positives. In this case, the classical algorithm, seeing only the training set shown above, makes an inductive leap that turns out to be invalid.

red	no	no	no	no
green	no	no	no	no
blue	yes	no	yes	yes
	brick	wedge	cylinder	sphere

But it is worse than this. If we expand the training set so as to include the exception <[blue wedge] [no]> the classical algorithm will fail to produce any meaningful definition at all. This is because there is no attribute value that is shared between all the positives but not seen in any of the negatives. Therefore it is impossible to produce a definition expressed in these terms. Putting it geometrically, there is no rectangular region definable in terms of a list of shared attributes that both includes all the positives and excludes all the negatives.

The general conclusion is that we cannot base a satisfactory definition of the expanded training set solely on a (single) list of shared attributes. Since the classical algorithm uses this form of definition, we know that it is bound to fail on this example. To handle it we need a more powerful and more flexible way of defining a particular target mapping.

A number of possibilities immediately present themselves. For example, we could use simple logical formulae. This might mean defining the target concept in terms of the conjunctive-normal-form expression 'blue and (brick or cylinder or

---

[3] Of course it is only an 'exception' with respect to the rule we have formed.

sphere)'.[4] Another possibility would be to use specifications for arbitrary rectangular regions of the (geometric form of the) instance space. For example, we could represent the target mapping in terms of a definition that isolates the region containing **[blue cylinder]** and **[blue sphere]** and the one containing **[blue brick]**.

Unfortunately, neither of these two approaches is particularly satisfactory. In both cases, the number of possibilities that we will need to search through to find a satisfactory hypothesis increases very rapidly with the size and complexity of the instance space. This means that in realistic examples, the search process is likely to be intractable. To drive this point home, let us consider the second possible method — exploring the space of all possible rectangles.

To work out how many rectangular regions we can find in an arbitrary discrete space we begin by counting up the number of ways in which we can place two boundaries in one dimension. We can position a boundary just below the first value, just below the second value, just below the third value, etc. If we position the first boundary just below the first value, we can position the second boundary just below the second value, just below the third value, etc., all the way up to just above the nth value. If we position the first boundary just below the second value, then we can position the second boundary in any position from just below the third value all the way up to just above the nth value. We can therefore find the total number of boundary combinations by summing all the values from 1 to n (i.e. all the possible positions for the second boundary given all the possible positions of the first boundary). There are then

$$\sum_i^n i$$

possible boundary arrangements in a dimension of n values. If we have a space of m dimensions all of which have n values then we have:

$$(\sum_i^n i)^m$$

possible rectangular regions. With only 25 values per dimension and 20 dimensions, we have more than 10^{50} possible hyper-rectangles. With this number of possibilities, the task of searching for a satisfactory hypothesis (which may of course involve

---

[4] ID3 (discussed in Chapter 6) can be used to generate representations like this.

more than one rectangle) is likely to take an unacceptably large amount of processing. The conclusion is unavoidable: we need a better approach!

2.3. The version space

Fortunately there are several, as we shall see. One of the longest-standing and best-known methods in symbolic learning is the algorithm known as *candidate elimination*. This algorithm provides a neat solution to the problem of search complexity. Instead of trying to search through the hypothesis space considering one node at a time, it attempts to narrow the space down by systematically eliminating portions that are known to contain unsatisfactory hypotheses. Where large portions can be eliminated at a stroke, this approach has the potential to be more efficient than straightforward search (which eliminates one hypothesis at a time). But of course it requires an efficient representation for the space of hypotheses.

How can we represent the hypothesis space efficiently? Let us make some observations: (1) we want a way of representing a space of *satisfactory* hypotheses; (2) a satisfactory hypothesis is one which covers observed positive instances and excludes observed negative instances; (3) for any collection of observed instances there will be a set of *maximally general*, satisfactory hypotheses and some set of *maximally specific*, satisfactory hypotheses. Putting all this together we arrive at the insight underlying the candidate elimination algorithm; namely, that these two sets effectively provide a definition of the *complete* set of satisfactory hypotheses. The set constitutes a definition since we can always decide whether an arbitrary hypothesis is satisfactory by testing to see if it is no more general than any of the most general hypotheses and no more specific than any of the maximally specific hypotheses.

The idea that we can construct a definition for a set of satisfactory hypothesis by identifying its two 'boundaries' in the *generality ordering* of hypotheses is a subtle one which requires some careful thought.[5] Such definitions are called *version space representations* and they play a central role in the candidate elimination algorithm, as we will see. The two components of the version space — the set of maximally general, satisfactory hypothesis and the set of maximally specific, satisfactory hypotheses — are known, respectively, as G or the *general boundary*, and S or the *specific boundary*. A version space in which G is identical to S is said to be *empty*.

A visualization of the version space is shown in Figure 2.2. The hypothesis space

---

[5] Since the coverage of some hypothesis h_1 may overlap but not subsume the coverage of some other hypothesis h_2, the generality ordering is usually a *partial* ordering.

here is represented by the large upper rectangle and the instance space is represented by the long rectangle at the bottom. The target mapping is represented using plus signs to label positive instances and minus signs to label negative instances.[6]

The various pyramid shapes in the hypothesis space represent hypotheses and their coverage. The one labelled **G1** and the one labelled **G2** represent two maximally general, satisfactory hypotheses, i.e. the general boundary of a version space representation. The one labelled **S1** and the one labelled **S2** represent two maximally specific, satisfactory hypotheses, i.e. the specific boundary of a version space. The base of each pyramid bounds that 'portion' of the instance space (i.e. that subset of instances) covered by the relevant hypothesis. Points within a pyramid correspond to subsumed hypotheses. Thus the hypothesis **G2** covers all instances in that portion of the instance space bounded by the bottom edge of the corresponding pyramid, and subsumes all hypotheses that fall inside it.

The version space defined by the two sets of satisfactory hypotheses includes every hypothesis whose generality lies within the general boundary and the specific boundary. Visually the specific boundary is the upper profile of the **S1** and **S2** pyramids. The general boundary is the upper profile of the **G1** and **G2** pyramids. Any hypothesis which lies between these two profiles is 'in' the version space, including the hypotheses that define the boundaries. Note that use of the term 'empty' to describe version spaces in which $G = S$ is slightly confusing since it seems to suggest (incorrectly) that the space does not include the hypotheses which actually define the boundaries. However, this is not the case. The version-space representation defines the set of hypotheses that are intermediate in generality between G and S or contained explicitly in G or S.

2.4. The candidate elimination algorithm

The advantages of the version-space representation become obvious when we consider how the process of eliminating portions of the space is achieved in the candidate elimination algorithm. For simplicity, we will concentrate on the case where there is a *total* generality ordering over our hypotheses. In this case any hypothesis either subsumes or is subsumed by some other hypothesis. This implies that G and S are always singleton sets and can be thought of as single hypotheses, i.e. G can be viewed as the maximally general, satisfactory hypothesis and S can be viewed as the maximally specific, satisfactory hypothesis.

---

[6] Note that this visualization is only valid in the case where the partial ordering is a tree.

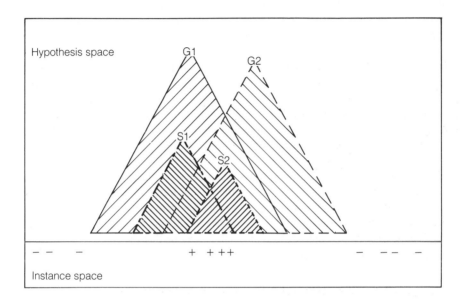

Figure 2.2. Version space visualization.

Consider the situation where we want to modify a version-space representation so as to take account of a newly presented instance. Assume that our aim is to modify the representation so as to ensure that all the contained hypotheses are satisfactory with respect to the new instance as well as to all the previously presented instances. If the instance is a negative and is covered by G then G can no longer be satisfactory. We must find a hypothesis that is less general than G. This entails working 'down' through the generality ordering looking for a hypothesis that *excludes* the new negative. (Provided that we never jump over any hypotheses on our way down the ordering, we know that the first satisfactory hypothesis we find is the one we want.) If, on the other hand, the instance is a positive that is not covered by S, then we must work our way up through the generality ordering looking for a hypothesis that does cover the new instance. The new G and S we find by this process of working 'inwards' in the generality ordering necessarily defines the new version space of satisfactory hypotheses.

In essence the candidate elimination algorithm is the application of this modification procedure to a sequence of presented instances. As we noted, in the general case the algorithm manipulates a version space that is defined in terms of a set of maximally general, satisfactory hypotheses and a set of maximally specific, satisfactory hypotheses. Thus, in modifying a boundary, the procedure has to substitute one set of hypotheses with another, rather than one hypothesis with another. However, the character of the process remains the same.

In the simplest case the algorithm terminates as a result of the supply of new instances being exhausted. However, it can also terminate as a result of G becoming identical to S. Processing cannot continue beyond this point since any further refinement of S would lead to it becoming more general, overall, than G. While any further refinement of G would lead to it becoming more specific, overall, than S. In either case the representation would become meaningless.

If there are still instances left to process when $G = S$ we have a potential *contradiction*. That is to say, it may turn out that there is an unseen instance that the current version space classifies in the wrong way (e.g., a negative that is covered by one of the embodied hypotheses or a positive that is excluded by all of them). On the other hand, there may be no contradiction after all. It may be that the final version space is satisfactory for the entire training set.[7]

A simplified definition of the candidate elimination algorithm[8] is as follows:

Candidate elimination algorithm

Initialize by setting G to be the set of maximally general hypotheses and S to be empty. Then, for each presented instance do the following two steps.

(1)   If the instance is positive then update S so as to ensure that it still contains the set of most specific hypotheses that mutually cover all the seen positives.

(2)   If it is negative then update G so as to ensure that it still contains the set of most general hypotheses, none of which cover any seen negative.

The algorithm terminates if there are no more instances to process or if G is identical to S. Ideally, any implementation of this algorithm should check for the emergence of an inconsistency, i.e. it should check to see whether an attempt is being made to make S more general than G or G more specific than S. In this situation the algorithm

---

[7] Determination of the precise situation at termination is not a specified part of the algorithm.

[8] For a more faithful reproduction see Dietterich *et al.* (1982, p. 388).

should return some indication of failure. If the algorithm manages to continue processing until one of the two termination criteria is met, then it should return the version space in its final form.

2.5. Comments

The main aim in the present chapter has been to introduce the candidate elimination algorithm and the concept of the version space. A brief review of the limitations of the classical learning algorithm led us to consider the need for an algorithm that enables more flexible definitions to be produced in a feasible amount of time. And this led us directly to candidate elimination which is one of the best known of all symbolic learning algorithms.

The most remarkable feature of the algorithm is the way in which it carries out the 'search' of the hypothesis space. Instead of exploring nodes (hypotheses) one by one, it systematically eliminates complete portions of the space from consideration, working towards the point at which there are no new instances left to process, or in which the version space is empty. The method for eliminating portions of the space involves traversing the partial generality ordering over hypotheses. Thus, the general efficiency of the algorithm depends crucially on how easily this can be done. In the next chapter we will look at a way of defining the hypothesis space that greatly facilitates generality-ordering traversal and thus yields an efficient implementation of candidate elimination.

2.6. Further reading

Winston's work on arch learning is described in (Winston, 1970; 1975). Mitchell first presented the candidate elimination algorithm to an international audience at the Fifth International Joint Conference on Artificial Intelligence (Mitchell, 1977). However, the article in Dieterich *et al.* (1982) on candidate elimination is probably the most accessible reference for this algorithm. There is also a paper by Bundy × et al.* (1985) that provides a detailed, critical review of the algorithm and its specification.

2.7. Problems

(1)   Characterize the constraints that apply to concepts defined in terms of a list of shared attributes. Provide an example to illustrate your answer.

(2)   Does a version space represent a set of instances? Illustrate your answer with an example.

(3)   How many hyper-rectangular regions are there in a discrete space of 5 dimensions where each dimension has 8 values? How did you compute the answer?

(4)   What are the components of a version-space definition? What does a version space contain? And what information does the definition (of the version space) presuppose?

(5)   What are the principal advantages of version-space definitions for the purposes of computational learning?

(6)   How does the candidate elimination algorithm manipulate version-space representations and what is the termination criterion for the algorithm?

(7)   Where there is a total generality ordering over hypotheses S and G are always singleton sets. Explain why this is the case.

3

Focussing

3.1. Introduction

Focussing is an implementation of candidate elimination in which the instance and hypothesis spaces are defined using a set of generalization hierarchies or lattices. This approach has several advantages. First, it means that hypotheses and version spaces can be defined in terms of simple, ordered sets of nodes. Second, it means that generality-ordering traversal involves straightforward tree-climbing and tree-descent operations. Third, it means that the general boundary G and the specific boundary S are always guaranteed to be singleton sets. This greatly simplifies matters, as we will see.

Another, possibly more important reason for defining hypotheses in terms of generalization hierarchies is that it gives us a way of exploiting background knowledge. We can best show this using an example. Imagine that we are concerned with the domain of *vehicles*. Instances in this case might be pairs of attribute values, for example:

```
[huge car]
[big  moped]
```

Our background knowledge may tell us that certain attribute values naturally belong together, i.e. it may tell us that `big` and `huge` belong together in that they both indicate largeness. The instances in a *class* (i.e. the instances that all have the same target output) are likely to have attribute values that belong together. Hypotheses aim to identify classes, so plausible hypotheses are going to be ones that allow us to identify classes in terms of values that belong together.

To exploit this background knowledge we can define the hypothesis language so that it includes *only* plausible hypotheses. One way of doing this involves defining it in terms of generalization hierarchies that capture the way in which certain values belong together. In the present case, we might use the hierarchies shown in Figure

3.1. The hierarchy on the right expresses the notion, for example, that **bike**, **moped** and **car** belong together and are subsumed under the **vehicle** class. The hierarchy on the left expresses the notion that **big**, **vast** and **huge** belong together and are subsumed under the **large** class.

To make sure that our hypothesis language contains only plausible hypotheses we have to make sure that the way in which hypotheses identify classes of instances respects the knowledge we have about classes of values. One way to achieve this is to

(1)   define the hypothesis language as the set of all pairs that can be constructed by combining one node from each tree (with the proviso that one of the nodes should be an internal node), and

(2)   specify that the set of instances that are covered by a given hypothesis are all those vectors that can be constructed by pairing up leaf nodes from the subtrees of the nodes in the hypothesis.

Hypotheses can now be defined as pairs such as **[small vehicle]** and **[large plane]**. *Instances* can be defined as pairs such as **[big car]** and **[tiny bike]**. With hypotheses being constructed from internal nodes in the hierarchies, we know that they are bound to generalize over *plausible* classes of instance values, i.e. we

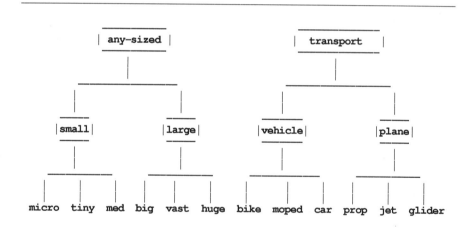

Figure 3.1. Generalization hierarchies defining 'vehicles' space.

know that they will necessarily respect the domain knowledge that we have expressed in the generalization hierarchies. Furthermore, we also have an easy way of deriving the coverage of a particular hypothesis. All we have to do is take each component of the hypothesis in turn, generate all the leaf nodes that are in its subtree, and then construct the Cartesian product of all the sets so produced.

For example, the coverage of the hypothesis:

[small vehicle]

is just the set of all pairs that can be constructed by pairing up leaf nodes from the subtrees of small and vehicle, namely:

```
[micro bike]
[micro moped]
[micro car]
[tiny  bike]
[tiny  moped]
[tiny  car]
[med   bike]
[med   moped]
[med   car]
```

In fact, the coverage of a hypothesis in this sort of hierarchy-based language can be worked out geometrically. Using the usual method, we draw out the instance space as a rectangular grid using one dimension for each set of possible attribute values.[1] We make sure that the sequence of dimension values respects the left-to-right ordering of the nodes in the generalization hierarchies so that we can attach the hierarchies to the axes of the space as shown in Figure 3.2.

A given hypothesis effectively marks a node in each tree and any node subsumes a given subrange of a dimension. Thus any hypothesis effectively identifies a subrange in each dimension. If we put these subranges together we get a rectangular region whose cells correspond to the instances covered by the hypothesis. In Figure 3.2 the boundary of the region identified by [small vehicle] is highlighted. Note that the region contains all the cells corresponding to the instances listed above.

---

[1] Once again, we are dealing with a case where there are only two sets of attribute values. This means we can draw the space as a 2-dimensional grid.

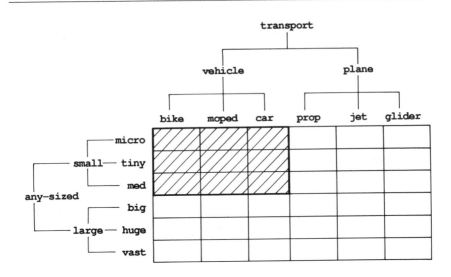

Figure 3.2. Coverage of hierarchy-based hypothesis.

3.2. Mark raising and lowering

We said above that where the hypothesis language is defined using hierarchies there is always just one maximally general, satisfactory hypothesis and one maximally specific, satisfactory hypothesis. Why is this the case? A hypothesis includes one node from each tree. In effect it places a *mark* on one node in each tree. If the hypothesis is satisfactory, then it must cover a maximum number of positive instances. This means that, in each tree, the corresponding mark must be at or above a certain node, namely, the node that subsumes a maximum number of values from positive instances. If the hypothesis is maximally general, the mark must be as far above this node as possible. If the hypothesis is maximally specific, the mark must be at the node. Since we are dealing with *hierarchies* we know that, in both cases, there is a unique position for the mark. Therefore we know that there can only ever be one maximally general, satisfactory hypothesis and one maximally specific, satisfactory hypothesis.

Where both *G* and *S* are defined using single hypotheses, implementing the generalization and specialization operations of candidate elimination involves manipulating hypotheses so as to alter the positions of marks. In fact we can conveniently view specialization as the operation of raising the marks corresponding to S and lowering the marks corresponding to G. Since the former can never appear above the latter, they are referred to as *lower marks*, while the marks defined by G are called *upper marks*.

Initialization of the algorithm takes place after presentation of the first positive instance and involves placing marks in the hierarchies. We have to place upper marks on all the root nodes and lower marks on the leaf nodes identified by the first positive instance. The G hypothesis corresponding to the upper marks covers all possible instances. The S hypothesis corresponding to the lower marks covers just the initial, positive instance.

After presentation of a new positive instance, the algorithm has to find the new S hypothesis that covers all seen positive instances. To do this it raises the lower mark in each hierarchy until the mark is above the leaf node that appears in the instance vector. Note that the S hypothesis corresponding to the new lower marks will necessarily cover the new instance. After presentation of a negative instance, the algorithm has to find the new G hypothesis that covers no seen negative instances. To do this it lowers the upper mark in *one* hierarchy until it is no longer above the leaf that appears in the instance vector. The G hypothesis corresponding to the new upper marks necessarily excludes the new instance.

The process continues until such time as all the instances have been processed or the upper and lower marks in each tree are on the same nodes. Clearly, at this point, the termination condition for candidate elimination $(G = S)$ is satisfied.

3.3. Near and far misses

Note that the raising and lowering operations are not perfect complements. Specializing G involves lowering the upper mark in *one* hierarchy only since it is sufficient that just one of the instance values is not a descendant of G for G not to cover the instance. If we have more than one way to specialize G, the instance is referred to as a *far miss*. If there is just one way, the instance is a *near miss*.[2] Where we have an instance that forms a far miss (i.e. where G can be specialized in more than one way) there are two possible strategies that can be employed for exploring the possible specializations.

---

[2] Winston made the exploitation of near misses a central feature of his ARCH program.

- We can adopt a depth-first strategy. Here we first try moving the upper mark down one level in the first hierarchy. If this is not sufficient we try moving the mark down another level — and so on. If the mark gets all the way to a leaf node we go on to the next hierarchy and try again there.

- We can also adopt a breadth-first strategy. Here we first try moving the upper mark down one level in the first hierarchy. If this is not sufficient we try moving the upper mark in the *second* hierarchy down one level. If this is not sufficient we go on to the third hierarchy, etc. If we run out of hierarchies, we come back and try moving the upper mark down another level in the first hierarchy.

The depth-first strategy is likely to be much easier to implement but the breadth-first strategy may be more effective. It will ensure that upper marks are always kept as high as possible; i.e. that the generality of the values in G (as defined by the hierarchies) is always maximized. This will typically help to *minimize* the risk of producing a contradiction.

3.4. A sample interaction with focussing

Let us look at an example run of the focussing algorithm. The instance space for this example is the 'vehicles' domain introduced previously. It is defined in terms of two generalization hierarchies and, as we have seen, can be viewed as forming a 2-dimensional space. The target mapping is the membership function for a certain, unspecified, target concept. There are, therefore, just two target outputs, and these are written as [yes] and [no] in the usual way. The training set containing five training pairs is as follows:

```
<[tiny moped]  [yes]>
<[tiny car]    [yes]>
<[big  jet]    [no]>
<[med  car]    [yes]>
<[med  jet]    [no]>
```

We will trace the behaviour of focussing using the geometric representation. We will look at the position of marks (and the regions they define) after processing each pair in the training set. The first pair is <[tiny moped] [yes]>. This triggers initialization. Upper marks are placed on all the root nodes and lower marks are placed on the leaf nodes marked by the instance values. Following initialization, the situation is as shown in Figure 3.3 (1). Note how the current S covers only one instance, namely the instance given in the training pair. The general boundary G covers every possible instance. At this point the version space includes every hypothesis that is at least as

(1)

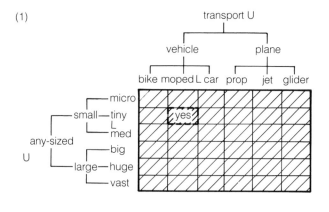

(2)

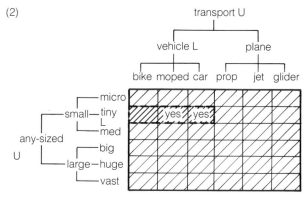

(3)

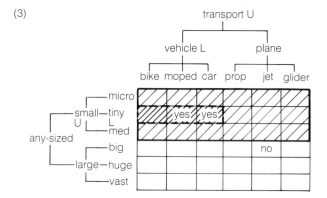

(4)

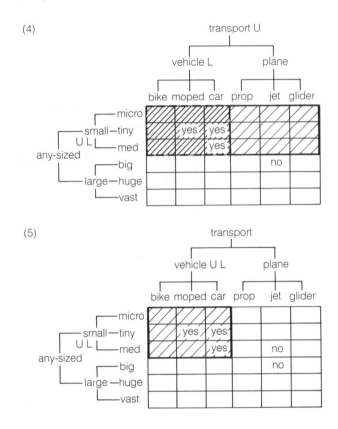

(5)

Figure 3.3. Focussing in action.

general as S and at least as specific as G.

The second training pair (<[tiny car] [yes]>) is another positive. It therefore causes the specific boundary to be generalized, see Figure 3.3 (2). In geometric terms it causes the S region to expand. Note how the lower mark in the transport tree has been raised to vehicle causing a corresponding expansion in the S region. Note also the inductive leap that occurs at this point.

The third training pair (<[big jet] [no]>) is a negative. It causes the general boundary to be minimally specialized so as to exclude the new instance. The upper mark is moved down from any-sized to small and the specific boundary contracts accordingly, see Figure 3.3 (3). Note that this instance forms a far miss: specialization might have involved moving the upper mark down in the transport tree.

The fourth training pair (<[med car] [yes]>) is another positive and therefore triggers further generalization. The lower mark in the **size** tree is moved up to **small** and the *S* boundary expands accordingly, see Figure 3.3 (4). Now that the upper and lower mark in the **size** tree are both on the same node, no further manipulation of the marks in this tree is possible. From here on processing must concentrate on the **transport** tree.

The final training pair (<[med jet] [no]>) is a negative. Specialization moves the upper mark in the **transport** tree down to **vehicle**. The *G* boundary contracts and is now exactly superimposed on the *S* boundary, see Figure 3.3 (5). No further processing is possible. But since there are no more training pairs in the training set no further processing is necessary. The final hypothesis, derived from the marked nodes, is **[small vehicle]**. *G = S* so the version space is 'empty'.

3.5. Problems with focussing

The example we have looked at is, of course, an ideal case. In more typical circumstances, focussing is quite likely to run into difficulties. There are at least three types of problem that may beset this algorithm.

(1) The structure of the generalization hierarchies can be such as to prevent a satisfactory hypothesis being derived. In the situation depicted in the diagrams below, it is impossible to generalize over the two positives without also including the single negative. *Tree-hacking* is a technique that involves detecting this situation and rectifying it by introducing new structure into the hierarchies. The right-hand diagram below shows the result of a tree-hacking modification applied to rectify the situation depicted on the left:

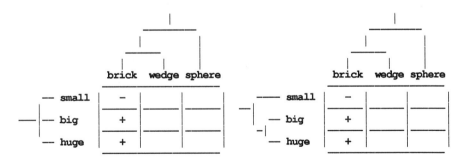

(2) In coping with far misses, focussing has to choose randomly between a number of possible specializations. If the choice is wrong, a satisfactory concept cannot

be constructed. The only solution involves keeping track of all choices made so as to be able to backtrack.[3] An illustrative situation is shown in the diagram below. If the algorithm tries to exclude the negative [big sphere] by putting an upper mark on the parent of **brick** and **wedge**, it will not be able to process the forthcoming positive [small sphere].

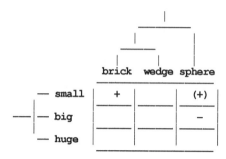

(3) There are some pathological situations that have no obvious solution. In the situation depicted below there is no generalization covering both positives that does not also cover the negative. Moreover, tree-hacking can only produce new boundary positions within the defined space. Since there is no combination of boundaries that would enable the positives to be separated from the negatives, we know that tree-hacking cannot help here. The problem is a deep one. The assumption that instances in different classes will be *dis*similar has broken down. In this situation, instances in different classes have a maximum degree of similarity. Therefore, the similarity-based approach inevitably fails.

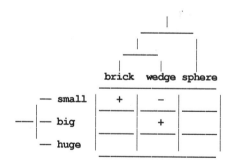

---

[3] A better solution, as advocated by Winston, may be to ignore all far misses.

3.6. Concluding comments

Although the focussing algorithm has not been used to any great extent in applications work, it does represent an interesting case, if only because it shows how we can use background knowledge (bias) in learning. It does this by having the hypothesis space defined in terms of generalization hierarchies, i.e. representations that themselves capture background knowledge about the domain. The advantages conferred by this arrangement are balanced by the limitations that they introduce. The fact that focussing *requires* the generalization hierarchies (i.e. the background knowledge) to be specified limits the applicability of the algorithm to those cases where the required background knowledge is actually available. In practice, background knowledge is very often unavailable and so the focussing algorithm cannot be applied.

3.7. Further reading

The best analysis of focussing is currently provided by Bundy *et al.* (1985). The article by Wielemaker and Bundy (1985) is a full discussion of tree-hacking technique. See also Murray (1987) for a variant of the focussing approach which addresses the problem of 'disjunctive concepts'.

3.8. Problems

(1)   In what sense do generalization hierarchies capture domain knowledge? How can we use generalization hierarchies to give a concept learning algorithm a strong and correct bias? Provide an example to illustrate your answer.

(2)   What is the syntactic form of a hypothesis in a language based on generalization hierarchies and what is the syntactic form of an instance? Describe an algorithm for deriving the set of instances that are covered by this sort of hypothesis.

(3)   An instance space is based on the generalization hierarchies shown below. Instances are pairs containing a leaf node from each hierarchy (e.g., [pink cube]). Hypotheses are 2-tuples containing a node from each hierarchy (e.g., [uniform brick]). How can we work out how many descriptions there are in all? How can we enumerate them? Finally, how can we implement concepts?

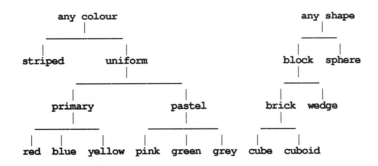

(4)   An implementation of the focussing algorithm that uses the hypothesis language shown in Problem 3 is presented with the following sequence of positive and negative instances:

```
<[green      cube]    [yes]>
<[striped    sphere]  [no]>
<[pink       cuboid]  [yes]>
<[striped    wedge]   [yes]>
```

Describe the way in which the algorithm manipulates upper and lower marks as it attempts to construct a concept for these instances. What is the final output from the algorithm?

How is the situation altered if the sequence is as follows:

```
<[green      cube]    [yes]>
<[striped    sphere]  [no]>
<[pink       wedge]   [yes]>
```

What is the final output in this case?

(5)   Explain why, in focussing, the first training instance must be positive.

(6)   Why is it the case that keeping upper marks as high as possible reduces the risk of a contradiction?

(7)   Explain how we can adapt an implementation of focussing so that it implements tree-hacking in those cases where the structure of the hypothesis space is 'detectably' inappropriate.

4

AQ11

4.1. Introduction

Candidate elimination is essentially a concept learning method. This means it can only be used to learn target mappings that have two distinct outputs (e.g., [yes] and [no]). The algorithm can, however, be adapted for use with target mappings which have more than two outputs. Remember that such mappings occur in classification learning problems, such as is defined by the training set shown in Figure 4.1.[1] The target mapping here gives classifications for instances that are descriptions (based on binary features) of particular species of amphibious creature.

The simplest way of using the candidate elimination algorithm for the purposes of learning a representation for such a mapping involves using an algorithm known as *Aq*. In executing this algorithm, we first separate out all the instances into *classes*, where a class is simply a set of instances (inputs) that all have the same target output. Then we get each class in turn and run candidate elimination, treating all instances in the class as positives and all instances outside the class as negatives. At the end of the process we will have one hypothesis for each class.[2]

It would appear at first sight that we can obtain classifications of an unseen instance *X* simply by determining which of our hypotheses covers *X*. But unfortunately, this approach does not succeed in general. The problem is that the coverages of the hypotheses may not be mutually exclusive or exhaustive. This means that we may have an unseen instance that is covered by more than one hypothesis or by none. For example, it may turn out that the unseen instance:

---

[1] This training set is derived from the decision tree for British amphibians shown in the *Education Guardian*, 5 March 1991.

[2] Assuming all the applications terminate successfully

TAIL	WARTY_SKIN	YELLOW_STRIPE	SPOTTED_THROAT		CLASS
<[no	no	yes	yes	]	[common_frog]>
<[no	no	yes	no	]	[common_frog]>
<[no	yes	no	yes	]	[common_toad]>
<[no	yes	no	no	]	[common_toad]>
<[no	yes	yes	yes	]	[natterjack_toad]>
<[no	yes	yes	no	]	[natterjack_toad]>
<[yes	yes	no	yes	]	[great_crested_newt]>
<[yes	yes	no	no	]	[great_crested_newt]>
<[yes	no	yes	yes	]	[smooth_newt]>
<[yes	no	no	yes	]	[smooth_newt]>
<[yes	no	yes	no	]	[palmate_newt]>
<[yes	no	no	no	]	[palmate_newt]>

Figure 4.1. Training set for classifying amphibians.

[no no no yes]

is covered by the hypothesis for **common_frog** and by the hypothesis for **common_toad**. So what should we return as its classification? A solution to this problem is provided by the algorithm known as *AQ11*. This algorithm uses candidate elimination roughly in the same way as Aq but it takes steps to ensure that, as far as possible, hypotheses are mutually exclusive and exhaustive.[3] Before we look at AQ11 let us consider the behaviour of Aq in more detail.

4.2. Non-determinacy problems

Let us concentrate on the ways in which Aq can *fail* to produce a satisfactory result. As we have said, the version-space representations we get from repeated applications of candidate elimination may be neither empty nor mutually exclusive in their coverage. We can show the problems this leads to with an example. Imagine that we have the following training set (the text to the right of the training set shows what the target outputs stand for):

---

[3] In fact, Aq has some other features; in particular it uses a heuristic for choosing the positive to present first in any given case. The heuristic ensures that it always selects an input which has not been covered by any representation in any previous *G*.

```
<[huge bike]    [G2]>      Giant 2-wheeler
<[huge moped]   [G2]>

<[micro jet]    [FP]>
<[tiny jet]     [FP]>      Fast plane
<[med jet]      [FP]>

<[tiny moped]   [CT]>
<[tiny car]     [CT]>      Conventional Transportation
<[med car]      [CT]>
```

The instance space is the familiar 2-dimensional vehicles space. So we can represent the training set geometrically by labelling points in the space with their target outputs. The configuration of points looks like this:

	bike	moped	car	prop	jet	glider
micro					FP	
tiny		CT	CT		FP	
med			CT		FP	
big						
huge	G2	G2				
vast						

What happens when we run Aq on this training set? Assuming that we process instance classes in the sequence in which they are given we first turn all the training pairs which have **G2** as the target output into positives (i.e. we replace the target output with **[yes]**) and all the other pairs into negatives (i.e. we replace their target outputs with **[no]**). We then run the candidate elimination algorithm on the training set so produced. This gives us a general boundary (the most general hypothesis covering no negative instances) and a specific boundary (the most specific representation covering all positive instances). In geometric terms, it gives us the largest, feasible rectangle which encloses no cells containing negative instances, and the smallest feasible rectangle which encloses all positives. We show these rectangles below:

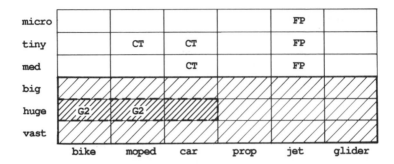

This version space is not empty. There is a valid hypothesis (i.e. rectangle) that would fit between the *G* and the *S* boundaries. This means that there is a representation which is (1) at least as general as *S* and (2) at least as specific as *G* but which is not identical to either *S* or *G*. The representation in question is **[large vehicle]**.

Imagine that we now repeat the whole procedure using the inputs which map on to **FP** as positive and all the others as negatives. In this case we produce a version space which has the following form:

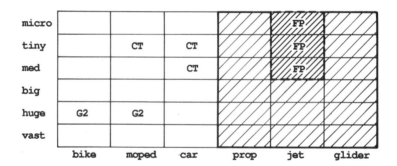

Finally, we repeat the procedure using the inputs which map on to **CT** as positives. This produces an empty version space:

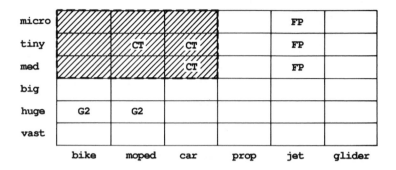

Unfortunately, there is no straightforward way of using the representations we have accumulated for the purposes of generating outputs for arbitrary inputs. Two of the runs of candidate elimination produced non-empty version spaces. This gives us a problem: if we want to classify an input in the usual way — by seeing what hypothesis covers it — we have to first decide whether we are going to use general boundaries or specific boundaries.

If we decide to use general boundaries then a given instance may have *n* different classifications. That is to say, a given cell may be inside one of *n* different general boundaries. The instance [huge jet] is a case in point. It is inside the general boundary represented by [any-sized plane] and the one defined by [large transport].

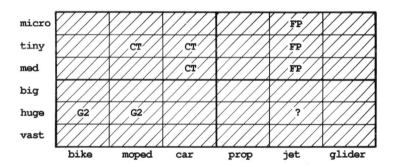

If we decide to use specific boundaries then a given input is less likely to fall into more than one region. However, it may fall into no region at all. That is to say, there will be many cells which are not inside any particular specific boundary. Again, [huge jet] is a case in point.

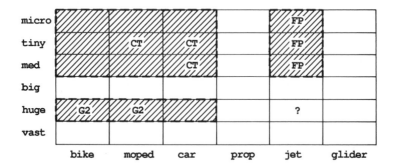

The overall conclusion is that Aq by itself does not give us a satisfactory solution to the problem of target mappings with multiple (i.e. more than two) outputs. To deal effectively with such learning problems we have to use AQ11, a direct descendant of Aq.

4.3. From Aq to AQ11

AQ11 is the same algorithm as Aq but with one small difference. It uses previously constructed hypotheses as 'dummy' negatives in addition to the negatives that it derives from instances in other classes. Of course, this approach is not possible unless hypotheses are of the same syntactic form as instances. But typically they are.[4] In the present case, both hypotheses and instances are pairs of nodes from the underlying generalization hierarchies. Thus, while a negative derived from an ordinary training pair might look like this:

<[big bike] [no]>

a negative derived from a representation would look like this:

<[large vehicle] [no]>

Provided the candidate elimination implementation is able to consider such constructions as ordinary training pairs, processing can proceed in the normal way.

The main advantage of this approach is that it ensures that, whenever candidate elimination builds a version space, it will make sure that the general boundary does not

---

[4] This is called the 'one representation trick' in Dietterich *et al.* (1982).

overlap any previously constructed general boundaries. Thus, at the end of processing, we have a set of general boundaries which are guaranteed to be mutually exclusive (even though they may be non-exhaustive). We can then use these to derive classifications in the suggested way.

If we give AQ11 the example considered above, i.e. the training set:

```
<[huge   bike]     [G2]>
<[huge   moped]    [G2]>
<[micro  jet]      [FP]>
<[tiny   jet]      [FP]>
<[med    jet]      [FP]>
<[tiny   moped]    [CT]>
<[tiny   car]      [CT]>
<[med    car]      [CT]>
```

it produces representations as follows:

```
<[small plane]      [FP]>
<[small vehicle]    [CT]>
<[large transport]  [G2]>
```

These represent mutually exclusive regions of input space as is shown below. Note how the G2 input group (the first to be processed) has the most general representation:

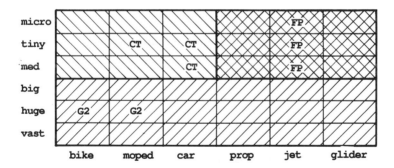

Naturally, there are various problems with AQ11. Since it uses candidate elimination, it is subject to all the problems that algorithm is subject to. In particular, it will not be effective if any of the classes has any of the problem characteristics outlined at the end of Chapter 3.

Another problem is that the hypotheses produced will vary depending on the order in which we present the classes. In general, we can expect that the hypotheses learned first will be more general than the ones learned later. In geometric terms, early calls on candidate elimination will tend to produce general boundaries which enclose much larger portions of the instance space since, in the early stages, a larger proportion of the input space is still 'up for grabs'.

4.4. The soybean study

AQ11 is famous as the learning method which was used in the *soybean experiment*. This experiment was carried out by Michalski and Chilausky in the late 1970s and early 1980s. They introduce the work they did as follows:

> In the case study, 15 soybean diseases were selected as being representative of the nature and scope of the problems which are faced in the diagnosis of plant diseases . . . A description space for diagnosing the selected soybean diseases was developed in conference with an expert in soybean pathology. The variables used were 35 plant and environmental descriptors and one decision variable (specifying diagnosis). (Michalski and Chilausky, 1980, p. 67)

To a first approximation, a *descriptor* can be thought of as forming one dimension of the 35-dimensional instance space. Most of the descriptors that were used range over nominal variables. For example, the 'condition-of-roots' descriptor ranges over the values:

Normal, Rotted, Galls-or-Cysts-present

Other descriptors range over ordered variables, e.g., the 'time-of-occurrence' dimension ranges over:

April, May, June, . . . October

The instance space is subdivided into three main subspaces corresponding to the three main types of descriptors: namely, Environmental, Plant-global and Plant-local. Each instance is effectively a 35-tuple. An example is shown in Figure 4.2.

When run on a large training set containing empirically derived observations of soybean disease states, AQ11 produced 15 decision hypotheses — one for each type of disease. The rules (hypotheses) produced by AQ11 were written in an extended logic notation and some were very complex. For example, the rule for Brown spot disease is given in Figure 4.3.

Environmental descriptors
    Time of occurrence = July
    Plant stand = normal
    Precipitation = above normal
    Temperature = normal
    Occurrence of hail = no
    Number years crop repeated = 4
    Damaged area = whole fields

Plant global descriptors
    Severity = potentially severe
    Seed treatment = none
    Seed germination = less than 80%
    Plant height = normal

Plant local descriptors
    Condition of leaves = abnormal
        Leafspots--halos = without yellow halos
        Leafspots--margin = without watersoaked margin
        Leafspot size = greater than 1/8 inch
        Leaf shredding or shot holding = present
        Leaf malformation = absent
        Leaf mildew growth = absent
    Condition of stem = abnormal
        Presence of lodging = no
        Stem cankers = above the second node
        Canker lesion color = brown
        Fruiting bodies on stem = present
        External decay = absent
        Mycelium on stem = absent
        Internal discoloration of stem = none
        Sclerotia--internal or external = absent
    Condition of fruits--pods = normal
        Fruit spots = absent
    Condition of seed = normal
        Mold growth = absent
        Seed discoloration = absent
        Seed size = normal
        Seed shriveling = absent
    Condition of roots = normal

Figure 4.2. Soybean-disease instance (after Michalski and Chilausky, 1980).

[precipitation >= *n*]
[# years crop repeated > 1]
[damaged area /= whole fields]
[leaves = abn]
[leafspots halos = no yellow halos]
[leafspots watersoaked margin = abs]
[leafspot size > 1/8 inch]
[leaf malformation = abs]
[roots = *n*]

OR

[precipitation > *n*]
[leaves = abn]
[leafspots = no yellow halos]
[leafspots watersoaked margin = abs]
[leafspot size > 1/8 inch]
[roots = *n*]

OR

[time = Apr..Jun]
[damaged area /= whole fields]
[leaves = abn]
[leafspots halos = no yellow halos]
[leafspots watersoaked margin = abs]
[leafspot size > 1/8 inch]
[leaf shredding = abs]
[leaf malformation = abs]
[roots = *n*]

Figure 4.3. Soybean-disease diagnosis rule (after Michalski and Chilausky, 1980).

A striking result of the soybean experiment was the fact that the rules derived by AQ11 actually out performed human experts. The inductively derived rules achieved 100% correct diagnoses while rules derived directly from questionnaires filled in by experts achieved only 96.2% correctness. This demonstration of the power of machine learning techniques helped to establish machine learning as a major subfield of AI with serious, practical applications. However, the explanation for the apparent superiority of AQ11 over human experts is not entirely clear. A contributing factor may have been AQ11's willingness and ability to produce large and unwieldy rules. The rule that we see in Figure 4.3 seems rather long but it is, in fact, of average length. Some of the rules produced by AQ11 contain more than 70 separate terms ('selectors'). The rules derived directly from the experts tended to be somewhat shorter.

4.5. Further reading

Dietterich *et al.* (1982) provide an excellent introduction to Aq and AQ11 (see pages 398-400 and 423-7) but the paper by Michalski and Chilausky (1980) is the main reference for the soybean experiment.

4.6. Problems

(1)   What is the simplest way of using candidate elimination to learn a target mapping that has more than two distinct outputs? What is the name of this algorithm and what problems are associated with it?

(2)   In what ways does AQ11 differ from Aq?

(3)   Invent a learning problem that causes AQ11 to produce a non-exhaustive set of hypotheses (i.e. which leaves the classification of some instances undefined).

(4)   If we use Aq to derive a set of specific boundaries for a given set of classes, will an unseen instance ever have a multiple classification? In what circumstances will this occur?

(5)   Why does training-set order have an impact on the representations produced by AQ11?

(6)   Will Aq produce satisfactory representations for the target mapping depicted below (using the vehicles language)? Would AQ11? Justify your answer.

	bike	moped	car	prop	jet	glider
micro			CT			
tiny			CT	FP		
med	CT		CT		FP	
big		G2				FP
huge				FP		
vast			G2			

5

Information theory

5.1. Introduction to the basic formula

Up to this point we have been looking at some of the mechanisms which have been developed through empirical work in machine learning. In this chapter we will change tack and take a brief look at a more theoretical issue: *information theory*. It is necessary to look at information theory for two reasons. First, it provides us with the basic concepts necessary for understanding the implementation of the similarity-based learning mechanism ID3 which we will be dealing with in Chapter 6. Second, it provides us with a principled justification for similarity-based learning in general, which is something that, so far, we are still lacking.

The original formulation of information theory was presented in a book called *A Mathematical Theory of Communication* (Shannon and Weaver, 1949). This book did not claim to provide a theory of information in the sense in which 'information' is usually understood. However, its concern with the development of an information *measure* has caused it to be often perceived — rightly or wrongly — as having done so.

The basic model presented to us by information theory fits fairly well with our pretheoretic notions about what information is and how it behaves. The model says that information can be viewed as something that

* originates in a particular place, called the *source*,

* is transmitted in a certain form, called the *message*, and

* is received by some information-processing agent called the *receiver*.

So far so good. But the interesting thing about information theory is the way in which it allows us to *measure* information. It says that we can quantify the amount of information that is conveyed in a message by looking, not at the message itself, but rather at the receiver — and in particular at the receiver's view of the message. The theory does not specify what sort of entity the receiver actually is. It could be a biological organism of some kind (e.g., a human being) or it could be some electronic mechanism. However, to understand what information theory is about we need to think of the receiver as having some kind of 'knowledge' of the space of possible messages and their respective probabilities. Once we have this image firmly in mind, we can see that the amount of information contained in a message is related to the receiver's estimate of its probability. If the receiver estimates the probability of receiving a certain message as 0.9 then in some sense the receiver knows that this is a message which is rather likely to be received. Thus very little surprise is caused when it arrives. Conversely, if the receiver estimates the probability of receiving a certain message as 0.1 then its arrival yields a much bigger surprise.

The underlying idea here is that we can measure the amount of information in a message in terms of the degree to which the receiver is surprised by the message. The greater the surprise, the greater the information, and vice versa. Whether or not this is a suitable way of defining information in general is a difficult issue, as we will see. However, the great advantage of the approach is that it leads directly to a simple method for computing the amount of information in a given message. We simply define information as being inversely equal to the probability of the incoming message (as estimated by the receiver):

$$\text{information}(M) = - \text{probability}(M)$$

where M is the message in question. In fact the formula proposed by Shannon is not quite this simple. Shannon argued that, for various reasons, it makes sense to measure information in terms of the (inverse of the) base 2 logarithm[1] of the assigned probability (Shannon and Weaver, 1949). In other words he proposed using the following formula:[2]

$$\text{information}(M) = - \log_2 \text{probability}(M)$$

It turns out that (rounded up to the nearest whole number) this formula gives us the number of digits we need if we want to give a unique binary encoding to each

---

[1] The base n logarithm of some number x is just the number of times we have to 'raise' n (i.e. multiply it with itself) to obtain x. Thus $\log_2$ of 16 is 4 because $2 \times 2 \times 2 \times 2 = 16$.

[2] This was originally associated with Hartley (1928) and Nyquist (1924). It is possible to use any base logarithms but using base 2 has some advantages, as we will see.

possible message. As a result, the value of the formula is said to measure the information content of the message in *bits* (short for *b*inary dig*its*).

5.2. Entropy

Shannon showed how we could take the argument one step further and use the information formula as a way of measuring the *uncertainty* of the receiver. The approach here involves defining uncertainty in terms of the expected level of surprise of an arbitrary message. Again, this fits our intuitions well. If the receiver assigns roughly equal probabilities to all messages then the expected level of surprise (of an arbitrary message) is relatively high. Thus the receiver's uncertainty is high. Conversely, if the receiver is able to assign very high probabilities to certain messages and low probabilities to others then the expected level of surprise is relatively low. And the uncertainty is low too. The receiver 'knows' what is coming. But how should we compute the expected surprise?

If the receiver gives all messages the same probability then, clearly, the expected surprise is just the surprise (information) level for any of the possible messages, i.e. it is just:

$$\text{expected-surprise}(M) = - \log_2 \text{probability}(M)$$

where M is any message. But typically, the receiver will give different probabilities to different messages. To compute the expected surprise we have to work through all the possible messages multiplying the surprise level for each one with its estimated probability. This is an ingenious approach since it uses the probability estimates twice over: first, to give the original levels of surprise and, second, to give the probability that the given level of surprise will be the surprise actually experienced by the receiver.

The formula which gives us the overall uncertainty level (or expected surprise) is known as the *entropy* formula.[3] It has the following form:[4]

---

[3] It is called this since it has the same form as the equation used to measure thermodynamic entropy in statistical mechanics.

[4] The Σ symbol is the *summation sign sigma*. When tacked on to the front of an expression it signifies that the value of the complete expression is computed by summing up all instantiations of the formula, given the indicated constraints.

$$\text{uncertainty} = - \sum_i P_i \log_2 P_i$$

given the proviso that

$$\sum_i P_i = 1$$

Here P_i is the probability of the ith message.

5.3. Why use a logarithmic relationship?

It is interesting to ask why Shannon proposed to measure information in terms of the base 2 logarithm of the probability. It turns out that this approach has several advantages, the principal one being that it means information can be added up. Provided that we use a logarithmic relationship in the formula, it is always the case that if message X contains a certain amount of information and message Y contains a certain amount of information, then the amount of information contained in both messages is just the sum of the two individual amounts.[5] For example, imagine that:

$$\text{probability}(M_1) = 0.2$$
$$\text{probability}(M_2) = 0.3$$

This means that the probability of receiving both X and Y is:

$$\text{probability}(M_1 \text{ and } M_2) = 0.2 \times 0.3 = 0.06$$

and that the amount of information contained in both messages is therefore:

$$- \log_2 0.06 = 4.06$$

This is the same as the sum arrived at when we add up the amount of information received from X and the amount obtained from Y:

$$-\log_2 0.2 + -\log_2 0.3 = -\log_2 0.06 = 4.06$$

Another advantage of using logarithmic values is that fact that it suggests an intuitive

---

[5] This assumes that X and Y are not interdependent in any way.

link between the level of uncertainty in a given case and the amount of work we have to do to dispel the uncertainty. Imagine that we have to find a particular book in an alphabetically sorted list containing 128 elements. We do not know what or where the book is, but we can find out whether it comes before or after a given point in the list.

Initially, the probability of the book being in any particular location is just 1/128, since there are 128 possible locations. This means that the information content (in bits) of a message which tells us the exact location of the book is:

$$- \log_2(1/128) = 7$$

bits.

Now, imagine that we try to find the location of the book using the well-known 'binary chop' strategy. This involves first asking whether the book comes before or after the middle element of the list. If it turns out to come before that point, then we have to ask whether it comes before or after the middle point of the initial half. The process continues until we have identified the correct location. The number of steps involved in finding a given location in a list using the binary chop algorithm is:

$$\log_2 n$$

where n is the number of items in the list. Now

$$\log_2 128 = 7$$

and 7 is just the number of bits of information in the message which informed us where the book was. This is not a coincidence! The number of binary chops needed will always be the same as the number of bits of information content (rounded up to the nearest whole number).[6] The overall implication is that we can think of information content as measuring uncertainty in the sense that it effectively measures the amount of work (binary chops) it would take to dispel the uncertainty completely.

---

[6] Looking at it another way, the information is just the number of yes/no questions we need to ask in order to identify an arbitrary member of a set of instances defined in terms of boolean attributes.

5.4. Information and meaning

Shannon emphasized the fact that we should not confuse information with *content* or *meaning*.[7] However, there is an ongoing debate concerning the precise nature of the link between information and content. To understand this debate we need to look more carefully at what is going on under the surface in information theory. First of all, let us note that there are various readings of Shannon's warning. Three possibilities are as follows.

- Information is a quantitative measure of content but quantitative measures cannot tell us anything about qualitative properties. Meaning/content is a qualitative property therefore information tells us nothing about meaning.

- Information is a quantitative measure of something (some statistical property, perhaps to do with signal processing) but *not* content.

- Content is a purely qualitative property which cannot be quantified.

Some authors have attacked the assumption contained in the first reading, namely that there is a clearly delineated boundary between quantitative and qualitative properties. Consider, for example, the fact that a particular object can contain 10 gallons of liquid. This is, presumably, a quantitative property of the object. But as such it seems to embody information about qualitative properties (e.g., that the object is some kind of tank).[8] This suggests that quantitative measures may be able to tell us something about qualitative properties.

Other aspects of the information theory debate arise as a result of a failure to recognize that information (in Shannon's theory) is essentially *subjective*. The information content of a message is not an independent property. It all depends on the 'views' of the receiving agent. The amount of information contained in a message received by some agent is measured in terms of the probability of the message as assigned *by the agent*. Shannon did not pay much attention to this issue because he was concentrating on a context in which the agents were electronic devices rather than living individuals capable of forming multiple interpretations of the same message.

But the fact that information content is measured in terms of the probability

---

[7] See page 1 of Shannon's section in Shannon and Weaver (1949).

[8] This example was suggested by Dretske's (1981) 'bucket' example.

assignments inherent in the receiver also implies — somewhat surprisingly — that a given message can have more than one information content. This arises in the case where a particular message is given more than one interpretation by a receiver, with each interpretation having a particular probability associated with it. In this context the message has one information content for each possible interpretation.[9]

5.5. Learning

Can we derive an information-theoretic justification for similarity-based learning? If so, what is it? Let us think of instances as inputs or messages from an environment. We can now ask: What is the information content of an input? If the receiver is completely lacking in knowledge about the environment then all inputs must be considered equally likely. The a priori probability of receiving a particular input is, then, just $1/n$ where n is the number of possible inputs (messages). This means that the information content of an input is:

$$- \log_2(1/n)$$

bits. If, in the target mapping, one output is always associated with one or more inputs then the number of distinct outputs will generally be less than the number of distinct inputs. Thus the information content of an output, treated as a forwarded message, will be lower than the information content of an input. The smaller the number of distinct outputs, the lower their information content.

Since learning is necessarily the formation of (representation of) a many-to-one mapping, it can be viewed as the achievement of a reduction in the information content of inputs (messages from the environment) by 'forwarding' them via the target mapping. A reduction in the information content of inputs means a reduction in uncertainty about the environment, which itself seems to correspond to an increase in knowledge. This is a satisfactory result since it corroborates our intuition that an increase in knowledge is the main result of learning.

---

[9] The fact that information is a subjective property (in Shannon's formulation) may be seen as a disadvantage by those concerned with the epistemological question of how knowledge can be justified. Dretske (1981), for example, has provided an information-theoretic model in which information is construed as a fundamentally objective property which 'flows' from the world into the mind of the receiving agent. A central notion in this theory is the idea that in the case where there is a correspondence between an actual realization of one possibility in the world and the perception of same in a receiving agent, information can be said to have flowed from the world to the receiver.

However, there is a problem. To reduce the information content of inputs to zero, the receiver need only map *all* inputs on to a single output. In this case the probability of receiving the output is 1 and the information content of outputs is zero. In this case the receiver is not surprised by *anything*. This sounds rather paradoxical!

But the paradox is apparent rather than real. If the receiver maps all inputs on to one output, that output tells the receiver absolutely nothing about what the original input was: the forwarding process has effectively obliterated the original message. On the other hand, if the receiver maps almost all inputs on to unique outputs, then a given output can give a completely accurate indication of what the input was. In reducing the absolute number of outputs the receiver reduces their information content but also, inevitably, increases their ambiguity. In terms of information theory, this introduction of ambiguity is understood in terms of the introduction of noise, or more precisely, *equivocation*.

By mapping unique inputs on to non-unique outputs the receiver reduces their information content but pays a price in terms of increased equivocation. Ideally, the receiver must find some way of minimizing both the information content of inputs *and* their equivocation. To minimize input information it is necessary to make the set of distinct outputs as small as possible, i.e. to map as many inputs as possible on to the same output. To minimize the equivocation of outputs, the receiver must minimize their ambiguity, i.e. must minimize the degree to which messages are *perturbed* as they are forwarded via the target mapping. To achieve this minimization it is only necessary to ensure that any set of unique inputs which are mapped on to the same output are as syntactically similar as possible, and that the output is as similar to all of the inputs as possible. Provided the similarity of any set of inputs evoking a unique output is maximized (for any given level of information reduction), the average perturbation (inaccuracy) of inputs is minimized too.

5.6. The information/equivocation tradeoff

The similarity-based learner, then, is confronted with a *tradeoff* between information and equivocation. The learner can reduce the information content of inputs but only by allowing their equivocation (ambiguity) to increase. The learner can reduce equivocation but only by allowing the information content of inputs to increase. For some fixed reduction in input information, there is some *minimum* price that the learner must pay in terms of equivocation. The price is kept to a minimum only if maximally similar inputs are mapped on to unique outputs. For some fixed equivocation, there is some maximum reduction in input information which can be achieved. Again, this is only achieved if maximally similar inputs evoke unique outputs. Thus, there is a set of optimal ways of combining information reduction and equivocation increase.

We can visualize the situation in terms of a 2-dimensional graph in which information is plotted on the vertical axis and equivocation is plotted on the horizontal axis; see Figure 5.1. A given point corresponds to a particular information/equivocation combination. As we move down along the curve we obtain decreases in the information content of inputs in exchange for increases in their ambiguity. Points corresponding to feasible information/equivocation combinations form a region whose boundary represents the locus of optimal information/equivocation combinations, i.e. points from which we can achieve no improvement with regard to information (equivocation) without paying a price in terms of a deterioration with regard to equivocation (uncertainty).

In the special case where the receiver has no prior knowledge, uncertainty about the environment is minimized by moving to an optimal information reduction/equivocation combination. This is done by identifying groups of maximally similar inputs and mapping them on to maximally representative outputs (i.e. outputs which are as similar to members of the input group as possible). Similarity-based learning is, of course, a process which does exactly this. It attempts to map groups of inputs on to concepts in such a way as to maximize *intra*-group similarity and minimize *inter*-group similarity. Hence similarity-based learning can be seen as a way of optimizing knowledge about the environment. So, finally, we arrive at the desired justification of similarity-based learning.

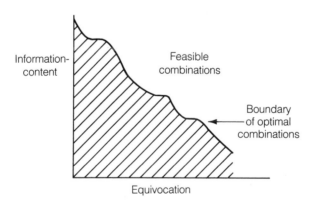

Figure 5.1. Information-content/equivocation tradeoff.

5.7. Concluding comments

Information theory has traditionally been something of a mire for those interested in the cognitive aspects of information. In some cases, the meaning of the term *information* as used in the theory has been too loosely interpreted and this has led to the emergence of difficulties such as the false paradox discussed above. However, despite these problems, the theory does seem to have implications beyond the area for which it was originally intended (i.e. electronic communications). In the area of learning it provides us with a much needed rationale for the well-established methodology of similarity-based learning. And, as we will see in the next chapter, it also provides a central foundation for the ID3 algorithm.

5.8. Further reading

The original text by Shannon and Weaver (1949) continues to be one of the best general references for this material but see also Llewellyn (1987) and Campbell (1984). The latter book is eminently suitable for those seeking a less technical introduction.

5.9. Problems

(1)   Information theory assumes an idealized model of an informational situation. What/who are the principal components in this model?

(2)   What is the qualitative form of the relationship between information and surprise and why?

(3)   How did Shannon define the information content of a single event (message) with probability *P?*

(4)   Why did Shannon argue that information should not be defined as a linear function of probability? What are the advantages of defining information in terms of log probabilities? (This requires some extra reading.)

(5)   What is the connection between the binary chop algorithm and the information measure?

(6) In what circumstances can we use the simple information measure:

$$\text{information}(M) = -\log_2 \text{probability}(M)$$

as a measure of uncertainty?

(7) What impact can similarity-based learning have on the information content of inputs?

(8) How can we trade off information content (of inputs) against equivocation? What criteria might we use in determining the best tradeoff?

(9) How would you go about measuring the information content(s) of a letter from a friend? What assumptions would you have to make in order to be able to do so?

(10) In what circumstances might it be appropriate to define information using base n logarithms (where $n > 2$)?

(11) Demonstrate that the level of uncertainty of a receiver who assigns equal probabilities to all possible messages is the same whether calculated using the entropy formula or the basic information formula.

6

ID3

6.1. Introduction

Although Ryszard Michalski's work with AQ11 demonstrated the way in which symbolic learning could be used to solve realistic problems, the method that has proved — in the 1980s at least — to be the most fruitful source of applications is Ross Quinlan's *ID3* algorithm.[1] This was derived from an algorithm originally described by Hunt *et al.* (1966) called the *Concept Learning System* or CLS. This algorithm constructs a representation in the form of a decision tree. In the tree, each leaf node corresponds to a unique target output. An arbitrary instance is processed by applying the tree to the instance. This yields a leaf node that in turn yields the target output.

One of the great advantages of CLS as a learning algorithm is the fact that it does not require the user to specify the structure of the instance space explicitly (e.g., by providing generalization hierarchies). The structure can be inferred directly from the training set. This greatly enhances the applicability of the algorithm. But in producing ID3, Quinlan added two features to the basic algorithm that improved it still further. First, he incorporated an information theoretic 'splitting' heuristic that enabled smaller and therefore more efficient decision trees to be constructed. Second, he added a process known as 'windowing' that enabled the algorithm to cope with very large training sets. With these advantages, ID3 quickly become a mainstay of symbolic learning and a central component in many commercial learning packages.

6.2. Conjunctive and disjunctive definitions

To understand the difference between ID3 and algorithms such as candidate

---

[1] ID3 stands for Inductive Dichotomizer 3.

elimination we need to first consider the difference between *conjunctive* and *disjunctive* concepts. Recall that target mappings with only two distinct outputs are often seen as the membership functions for concepts. When such functions are defined in terms of single regions of the instance space they are normally called *conjunctive concepts*.[2] When they are defined in terms of multiple regions they are called *disjunctive concepts*.[3] The distinction is drawn in these terms because a representation based on a single region can typically be defined using a single conjunctive expression, whereas a representation based on more than one region can normally only be defined using a disjunction of conjunctions.[4] Note that a hierarchy-based representation such as [small vehicle] corresponds to a simple conjunctive definition, namely:

$$X_1 = \texttt{small and } X_2 = \texttt{vehicle}$$

where X is the instance to be classified.

It is easy to produce examples of disjunctive concepts. Imagine that instances are made up of a colour value and a pattern value, such as

[white stripy]
[blue textured]

In this example {blue, green, orange} are the possible colours and {uniform, textured, stripy} are the possible patterns. The target concept covers all descriptions of 'loud' patterns. In particular, it covers [orange, uniform], [orange, textured], [blue, stripy], [green, stripy] and [orange, stripy] but *none* of the other possible instances.

This concept cannot be represented in terms of a single rectangular region in instance space (i.e. it cannot be represented as a conjunctive concept) because there is no attribute that is *shared* between all the positives. In geometric terms, there is no rectangle that encloses all the points corresponding to loud patterns but excludes all the points corresponding to non-loud patterns. However, the 'loud' concept could be defined in terms of the lists of shared attributes for two different groups: [orange] and [stripy]. This would correspond to an identification of *two* rectangles, as is shown

---

[2] They are sometimes called *implicitly disjunctive* due to the fact that they correspond to a disjunction that includes one term for each covered instance (Rendell, 1986).

[3] Occasionally, conjunctive concepts are called *monothetic* and disjunctive concepts are called *polythetic*.

[4] Of course we can always produce a conjunctive definition for multiple regions by introducing more powerful terms into our representation language.

in Figure 6.1.

6.3. The classification algorithm

In order to deal with disjunctive concepts of this sort we need to employ new learning methods. The CLS or *classification* algorithm is particularly well suited to the task of learning disjunctive concepts. The algorithm is a similarity-based, supervised method that accepts a set of training pairs and produces a hypothesis in the form of a decision tree (that is equivalent to a disjunctive rule). The main steps in the algorithm are as follows:

Classification algorithm

Initialize by setting variable T to be the complete training set. Then apply the following four steps to T.

(1)   If all elements in T are positive, create a 'yes' node and halt.

(2)   If all elements in T are negative, create a 'no' node and halt.

(3)   Otherwise select an attribute F with values $v_1, v_2, v_3, \ldots v_N$. Partition T into subsets $T_1, T_2, T_3, \ldots T_N$, according to their values on F. Create a branch with F as parent and T_1 etc. as child nodes.

(4)   Apply the procedure recursively to each child node.

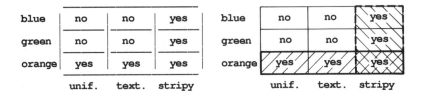

Figure 6.1. Disjunctive concept ('loud pattern').

6.4. Example

Let us look at an example of the classification algorithm in action. In this example, the instance space is 3-dimensional. The three dimensions correspond to a `size` attribute, a `shape` attribute and a `colour` attribute. The `size` attribute can take the values {`large`, `medium`, `small`}. The `shape` attribute can take the values {`sphere`, `brick`, `wedge`, `pillar`}, while the `colour` attribute can take the values {`red`, `blue`, `green`, `yellow`}. The training set contains seven pairs:

```
1. <[medium blue   brick]   [yes]>
2. <[small  red    wedge]   [no]>
3. <[small  red    sphere]  [yes]>
4. <[large  red    wedge]   [no]>
5. <[large  green  pillar]  [yes]>
6. <[large  red    pillar]  [no]>
7. <[large  green  sphere]  [yes]>
```

The algorithm initializes the decision tree to be a single node containing all the instances. In the diagrams below instances are represented as single digits. Input number one is represented by `1`. Input number two is represented by `2`, and so on. Thus the initial tree is just a set of all the digits between `1` and `7`:

$$\{1\ 2\ 3\ 4\ 5\ 6\ 7\}$$

In the first cycle, the algorithm selects an attribute on which to split the instances. It randomly chooses the `size` attribute. This has three possible values so three child nodes are created, one for each value. The child corresponding to `large` contains all the instances with this value (i.e. `4`, `5`, `6` and `7`). The child corresponding to `small` contains `2` and `3`. The child corresponding to `medium` contains all the instances containing this value but there is only one and it is a positive. Therefore the algorithm creates a `yes` node and stops extending this branch of the tree. The expanded decision tree looks like this:

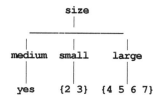

In the second cycle the algorithm is applied to both leaf nodes that contain instances of more than one class. In both cases, the algorithm chooses to split the instances using the **shape** attribute. In the case of instances **2** and **3** this produces two single-ton nodes that are immediately converted to leaf nodes. In the other case it produces three child nodes, one of which contains instances of different classes.

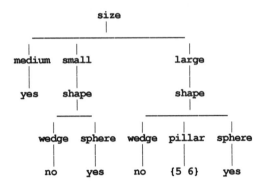

After the final cycle all the leaf nodes contain instances of the same class. The algorithm therefore terminates. The final decision tree is shown in Figure 6.2.

6.5. Deriving rules from decision trees

By construing all attribute-name nodes as disjunctive relations and all attribute-value nodes as conjunctive relations we can see the decision tree as a decision rule. The tree above corresponds to the following structure:

IF (**size** = **large**
   AND ((**shape** = **wedge**) OR (**shape** = **pillar** AND (**colour** = **red**))))
OR (**size** = **small** AND **shape** = **wedge**)
THEN **no**

IF (**size** = **large**
   AND ((**shape** = **pillar** AND **colour** = **green**) OR **shape** = **sphere**))
OR (**size** = **small** AND **shape** = **sphere**)
OR (**size** = **medium**)
THEN **yes**

We can derive a set of purely conjunctive rules (i.e. *disjunctive-normal form* or DNF formulae) by tracing out the paths to the positive nodes. For each attribute/value combination we construct an expression of the form 'attribute = value'. Each distinct attribute/value pair is joined by an AND. Thus, the tree above corresponds to the

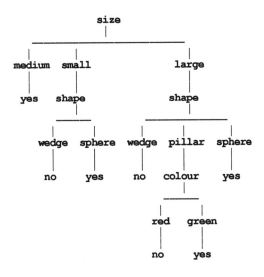

Figure 6.2. Final decision tree for blocksworld problem.

following formulae.

```
(size=medium)
(size=small AND shape=sphere)
(size=large AND shape=sphere)
(size=large AND shape=pillar AND colour=green)
```

6.6. The ID3 algorithm

The ID3 algorithm improves on the classification algorithm in two ways. First, it uses the windowing technique. This helps it to cope with large training sets. Second, it uses a heuristic to decide how best to split the instances at each stage of the tree growing process. This enables it to build more efficient (i.e. shallower) decision trees. We will consider both these enhancements, starting with windowing.

6.6.1. Windowing

If the training set is very large then, rather than process the entire set in one go, it may be more efficient to process a small sample first. If the sample is representative of the complete set the decision tree produced will be similar to the one which we would get by processing the entire training set. Once we have produced a tentative tree we can then gradually perfect it. To do this we simply search through the training set looking for any instance/output pairs that are not properly represented and each time we find such an exception we modify the tree appropriately. This process is called *windowing*; it is a feature of the standard ID3 algorithm.[5]

6.6.2. The information theoretic heuristic

The most important way in which ID3 differs from the standard classification algorithm is in its use of a 'splitting' heuristic. Recall that the classification algorithm does not have any principled criterion for deciding how to split the instances at any given point. This means that the algorithm may build deep, inefficient decision trees.[6] In ID3 an information theoretic heuristic is employed for deciding how to split sets of instances. This enables the algorithm to produce shallower trees.

In an incomplete decision tree for a positive/negative target mapping (i.e. a concept) leaf nodes contain both positive and negative instances. So deciding which leaf node an arbitrary instance classifies at[7] will not necessarily lead to a deterministic classification. However, since such leaf nodes will contain some balance of positive and negative instances the tree *can* generate probabilistic classifications.

For instance, if there are five positives and three negatives at a leaf X, then an arbitrary instance that classifies at X can be assumed to be positive with probability 5/8 = 0.625. Being able to derive these probabilistic classifications means that we can work out the information content of any message that tells us the *true* classification of an instance — given the assumption that our knowledge is completely represented by the current decision tree.

---

[5] In recent work, windowing does not receive much attention. In fact some evidence is now available that suggests windowing typically provides very little benefit (Wirth and Catlett, 1988).

[6] A deep tree will require a large number of tests to produce a classification.

[7] We say that an instance 'classifies at' node X if X is the node arrived at by tracing a path down through the decision tree making choices according to the values in the instance.

Let us think of each distinct output as a message and assume that we are dealing with a two-valued output mapping (i.e. a concept) in the usual way. We can think of the output **yes** as corresponding to the message 'it's positive', and the output **no** as corresponding to the message 'it's negative'. If we can say that p is the known probability that a given instance is positive and q is the known probability that it is negative (where $q = 1-p$), the information content of a message that gives us the true classification is:

$$- p \log_2 p - q \log_2 q$$

This formula is just a special case of the generalized information content (entropy) formula. The special case applies where there are just two possibilities to consider (with probabilities p and q).

6.6.3. Information needed and information gain

The information required for a deterministic classification of an arbitrary instance (that currently classifies at some given non-uniform leaf node) is just the information content of a message that provides the true classification. Our aim in building a decision tree is to arrive at a situation in which the information requirement is zero for all possible instances, i.e. a situation in which we can always generate the correct classification from the decision tree. In building the tree we should, then, at each stage, *minimize* the remaining information required. This is the idea underlying the ID3 heuristic.

To work out how much is achieved (i.e. how much the information requirement is reduced) by splitting the instances at some node on some particular attribute we first work out an *information needed* value for the current node. This is just the information required for a correct classification of an instance given the probabilities derivable from the mix of positives and negatives at the node. We then derive n child nodes by splitting the instances on the attribute. For each child we can derive the information needed for a correct classification of an instance that currently classifies at the child. We also compute an a priori probability that an arbitrary instance that classifies at the parent node *before* splitting will now classify at the given child. This probability is just the ratio between the number of nodes at the child and the number of nodes at the parent. If there are five nodes at the parent and two at the child, then the a priori probability that an instance that once classified at the parent will now classify at the child is just $2/5 = 0.4$.

The *expected information needed* (the amount of information we will still need after splitting) is just the total produced by summing the appropriately scaled *information-needed* values for all the children; i.e. by finding the sum of:

$$\text{information-needed(child)} \times (\text{size(child)} / \text{size(parent)})$$

for all children produced by the split. By subtracting the expected information needed (after the split) from the information needed (before the split) we get an *information-gain* value. ID3 selects the attribute that *maximizes* the information gain.

In effect the heuristic enables ID3 to choose the next split so as to maximize the *uniformity* of the new leaf nodes, i.e. the degree to which instances at a given node have the same type. This makes sense intuitively: the more uniform child nodes are, the closer we are to *completely* uniform nodes, i.e. ones that yield deterministic outputs. Of course, since the heuristic only looks one level ahead, it is vulnerable to what is known as the *horizon effect*. Deciding to split the instances in a certain way at a certain point may maximize the uniformity of the child nodes; however, it may not minimize the total number of times we will have to split the instances to get totally uniform nodes.

6.7. Example

Let us look at a worked example involving ID3. In this example we use the same instance space and training set as we used in the worked example for the classification algorithm. The target mapping is two-valued in the usual way and instances are descriptions of simple blocks. The training set is as follows:

```
1. <[medium blue  brick]   [yes]>
2. <[small  red   wedge]   [no]>
3. <[small  red   sphere]  [yes]>
4. <[large  red   wedge]   [no]>
5. <[large  green pillar]  [yes]>
6. <[large  red   pillar]  [no]>
7. <[large  green sphere]  [yes]>
```

The instance space is the 3-dimensional blocksworld language based on **size**, **colour** and **shape** attributes. In the displays, the instance/output pairs are labelled from **1** to **7** in the same way as before. The initial decision tree is therefore a single node containing all the pairs:

$$\{1\ 2\ 3\ 4\ 5\ 6\ 7\}$$

Now, this node is not uniform: some pairs are positives, some are negatives. There are seven pairs altogether, four positives and three negatives. Therefore the probability that an instance classifying at this node is positive is $4/7 = 0.57$; the probability that it is negative is $3/7 = 0.43$. So the information needed for a true classification is

Example 79

just the entropy of these two probabilities:

$$- (0.57 \times \log_2 0.57) - (0.43 \times \log_2 0.43) = 0.99$$

We now evaluate each possible way of splitting the instances. We (1) derive the child nodes, (2) compute the relative probabilities for positive and negative classifications, and then (3) derive an overall expected information-needed value. By subtracting the expected information needed from the current information needed we derive an information-gain value for each possible way of splitting. We then choose the split that achieves the highest gain.[8]

First of all we try splitting on the `size` attribute. This has three values: `large`, `medium` and `small`. We therefore produce three child nodes. The first one contains all the instances that include `large`:

{4 5 6 7}

There are two positives and two negatives in this set so the probability that an instance that classifies at this node is positive (or negative) is just 0.5. The information needed is therefore:

$$- (0.5 \times \log_2 0.5) - (0.5 \times \log_2 0.5) = 1$$

The next node contains all the instances that include `small`, namely:

{2 3}

This contains one negative and one positive. So the probability that a node classifying at this node is positive is 0.5 and the probability that it is negative is 0.5. Thus the information needed is again:

$$- (0.5 \times \log_2 0.5) - (0.5 \times \log_2 0.5) = 1$$

Finally, we inspect the node that contains all the instances that include `medium`. This contains only one positive instance: {1}. So now we have probabilities of 1 and 0, and an information-needed value of 0.

---

[8] Since the current information needed is constant we could equally well choose the split with the lowest expected information needed.

We can now calculate the expected information needed after splitting on **size**. We multiply all the information-needed values by the relevant proportions (i.e. probabilities):

$$(1 \times 4/7) + (1 \times 2/7) + (0 \times 1/7) = 0.86$$

The expected information gain from splitting on **size** is the expected information needed subtracted from the current information needed:

$$0.99 - 0.86 = 0.13$$

We now try splitting on **colour** and **shape** and derive information-gain values of 0.52 for **colour** and 0.7 for **shape**. Splitting on **shape** therefore achieves the highest information gain. The decision tree after this split is as follows:

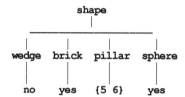

Only one node is non-uniform. This is the child of **pillar**. Applying the algorithm recursively to the instances **{5 6}** produces a further split on the **colour** dimension.

In fact this split produces a deterministic decision tree, i.e. a tree in which all the leaf nodes contain instances of the same type. The tree is shown below (compare it with the tree produced for the same data by the classification algorithm):

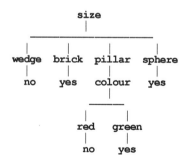

Example   *81*

6.8. A more realistic example

Obviously, to appreciate the real advantages of ID3 we need to look at a more realistic learning problem. The following example shows the results of applying a (non-windowing) ID3 to the problem of detecting toxicity in mushrooms of the Agaricus and Lepiota families. The original training set[9] for this problem contains over 8000 training pairs. The initial ten pairs are:

```
<[x s n t p f c n k e e s s w w p w o p k s u]  [poisonous]>
<[x s y t a f c b k e c s s w w p w o p n n g]  [edible]>
<[b s w t l f c b n e c s s w w p w o p n n m]  [edible]>
<[x y w t p f c n n e e s s w w p w o p k s u]  [poisonous]>
<[x s g f n f w b k t e s s w w p w o e n a g]  [edible]>
<[x y y t a f c b n e c s s w w p w o p k n g]  [edible]>
<[b s w t a f c b g e c s s w w p w o p k n m]  [edible]>
<[b y w t l f c b n e c s s w w p w o p n s m]  [edible]>
<[x y w t p f c n p e e s s w w p w o p k v g]  [poisonous]>
<[b s y t a f c b g e c s s w w p w o p k s m]  [edible]>
```

Each input here is a description of a sample of particular species of mushroom. Each input component corresponds to an attribute and the single character values correspond to attribute values. For example, the initial component of the input vectors corresponds to the attribute **cap-shape** (i.e. the shape of the cap of the mushroom). Its possible values are **x**, **b**, **c**, **f**, **k** and **s**. These correspond to different types of shape: **x** = convex, **b** = bell-shaped, **c** =conical, **f** = flat, **k** = knobbed and **s** = sunken. The target output is either **[edible]** or **[poisonous]**; the former indicates an edible mushroom and the latter indicates a poisonous one.

To obtain reasonable processing times a working training set of 200 pairs, and a testing set of 100 (different) pairs was randomly selected from the original database. Applying the classification algorithm (which selects attributes working from left to right) to this training set produced the tree shown in Figure 6.3. Note that the tree has been drawn on its side so as to save space.

The tree yields an overall error rate on the testing set of 20%. That is to say, it produces an incorrect classification on 1 in 5 of all testing pairs. The DNF definition for the poisonous class is as follows:

---

[9] This is taken from the UCI repository of machine learning databases. The training set was originally derived from Lincoff (1981).

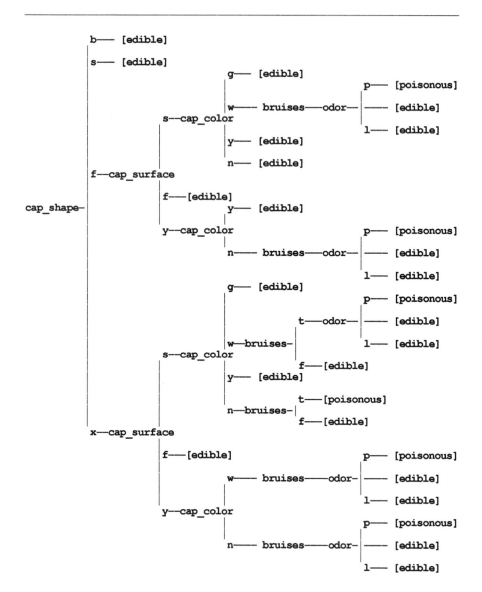

Figure 6.3. Mushroom decision–tree (classification algorithm).

```
(cap_shape=x AND cap_surface=s AND cap_color=n AND bruises=t)
(cap_shape=x AND cap_surface=y AND cap_color=n AND bruises=t AND odor=p)
(cap_shape=x AND cap_surface=y AND cap_color=w AND bruises=t AND odor=p)
(cap_shape=x AND cap_surface=s AND cap_color=w AND bruises=t AND odor=p)
(cap_shape=f AND cap_surface=y AND cap_color=n AND bruises=t AND odor=p)
(cap_shape=f AND cap_surface=s AND cap_color=w AND bruises=t AND odor=p)
```

Clearly, the representation produced by the classification algorithm in this case is quite complex. However, it turns out that there is in fact a very straightforward representation for this particular subset of the problem. This is brought out when we run ID3 on the training set. The decision tree produced is shown in Figure 6.4. From the tree we can derive a very simple DNF decision rule for the poisonous class, namely:

odor = p

The error rate of this representation is zero on both the training set and the testing set of 100 pairs.[10]

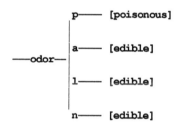

Figure 6.4. Mushroom decision-tree (ID3).

---

[10] Unfortunately, finding a rule which covers the entire mushroom training set is not so easy. Running a version of ID3 which terminates branches once the information needed at the leaf has fallen below 0.99, we can obtain a rule which obtains an error rate of about 24% on the training set.

6.9. Concluding comments

The ID3 algorithm has proved to be one of the most powerful methods in similarity-based learning. It is not a complex algorithm and therefore processes quite large training sets in a reasonable amount of time. Its usage of the information theoretic heuristic enables it to build compact decision trees (although its vulnerability to the horizon effect means that they are not guaranteed to be optimal) and its method for deriving the hypothesis space without requiring any special definitions (e.g., generalization hierarchies) means that it has been used widely both in the theoretical and the commercial spheres.

However, it is not a perfect algorithm. Its limitations spring from the fact that the hypotheses it constructs are essentially made up from sets of classical concept representations. Recall that the region of the instance space defined by a classical concept representation has a very particular 'shape'. Each of its boundaries encloses either an entire dimension (e.g., **red, green, blue,** ...) or just one value of it (e.g., **red**). This means that the algorithm is effectively incapable of defining regions that cover subsets (or subranges) of values in one or more dimensions.

Does this really matter? If we view the hypothesis space as the set of all regions in the instance space, then we can see that ID3 has a strong bias — in the sense that it can only define a small proportion of all possible regions. Potentially, this bias is both a strength and a weakness. If a particular target mapping can be well represented in terms of long and thin regions then ID3 will be successful in producing an efficient representation of the mapping. But if it turns out that the mapping cannot be easily represented this way, then the algorithm will fail to produce a high-quality representation. (An example is described in Chapter 21.) The representation produced may have many paths defining degenerate regions that cover only a single instance. In the worst case *all* its paths are of this type and the representation is effectively a lookup table. The overall effectiveness of ID3, then, rather depends on the form and structure of the target mapping.

6.10. Further reading

The Concept Learning System is described in Hunt *et al.* (1966) while ID3 is described in Quinlan (1983). However Bundy *et al.* (1985) is also worth looking at for its coverage of the classification algorithm. See also Quinlan (1986) or the article by Thompson and Thompson (1986) for information on ID3. The proceedings presented in Bratko and Lavrac (1987) provide examples of applications work involving ID3 from the mid-1980s. For the psychological perspective on the classification algorithm see Smith and Medin (1981).

6.11. Problems

(1) Consider the concept of *table*. Should this be considered a disjunctive or a conjunctive concept? Illustrate your answer using an appropriate instance and hypothesis space.

(2) In the case where we have the target mapping depicted below, how might we modify the instance space so as to allow the mapping to be learned as a conjunctive concept?

	unif.	text.	stripy
blue	−	−	+
green	−	−	+
orange	+	+	+

(3) What is the termination criterion for the classification algorithm? In what cases is it likely to produce a shallow decision tree?

(4) Invent an example in which a random split of the current instances causes the generation of an unnecessarily deep decision tree. Use the instance space represented in the diagram above.

(5) Describe an algorithm that will take a representation of a decision tree and produce the corresponding set of DNF formulae.

(6) Any decision tree effectively identifies a set of regions in instance space. How many are there in general and what can we say about their shape?

(7) Devise a pathological training set that will defeat the information theoretic, splitting heuristic. The training set must be such that the heuristic leads to a split being made that does *not* minimize the total number of splits that have to be made to arrive at completely uniform nodes.

7

Unsupervised learning by clustering

7.1. Introduction

So far we have been concentrating exclusively on supervised learning. In this approach the learner is given explicit information about the target mapping in the form of example pairs. In *self-supervised* or *unsupervised* learning the learner receives no explicit information about pairs in the target mapping but rather information that is entirely implicit. In fully unsupervised learning, improvements in the behaviour of the learner do not involve the evaluation of actual outputs. Instead, the desired behaviour is achieved via a direct, algorithmic process which can usually be described in terms of an objective function. In many cases, the aim of the learning process is to discover regularities in the input data. Typically, 'discovering regularities' simply means partitioning the instances into similarity classes, i.e. finding *clusters* of instances in the instance space. So it is not surprising to discover that unsupervised learning procedures sometimes closely resemble statistical clustering procedures.

Although there is a difference between supervised and unsupervised learning, they may achieve the same effect when presented with a given set of instances — even though the unsupervised process actually ignores the training outputs. We have already seen how supervised learning may produce a representation of the target mapping that shows how the instances in a given class 'cluster together'. So it follows that an unsupervised procedure that searches for instance clusters directly may well discover the same basic structure as discovered by a supervised procedure.

In this chapter we will look at some basic methods in cluster analysis and then move on to cover two clustering-based procedures in symbolic learning.

7.2. Basic numerical taxonomy

Clustering is normally viewed as a type of statistical analysis rather than a type of unsupervised, symbolic learning. In fact, in its most basic form, it is typically placed under the heading of *numerical taxonomy* since it involves the production of a class hierarchy (i.e. a classification scheme) using a mathematical measure of similarity defined over an instance space. The instances in this space are typically collections of numeric measures of particular parameters.

Imagine that we have the instances shown in Figure 7.1. Here, each instance is a sequence of attributes for a particular animal, the name of which appears on the right

```
[0 0 1 0 0 1 1 1 0 0 1 0 1 0 0 4] piranha
[1 0 0 1 0 0 1 1 1 0 0 4 1 0 1 1] cheetah
[1 0 0 1 0 1 1 1 1 0 1 2 1 0 1 1] sealion
[1 0 0 1 0 0 0 1 1 0 0 4 1 0 1 1] giraffe
[1 0 0 1 0 0 1 1 1 0 0 4 1 0 1 1] lion
[0 0 1 0 0 1 1 1 0 0 1 0 1 0 0 4] bass
[0 0 1 0 0 1 1 1 0 0 1 0 1 0 1 4] pike
[0 0 1 0 0 1 1 1 0 0 1 0 1 0 0 4] catfish
[1 0 0 1 0 1 1 1 1 0 1 0 0 0 1 1] seal
[1 0 0 1 0 0 0 1 1 0 0 4 1 0 1 1] elephant
[0 0 1 0 0 1 1 1 0 0 1 0 1 0 0 4] herring
[1 0 0 1 0 0 0 1 1 0 0 4 1 0 1 1] antelope
[0 0 1 0 0 1 1 0 0 0 0 8 0 0 1 7] octopus
[0 0 1 0 0 1 0 1 1 0 0 1 0 1 1 0 4] carp
[0 0 1 0 0 1 0 1 1 0 0 1 0 1 0 0 4] seahorse
[0 0 0 1 0 1 1 1 1 1 0 1 0 1 0 1 1] dolphin
[0 0 1 0 0 1 0 1 1 0 0 1 0 1 0 0 4] haddock
[1 0 0 1 0 0 1 1 1 0 0 4 1 0 1 1] mongoose
[1 0 0 1 0 0 0 1 1 0 0 4 1 1 1 1] calf
[1 0 0 1 0 0 0 1 1 0 0 4 1 1 1 1] reindeer
[0 0 1 0 0 1 1 1 0 0 1 0 1 0 1 4] dogfish
[0 0 1 0 0 1 0 1 1 0 0 4 0 0 0 5] toad
[1 0 0 1 0 0 0 1 1 0 0 2 0 0 1 1] gorilla
[1 0 0 1 0 0 1 1 1 0 0 4 1 0 0 1] mole
[1 0 0 1 0 0 0 1 1 0 0 4 1 0 1 1] buffalo
[0 0 0 1 0 1 1 1 1 1 0 1 0 1 0 1 1] porpoise
[1 0 0 1 0 0 0 1 1 0 0 4 1 0 1 1] deer
[0 0 0 0 0 1 1 1 1 0 1 0 0 1 0 0 3] seasnake
[1 0 0 1 0 0 0 1 1 0 0 4 1 1 1 1] goat
[1 0 0 1 0 1 1 1 1 0 0 4 1 0 1 1] mink
[1 0 0 1 0 0 1 1 1 0 0 4 0 0 1 1] bear
```

Figure 7.1. Binary-valued animal instances.

of the instance. Attributes 13 and 17 specify the number of legs and the 'type' of the animal respectively. All the other attributes are *boolean*, i.e. they can have either the value 'yes' (represented here as 1) or the value 'no' (represented here as 0). The attributes correspond to the following predicates (reading left-to-right): 'has hair', 'has feathers', 'lays eggs', 'produces milk', 'can fly', 'is predator', 'has teeth', 'has backbone', 'breathes', 'is venomous', 'has fins', 'has tail', 'is domestic' and 'is catsize'.

The application of a clustering procedure to these instances produces the class hierarchy shown in Figure 7.2. Note how the groupings correspond approximately to species. Note in particular the major dichotomy between fishes and dry-land animals.[1]

Let us see how this clustering process can be carried out. The simplest method of all involves (1) setting up initial clusters each of which contains a single instance, and then (2) repeatedly joining together those clusters whose mutual similarity is highest. This is called

Agglomerative clustering algorithm

Initialize by setting D to be the set of singleton sets such that each set contains a unique instance. Then, until D has only one element, do the following two steps.

(1)   Form a matrix of similarity values for all elements of D (using some given similarity function).

(2)   Merge those elements of D that have a maximum similarity value.

Note that in this procedure we are effectively working bottom-up, trying to build ever larger clusters. An alternative procedure is *divisive clustering*. This works top-down (like ID3), repeatedly trying to break down the instances into smaller groups. Unfortunately, divisive clustering is potentially more time-consuming than agglomerative clustering. If we have no easy way of deciding how to split a given set of instances then divisive clustering involves searching through all possible ways of splitting n elements into clusters. The number of possibilities in this process is usually large. There are 2^n ways of splitting n elements into 2 groups, 3^n ways of splitting n elements into 3 groups, and so on. As a result, divisive clustering is less commonly used than agglomerative clustering.

---

[1] The groupings suggest that the data may contain some erroneous descriptions.

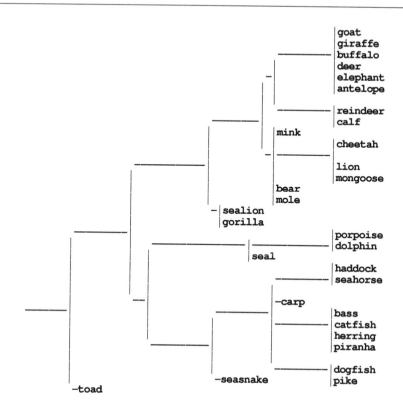

Figure 7.2. Agglomerative clustering of animal instances.

7.2.1. Euclidean and city-block distances

The basic clustering algorithms are very straightforward. However, the question of how to compute 'similarity' is a complicated one. There are two issues to be considered:

- How should we compute the similarity of two distinct instances?

- How should we compute the similarity of two *groups* of instances?

If instances are just vectors of numbers, then we can measure their syntactic similarity by measuring their closeness (inverse distance) in the instance space. This can done using a *Euclidean metric*, a *city-block metric* or some other standard measure of distance. The Euclidean and city-block distances between instances x and y are defined as follows:

Euclidean distance: $\sqrt{\sum_i (x_i - y_i)^2}$

City-block (Manhattan) distance: $\sum_i |x_i - y_i|$

If we think about the instances as points in a geometric space, then their Euclidean distance is just the same thing as their 'as-the-crow-flies' distance. Their city-block distance is just the total distance we would cover in going from one point to the other walking parallel to the axes of the space. The distinction is characterized in Figure 7.3. (In clustering the animal data we used the Euclidean distance metric.)

7.2.2. Single-linkage and complete-linkage methods

We now look at some of the common methods for computing the similarity (closeness) of clusters. The simplest methods are the single-linkage method and the complete-linkage method.

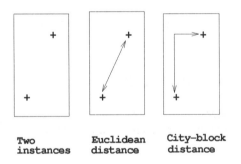

Figure 7.3. Euclidean and city-block distances.

- In the *single-linkage* method, the distance between two groups is defined as the distance between their two closest points.

- In the *complete-linkage* method, the distance between two groups is defined as the distance between their two most distant points.

Two other common methods are the centroid method and the group-average method.

- In the *centroid* method, the distance between two groups is defined as the distance between their centroids. (This was the method we used in clustering the animal data.)

- In the *group-average method*, group distance is defined as the average of the distances for all pairs in the Cartesian product of the two groups.

The single-linkage method is computationally inexpensive; however, it is vulnerable to a phenomenon known as *chaining*. This occurs whenever the data set contains a set of points in which each point is close to its nearest neighbour but relatively distant from all other points in the chain. The single-linkage method applied to a cluster containing such a point will keep expanding the cluster by adding in the next point along the chain. The final result is a chain-like 'cluster' that contains very distant points. The group-average method is robust against such effects but computationally rather expensive. Computing the distance between two groups involves measuring the distance between $n \times m$ points, where n is the number of points in one group and m is the number of points in the other.

7.3. Conceptual clustering

As we noted, there are many unsupervised learning algorithms that are based on a process very similar to agglomerative clustering. These algorithms carry out what is known as *conceptual clustering*. The main difference between clustering and conceptual clustering is that conceptual clustering enables contextual information to be taken into account. In conventional clustering procedures the only information available to the algorithm consists of the instances themselves. Therefore these algorithms cannot take account of semantic relationships among instance attributes, or global concepts that might be of relevance in forming a classification scheme.

The aim in conceptual clustering is the same as in conventional clustering, namely, to derive a hierarchical classification. But in conceptual clustering there is the additional intention that each node in the hierarchy should form a coherent *concept*. 'Coherent' can, however, mean a number of different things. It can mean that the class representation should be

- compact,

- easily represented in terms of a definition or rule that has a natural interpretation for humans, or

- easily transformed into a representation that can help in the achievement of goals.

Here we will look at two important conceptual clustering systems. First, we will look at Lebowitz's UNIMEM system. Second, we will look at the more recent COBWEB system, developed by Fisher.

7.4. UNIMEM

UNIMEM is essentially a divisive clustering algorithm. As such it bears some resemblance to ID3 and the classification algorithm in the way in which it produces a class hierarchy. To introduce it, let us first look at a well-known method for interactively extending a decision tree.

Consider the decision tree shown in Figure 7.4. This tree is for classifying cars. All the attributes tested by the tree are two-valued. Thus all internal nodes have exactly two branches. The one to the left leads to the subtree to be used in the case that the instance being tested *does* have the attribute in question. The one to the right leads to the subtree to be used in the case that the instance *does not* have the attribute.

The decision tree can be automatically extended within an interaction with a knowledgeable user. Imagine that the user asks for a classification of a given instance. The algorithm descends through the tree, testing attributes of the instance and choosing branches in the usual way. When it arrives at a leaf node it produces the corresponding label as a tentative classification. If the user indicates that the classification is incorrect the program responds by asking what question would discriminate between the new instance and the suggested classification. If the instance is a Porsche and the classification is 'BMW' (as it might be, given the present tree), the user might suggest the question 'Is it a two-seater?'. The program then asks what name should be associated with a fast, expensive, two-seater. The user says 'Porsche' and

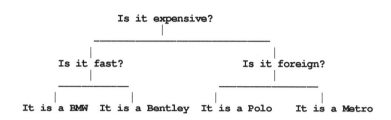

Figure 7.4. Decision-tree for classifying cars.

the program creates a new subnode in the tree as shown in Figure 7.5.[2]

Like this simple program, the UNIMEM system uses a tree structure as its basic representation. Moreover, it exhibits roughly the same behaviour. If asked to classify an instance it searches down its internal decision tree, testing attributes and returns a classification based on the relevant leaf nodes. If asked to update the tree so as to represent a new instance, it searches down the tree looking for a suitable place to add

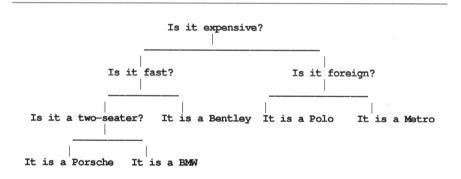

Figure 7.5. Extended decision-tree for classifying cars.

[2] Of course, in the case where attributes are not two-valued, the program would have to ask the user to provide the complete set of values for the attribute in question.

in new structure. But while the simple program described above uses a tree in which each node tests a single attribute (i.e. a *monothetic* tree) UNIMEM uses a tree in which each node can test an arbitrary number of attributes (i.e. a *polythetic* tree).

This has ramifications both for classifications and for the mechanism by which the tree is updated. In considering the classification aspect, we should note that each node in UMIMEM's tree is a complex definition and therefore covers a certain set of instances. These nodes are not mutually exclusive — their coverage may overlap. Thus, when UNIMEM searches down through the tree for a classification of a given instance, it cannot stop after finding the first satisfactory node. It has to continue in order to find all the nodes that cover the instance.

In considering the updating mechanism we should note that UNIMEM's method for extending the tree is automatic and therefore does not require interaction with a knowledgeable user. The basic idea is to add new nodes into the tree as and when they appear to be warranted by the presented instances. In order to do this UNIMEM actually stores each presented instance at all the nodes that cover it. If it ever appears that there are two instances stored at a node that are particularly similar to one another, then an extra child node is created whose definition covers the two instances in question. (The two instances are then relocated to this new node.) As new instances are processed, new specializations are created and the hierarchy thus 'grows' downwards.

For present purposes it is most convenient to view UNIMEM as a learning algorithm. As such we can see it as using a type of clustering algorithm to gather instances together into classes. However, since the mechanism actually *stores* new instances inside the tree, we can also view it as a type of memory device — a *generalization-based memory*. The structure of the hierarchy enables given classes of instances to be accessed much more efficiently than would be the case if all the instances were stored in a linear memory structure. This is because it supports inheritance of properties.

7.5. The processing loop in UNIMEM

The main instance-processing loop in UNIMEM is specified as follows:[3]

UNIMEM algorithm

----

[3] This is a simplification of the pseudo-code algorithm given in Lebowitz (1987).

Initialize the decision tree to be an empty root node. Then apply the following steps to each instance.

(1)   Search the tree depth-first for the most specific concept nodes that the instance matches.

(2)   Add the new instance to the tree at or below these nodes. This involves comparing the new instance to the ones already stored there and creating new subnodes (generalizations) if appropriate.

Note that an instance is considered to 'match' a node if it is covered by that node (i.e. concept). Typically, UNIMEM accesses an attribute-value data language. This means that match (coverage) is determined by testing to see what proportion of the instance's attributes are associated with the node (concept). If attribute values are ordered, then a distance function is used — just like in ordinary clustering — to determine the dissimilarity between a given concept and a given instance.

At any point in the search of the concept hierarchy, UNIMEM checks to see if the sum of the distances between the currently unaccounted-for instance attributes and those of the current node is too great (i.e. over some threshold). If it is, UNIMEM stops exploring the current branch.

The search process returns all the most specific nodes that explain (cover) the new instance. UNIMEM then generalizes each node in this set as necessary, so as to account for (cover) the new instance. It compares the new instance with all the other instances stored at the node. If it finds an instance that has enough attributes in common with the new instance, it creates a new subnode by generalizing the common attributes and stores both instances at the subnode. Otherwise it stores the instance at the node.

7.6. Example

Let us look at a worked example involving a 'toy' (highly simplified) reconstruction of UNIMEM. The data for the example are taken from a training set in which instances are attribute vectors for American flags. Each instance describes one flag for a particular state and the name of the state is shown to the right of the relevant training pair. The complete training set is listed in Figure 7.6. In the example, UNIMEM is presented with just the instance vectors from this training set. These are labelled 1, . . . , 12 in the displays below: 1 labels the Alabama instance, 2 labels the Arkansas instance, and so on.

		Stars	Bars	Strp	Hues	Xcrs	Icon	Hmns	Word	Num	Class	
1.	<[	0	0	0	3	1	0	0	0	0	] [C]>	Alabama
2.	<[	29	0	0	3	0	0	0	1	0	] [C]>	Arkansas
3.	<[	0	0	0	5	0	1	0	4	0	] [U]>	Connecticut
4.	<[	0	0	0	6	0	1	2	4	2	] [U]>	Delaware
5.	<[	0	0	0	6	1	1	1	15	0	] [C]>	Florida
6.	<[	13	1	0	3	1	1	0	3	1	] [C]>	Georgia
7.	<[	0	0	0	6	0	1	0	6	2	] [U]>	Illinois
8.	<[	0	2	0	5	0	1	0	10	0	] [U]>	Iowa
9.	<[	0	0	0	4	0	1	0	4	0	] [C]>	Louisiana
10.	<[	0	12	0	4	0	1	0	0	0	] [U]>	Maryland
11.	<[	1	0	0	4	0	1	1	6	0	] [U]>	Mass.
12.	<[	13	0	3	3	1	0	0	0	0	] [C]>	Mississippi

Figure 7.6. The 'flags' training set (after Forsyth and Rada, 1986).

The toy UNIMEM assumes that all values are ordinal and that the distance between two values is just their absolute difference. This means that the program defines the similarity of two inputs as the city-block distance. A generalization is just a range of values (e.g. 3, . . ., 8) and the degree to which a generalization does *not* cover an instance is just the degree to which the instance's values fall outside the ranges representing the generalization. A generalization of two instances is formed by finding the minimal ranges that subsume all values of both instances.

Initially UNIMEM has an empty generalization hierarchy. Thus, presentation of the first instance causes it to initialize the hierarchy as a single node containing the first instance. We represent sets of instances here in the usual way using integers and curly brackets:

{1}

After presentation of the second instance, UNIMEM decides to create a new subnode containing instances **1** and **2**:

{1 2}

Instance number **3** is not sufficiently similar (i.e. the city-block distance is too great)

Example 97

to instances **1** and **2** to be stored with them. It is therefore stored at the root node. The tree after presentation of instance number **3** therefore looks like this:

Instance number **4** is sufficiently similar to instance number **3** to warrant the generation of a new subnode. Thus the tree is extended as follows:

Instance number **5**, like instance number **3**, is not sufficiently similar to any of the instances stored at the two subnodes to be stored with them. It is therefore stored at the root:

Presentation of instance number **6** triggers the generation of a new subnode at which instances **5** and **6** are stored:

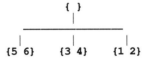

Presentation of instance number **7** triggers the production of a second level of structure in the tree. It is sufficiently similar to both **4** and **3** to warrant the production of two new subnodes:

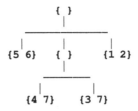

Presentation of instance number **8** has a very similar effect, only this time we get new generalizations involving instances **7** and **3**:

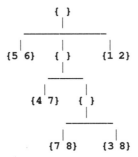

Instance **9** turns out to be sufficiently similar to instances **3**, **7** and **8**. As a result we see **9** stored at four different nodes in the tree. Storing an instance at such a large number of nodes effectively reduces the quality of the clustering since it increases the overall inter-class similarity. The implication is that our criterion for deciding whether two instances are sufficiently similar is too weak for this training set.

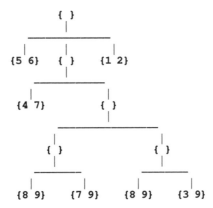

Presentation of instance number **10** produces no further decrease in clustering quality. It turns out to be insufficiently similar to all of the nodes in the tree and is

Example 99

therefore stored at the root:

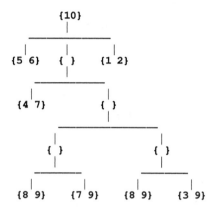

Instance number **11** produces an effect similar to that produced by instance number **9**. It is stored at four different nodes and average inter-class dissimilarity is therefore decreased still further.

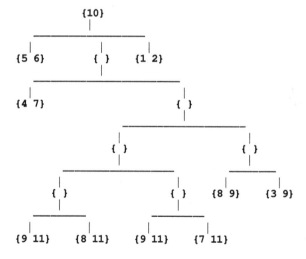

Instance number **12** turns out to be sufficiently similar to instance number **10** to warrant the generation of a new subnode. The final tree therefore looks like this:

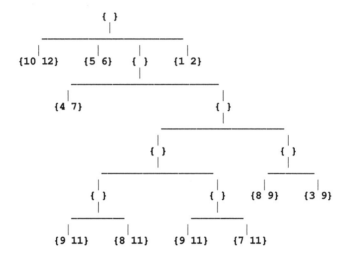

It is interesting to compare the concept hierarchy produced by UNIMEM with the tree produced using ordinary agglomerative clustering. The tree shown in Figure 7.7 is the concept hierarchy produced by UNIMEM in the example above displayed on its side with the root on the left.

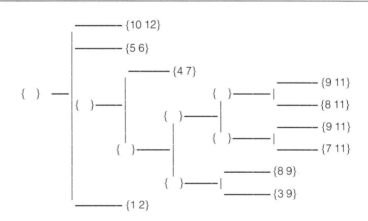

Figure 7.7. UNIMEM tree for 'flags' training set.

Example 101

The tree in Figure 7.8 was produced by clustering with a city-block distance function and the group-average method for computing cluster distance. Leaf nodes are represented as instance vectors but the corresponding integer labels have been appended to facilitate comparison. Notice how this tree brings out the fact that instances **3** and **9** are the most similar. Some of the difference between the two trees can be explained in terms of the fact that, in UNIMEM, the structure of the tree is order-dependent, whereas in hierarchical clustering this is not the case.

7.7. COBWEB and category utility

UNIMEM's aim is to build a hierarchy in which the clusters represent good concepts. However, its notion of what forms a good concept is represented in the form of the many system parameters that control its cluster-building behaviour. There are a fairly large number of these and the user must select appropriate settings for each one in order for the system to behave satisfactorily. Parameters that are particularly important include the one that specifies the degree of instance similarity that is required to

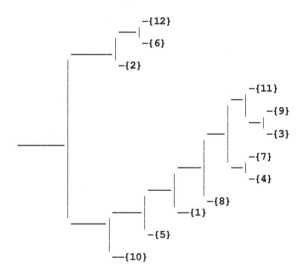

Figure 7.8. Agglomerative clustering of 'flags' training set.

warrant a new specialization, and the one that specifies the degree of coverage that is required in order for a definition to count as 'covering' a given instance. This heavy reliance on user-defined parameters is a disadvantage. However, more recent conceptual clustering systems have been able to overcome this problem to a certain extent.

The COBWEB system is a case in point. COBWEB is based on the idea that a 'good' clustering should *minimize* the distance between points within a cluster and *maximize* the distance between points in different clusters. If distance corresponds to dissimilarity then a high-quality clustering is one that maximizes intra-cluster similarity and minimizes inter-class similarity. The goal in COBWEB, then, is to find an optimum tradeoff between intra-class similarity and inter-class dissimilarity.

COBWEB defines the quality of a particular clustering in terms of the *expected* number of attribute values that can be correctly guessed for an arbitrary member of an arbitrary instance class. If instance values are nominal, the similarity of two instances depends only on the number of values they have in common. Thus a clustering that maximizes intra-cluster similarity and minimizes inter-class similarity must be one that affects the probability of two instances sharing an arbitrary value in a particular way. In particular, it must maximize it for two instances from the same cluster and minimize it for two instances from different clusters. COBWEB does exactly this and thereby maximizes clustering quality.

In fact, COBWEB attempts, at each stage, to maximize *category utility*. This is simply the increase in the expected number of values that can be correctly guessed on average. Since this will clearly reflect the degree of intra-class similarity we know that maximizing category utility will implicitly optimize the quality of the clustering. The use of this clustering heuristic means that COBWEB has to represent clusters in a manner that makes it possible to derive probabilities for particular values. It does this by keeping count of the number of times a particular value appears in the instances stored at a given node. Thus, each cluster (node) is associated with a set of counts. Each count is the number of instances stored at or below the node that have a particular value for an attribute. Probabilities are derived as ratios between counts in the obvious way.

The fact that clusters are represented in terms of probabilities means that COBWEB cannot deterministically decide whether a particular instance can be stored at a particular node. For each distinct instance it can only derive the probability of it being covered by a particular node in the tree. The nodes that cover the new instance with the highest probability are referred to in COBWEB parlance as the instance's *best hosts*. COBWEB attempts to store each new instance at all of its best hosts. But in doing this it also considers the possibility of (1) creating a new node for the instance, or (2) merging the two best hosts or (3) deleting (*splitting*) one or more of the children of the best host. It thus dynamically manipulates the tree so as to maintain a maximum-quality clustering at all times.

7.8. Comments

COBWEB and UNIMEM are far from being the only conceptual clustering methods. However, they do serve to give a flavour of this particular subfield of symbolic learning and to suggest what its limitations and possibilities might be. Both UNIMEM and COBWEB attempt to find a way of partitioning the instances into groups that (1) respects the similarity principle (i.e. the principle that instances in the same class should be similar to one another) and (2) respects a less well-defined notion of conceptual coherence or usefulness. COBWEB's approach to the latter is more principled than UNIMEM's since it relies on the single criterion, that the clusters should be configured so as to maximize the predictive capacity of the associated categories. And while it is probably the case that whatever clustering we can produce with COBWEB we can also (given an appropriate configuration of user-defined parameters) produce using UNIMEM, it seems reasonable to assume that, usually, generalizing to new domains will be easier using COBWEB rather than UNIMEM.

7.9. Further reading

Good references for statistical clustering and numerical taxonomy are Everitt (1974) and Anderberg (1973). Good (1977) considers the wider epistemological status of clustering while Romesburg (1984) provides a very elementary introduction to the field. Chatfield and Collins, (1980) provide a treatment that places cluster analysis in the context of statistical, multivariate analysis. Sokal (1977) is an authoritative survey article on clustering and classification. Fisher and Langley (1985) is an excellent survey article on conceptual clustering. See also Fisher (1987b). For alternative distance measures see Vogt *et al*. (1987, pp. 29-36) and Anderberg (1973).

UNIMEM is described in Lebowitz (1987) while a good reference for COBWEB is Fisher (1987a). Both of these articles appear in a single issue of the Machine Learning journal (vol. 2, no. 2). Articles by Michalski and Stepp, e.g., Michalski and Stepp (1983) and Stepp and Michalski (1986) provide a slightly different perspective on the general topic of conceptual clustering. They also focus on a different type of system.

7.10. Problems

(1)   What is the aim in numerical taxonomy?

(2)   In what sense is conceptual clustering related to similarity-based learning?

(3)   If we have data presented in the form of a training set, can we use them for the purposes of unsupervised learning? If so, how?

(4)   Using an example, describe the difference between an agglomerative clustering algorithm and a divisive algorithm. Which approach is likely to be computationally more efficient and why?

(5)   The Euclidean distance function can be used as a similarity measure provided that instances have certain properties. What are these properties?

(6)   What is the difference between single-linkage and complete-linkage clustering? What problems can arise with the former method?

(7)   What sort of clustering process is normally used in machine learning? What are its distinguishing characteristics?

(8)   What sort of representations are constructed by UNIMEM? What tasks might they be used for?

(9)   What is the difference between a monothetic and a polythetic decision tree? Does UNIMEM construct a monothetic tree? Does ID3? Does the classification algorithm?

(10)   How might UNIMEM generalize over descriptions whose components identify subranges of continuous variables?

(11)   What are the main steps in the UNIMEM algorithm and what is the termination criterion?

(12)   Contrast the UNIMEM system with Fisher's COBWEB system. What disadvantages might there by in the COBWEB approach to conceptual clustering?

(13) How does COBWEB's representation of clusters differ from UNIMEM's?

8

LEX and explanation-based learning

8.1. Introduction: the knowledge principle

In the 1970s and 1980s AI researchers placed increasing emphasis on the role of *background knowledge*. Lenat, for example, has identified the 'knowledge principle'. This is the notion that AI systems cannot hope to perform well without plenty of background knowledge. In Winston (1984), the idea that the knowledge principle will always have a (negative) impact on learning mechanisms takes the form of *Martin's law* - 'you can't learn something unless you almost know it already'.

Given this background it is paradoxical that a large proportion of all symbolic learning algorithms — and in fact all the algorithms we have looked at so far — use practically no built-in knowledge whatsoever. Such knowledge-free algorithms are said to carry out *empirical learning* since they form representations purely on the basis of observations (i.e. received inputs) without bringing any knowledge to bear. But empirical learning is far from being the only possibility that has been explored in symbolic learning. In fact, during the latter half of the 1980s, an increasing proportion of work was devoted to the investigation of knowledge-driven approaches.

One of the leading examples of this alternative form of learning is *explanation-based learning* or EBL. This is based on the observation that people frequently learn how to solve a problem by observing and understanding how some other person solves it. The implication seems to be that powerful learning (e.g., the sort exhibited by humans) may depend on being able to construct *explanations* for the behaviours of other cognitive mechanisms. Researchers have investigated the possibility by building systems that attempt to do just this, i.e. construct explanations for training inputs in terms of some prespecified *domain theory*.

We will look at explanation-based learning in more detail below. By way of introduction we will look at the LEX system. LEX contains within it some of the ideas
that are central to explanation-based learning. But the system is also important in its
own right since it shows how a standard symbolic learning procedure (candidate
elimination) can be combined with other processes for the purposes of producing
interesting learning behaviour.

8.2. LEX

LEX differs from the learning systems we have considered so far in the sense that it
does not attempt to find a representation for a target mapping (at least not in any
obvious sense) but rather attempts to improve its performance on a certain task. The
task in question is *symbolic integration*. This is the process by which we apply a
sequence of manipulations to a mathematical expression so as to get rid of the
integration sign (cf. performing syntactic manipulations on an equation so as to get
all the unknowns on one side). We do not need to know why one might want to do
this, or why particular manipulations are legal. We can just think in terms of an arbitrary formal system involving particular syntactic items and rules of manipulation.

8.2.1. The problem solver

Learning in LEX involves an interaction between two main components: a *problem
solver* and a *strategy modifier*. We will look at the problem-solver component first.
The input to the problem solver is a symbolic integration problem; i.e. an expression
containing an integration sign. The goal of the problem solver is to manipulate the
expression so as to get rid of the integration sign.

LEX has access to a set of integration operators (i.e. operators that manipulate
expressions) and it solves an integration problem by searching the space of possible
manipulations to find a sequence that gets rid of the integration sign. Each operator
describes one legal transformation (i.e. specifies one transition in the search space).
In Figure 8.1 we see a selection of operators. Note that some of them achieve a satisfactory goal state directly, i.e. they produce an expression with no integration sign in
it. Others produce intermediate states that will require further manipulation to remove
the integration sign.

The search space defined by this set of operators is very large. The branching factor
is just the total number of operators. If there are 25 operators, then the first two levels
in the problem space contain over $25^3 = 15625$ states. The normal way of getting
around this sort of search complexity is to use heuristics. However, whereas the

OP1	$\int r \cdot f(x) \, dx$	->	$r \int f(x) \, dx$

OP2   Integration by parts:
           $\int u \, dv$ -> $uv - \int v \, du$
        (the precondition is internally represented
        as $\int f1(x) \, f2(x) \, dx$, where $f1(x)$ corresponds
        to u and $f(x) \, dx$ corresponds to dv)

OP3	$1 \cdot f(x)$	->	$f(x)$
OP4	$\int f1(x)+f2(x) \, dx$	->	$\int f1(x) \, dx + \int f2(x) \, dx$
OP5	$\int \sin(x) \, dx$	->	$-\cos(x) + C$
OP6	$\int \cos(x) \, dx$	->	$\sin(x) + C$
OP7	$\int x^r \, dx$	->	$[x^{(r+1)}] / (r+1) + C$

Figure 8.1. Some LEX operators (after Mitchell *et al.*, 1983).

normal strategy would be to use a single heuristic function to discriminate between good and bad operator applications, LEX adopts a quite different approach. It associates each operator with a description of those cases in which the operator is likely to be of advantage — and only applies an operator if its description covers the current form of the expression. This strategy paves the way for a fairly straightforward learning strategy. To improve problem solving performance all we have to do is fine-tune the descriptions so as to make sure that they describe only those cases in which application of the corresponding operator will be of advantage.

8.2.2. Heuristics as concepts

But how can we carry out this fine-tuning? The point to note is that the role of the descriptions is to discriminate between two classes: the class of expressions for which the operator is appropriate and the class for which it is not appropriate. Since a description that discriminates between two classes is, in effect, a concept representation, we can treat the descriptions as *concepts* and use concept learning techniques for the fine-tuning. LEX's approach, in fact, is to use *supervised* concept learning for the purposes of refining descriptions. But, of course, to carry out supervised concept learning, a *training set* is required. In fact, to learn descriptions (concepts) for a whole set of operators a whole set of training sets is required.

LEX uses a rather neat trick to obtain these training sets. First it runs the problem solver on a sample integration problem. Then it looks at the trace of the problem solver and finds all the situations in which a given operator was applied. From each application, LEX derives a training pair. The input in the pair is just the expression to which the operator was applied. The output is 'yes' if application of the operator kept the problem solver on the solution path, and 'no' otherwise. Collecting all the pairs so generated for a particular operator together provides a training set that can then be used to refine the concept (heuristic) associated with that operator.[1]

8.2.3. The hypothesis space

Two questions remain: What concept learning method does LEX use? And how is the hypothesis space defined? The first question can be quickly dispensed with. LEX makes use of the candidate elimination algorithm for the purposes of refining descriptions. This means that, in general, descriptions are in the form of version-space representations and that the process of checking a particular expression for suitability involves deciding whether the expression is covered by a hypothesis in the corresponding version space.

The issue of the definition of the hypothesis space is not quite so straightforward. In LEX, the hypothesis space is based on generalization hierarchies, just as it is in focussing. However, the process by which hypotheses are derived differs slightly. The LEX hypothesis space is based on a *single* generalization hierarchy. This contains all the mathematical symbols which can go to make up symbolic expressions. Representations are constructed using *multiple* items from the hierarchy. This contrasts with the usual method in which hypotheses are constructed by taking one item from each of a set of hierarchies (cf. Chapter 3).

In Figure 8.2 we see part of the generalization hierarchy that defines LEX's hypothesis language. The hierarchy is tangled (a child node can have more than one parent) which means that there may be more than one maximally general/specific hypothesis covering a given set of cases. Thus the version-space hypotheses produced by candidate elimination will typically consist of a non-singleton general boundary and a non-singleton specific boundary. This contrasts with the simple case we concentrated on when dealing with focussing.

To a first approximation, the hypothesis space can be thought of as the set of all sequences of nodes from this tree. Similarly, the instance language is approximately

---

[1] Of course, if the problem generator does not provide a random sampling of the space of problems, then this approach may encounter various sorts of looping problems.

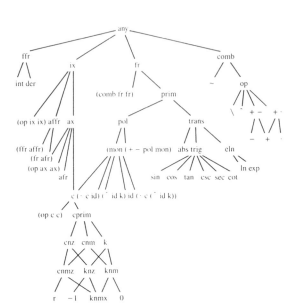

Special rules:
a. Something is an **afr** if and only if it is a nonnumeric atom that is not used explicitly elsewhere in the grammar.
b. Something is an **r** if it is a noninteger or Euler's constant.
c. Something is a **knmz** if and only if it is an integer that is neither 0 nor −1.

Figure 8.2. LEX generalization hierarchy (after Utgoff, 1986a).

the set of all sequences of *leaf* nodes from this tree (e.g., [$x + y$] or [sin ($x + y$)]).[2]

As we saw in Chapter 2, version spaces are defined in terms of a set of maximally general, satisfactory hypotheses and a set of maximally specific, satisfactory hypotheses. Each version space identifies the set of cases in which the corresponding

[2] In fact, in the implementation of LEX expressions were written in a standard Lisp notation so as to make the problems involved in dealing with arbitrary-sized tuples less severe.

operator is of advantage and thus serves as an application heuristic for the operator. For example, consider the following heuristic for symbolic integration:

IF the problem state contains an integrand that is the product of x and any transcendental function of x,

THEN try integration by parts, with u and dv bound to the indicated subexpression.

Implemented in LEX, this heuristic might take the form of the operator:

$$\int \sin(x) \ dx \ ==> \ -\cos(x) + C$$

being associated with a version space such as:

$$G: \ \{[\int f1(x) \ f2(x) \ dx]\}$$

$$S: \ \{[\int 3x \ \cos(x) \ dx]\}$$

where $f1$ and $f2$ denote functions. To make the version space work as a heuristic LEX obviously has to be able to bind components of the input expression with variables in the hypothesis, but this is a fairly straightforward operation.

8.2.4. Processing cycle in LEX

A simplified specification of the LEX algorithm is as follows:

LEX algorithm

Initialize by associating each operator with a suitably initialized version space. Then enter a loop involving the following four steps.

(1)   Generate an integration problem (problem generator).

(2)   Solve the problem by exploring the space of possible operations employing version-space heuristics as appropriate (problem solver).

(3)   Extract from the trace of the generated search space all the operator applications lying *on* the path to the solution node and all the operator applications lying *off* the path (critic).

(4)   Update each version space using the candidate elimination algorithm so as to ensure that each one covers any applications (of the associated operator) that are on the solution path and excludes any applications that lead away from it (generalizer).

Thus LEX can be seen in terms of a cyclical interaction between a problem generator, a problem solver, a critic and a generalizer (or concept learner).

8.3. Explanation-based learning

We now turn to explanation-based learning proper. As we suggested, LEX contains some of the ideas that have become central in EBL. In particular, LEX's method for deriving training sets by running a problem-solving component on a particular problem, becomes, in the context of EBL, a way of deriving an 'explanation' (i.e. a search trace) by applying a 'theory' (i.e. a set of operators) to a particular 'observation' (i.e. a problem). As in LEX, the explanation derived by this process is used to modify the underlying theory in an appropriate manner. However, the way in which this is typically done is rather different, as we will see.

To get a flavour for what EBL means, imagine yourself in the following scenario. You are watching two experts playing a game of chess. You are studying their moves carefully in the hope of improving your own game. You notice that, in the early stages of the game, both players display a reluctance to escape from check by moving their kings (i.e. they usually prefer to block the check if they can). You also notice that both players 'castle' as soon as possible. From the little knowledge you have of the rules of chess you guess that castling is not allowed once the king has been moved and from this you deduce a likely explanation for the players' reluctance to move their kings: they are trying to retain the option of castling. Having arrived at this explanation you decide to incorporate the 'stationary king' strategy into your own game.

What you have gone through in this imaginary example is a process of explanation-based learning. You have used your *knowledge* (i.e. theories) about chess to arrive at an *explanation* for certain observed phenomena and you have then used the explanation so as to obtain a small *improvement* in your own chess-playing skills. Unfortunately, although the EBL process — when described at this level — sounds fairly straightforward, it can actually be implemented in a wide variety of ways — far too many to cover exhaustively here. Our approach will therefore be to look at just one well-known variant of EBL. This variant goes under the name of *explanation-based generalization* or EBG.

8.4. Explanation-based generalization

Explanation-based generalization can be thought of as a supervised concept learning method that requires a single training pair, a *goal concept* expressed as a rule and a *domain theory* expressed as a set of rules and facts. The input part of the training pair is a set of facts. The output part is implicitly **[yes]**; i.e. EBG (in the simplest case) uses positive inputs only.

Processing the training pair is a two-stage operation. First, we take the head of the rule representing the target concept and try to satisfy it using the set of facts and rules forming the domain theory, the goal-concept rule and the facts forming the training input. We then take the proof tree generated and 'regress' the head of the goal-concept rule through it. This entails producing all those facts that were used in the proof and showing how goal variables were instantiated to the terms in the facts. The conjunction of facts produced forms a 'justified generalization of the training example, for which the explanation [proof] structure serves as a justification' (Mitchell *et al.*, 1986, p. 56). It effectively forms a generalized definition for the goal concept.

8.5. Example

Let us look at an illustrative example using the familiar vehicles domain. The domain theory in this example is made up of the following rules:[3]

```
carries(V,P)  :- crew(V,N), seats(V,M), P is N+M.

mpg(V,M)  :- cc(V,S), M is S/100.
```

The first rule says that a vehicle *V* carries *P* people if it carries *N* crew and has *M* passenger seats. The second rule says that the MPG of a vehicle *V* is *M* where *M* is the cubic capacity of the engine divided by 100. (This is clearly not a realistic rule. However it suffices for the example.) The goal concept is defined by the following rule:

```
economical(V)  :- carries(V,N), mpg(V,M), M/N > 4.
```

This says that a vehicle *V* is economical if the ratio between its MPG and its carrying capacity is more than 4.

---

[3] The rules are written in standard Prolog notation (Clocksin and Mellish, 1984).

The training input is a set of six facts:

```
max_speed(car, 100).

doors(car, 4).

fuel(car, petrol).

crew(car, 1).

seats(car, 3).

cc(car, 2000).
```

These collectively describe a fairly typical car whose engine capacity is 2000 cubic centimetres.

If we try to satisfy the goal concept using the given domain theory and training input we obtain the proof tree shown in Figure 8.3. From this tree we can redefine the goal concept in terms of those facts from the training input that are *used* in the proof, substituting in goal-concept variables as necessary. The produced definition is:

```
economical(X) :- crew(X,1), seats(X,3), cc(X, 2000).
```

This forms a representation of the target concept. Note the generalization effects (i.e. inductive leap) obtained. Using the new rule we assume that *any* type of vehicle that has 1 crew seat, 3 passenger seats and a cubic capacity of 2000 is economical. When we compare the new rule with the goal concept we see that the new rule covers a different but overlapping set of cases. It is the coverage of these new cases that constitutes the inductive leap. Of course, while this is a justified inference given the

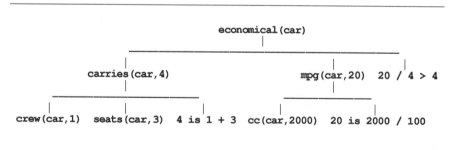

Figure 8.3. EBG proof tree.

Example   *115*

information that the algorithm is working with, it is not a particularly plausible rule. But this problem is more to do with the small size of the example than with the power of the EBG algorithm.

8.6. Comments

The chapter began by introducing LEX. This is a system that learns to perform symbolic integration problems. It forms an early example of the idea of using a problem trace (or proof tree) as a source of information for a learning algorithm. From LEX we moved on to look at explanation-based learning and EBG in particular. Explanation-based generalization is a knowledge-intensive learning mechanism that is capable of producing impressive learning performance. But the secret of its success is also its weak spot. The performance depends on the background knowledge that is given to the system as a domain theory. If this domain theory is flawed in some way then the learning process may not succeed in producing a satisfactory result. This dependence on a perfect domain theory is one of the major problems with EBG. In LEX it is not really an issue since a perfect domain theory is readily available. But in systems that work in less well-understood domains the situation may be very different.

Clearly, the whole question of how knowledge can best be employed within a learning process is a difficult and complex one. We can safely assume that explanation-based generalization represents just one case in a vast range of possibilities. But, unfortunately, the prior question of whether or not extensive knowledge is actually *required* for the purposes of learning is one that cannot be answered at the present time. As fashions change in the various subfields of computational learning, we can expect that the assumed answer to this question will be continuously updated.

In the past the general feeling has certainly been that extensive knowledge is probably essential for more advanced forms of learning. However, more recently, the validity of this assumption has begun to look less certain. The change is due, in part, to the great upsurge in connectionist work that has demonstrated how one can obtain powerful learning behaviours from relatively simple, empirical methods. It is to this body of work and the algorithms and systems with which it is concerned, that we now turn.

8.7. Further reading

The two classic papers on explanation-based learning are DeJong and Mooney (1986) and Mitchell *et al.* (1986). These both appear in the same issue of the Machine Learning journal (vol. 1, no. 1). The main reference for LEX is Mitchell *et al.* (1983). An excellent and up-to-date survey article is Elman (1989) but see also Minton and Carbonell (1987).

8.8. Problems

(1)   What are the main components of the LEX system and how do they interact?

(2)   Is it true to say that the difference between similarity-based and explanation-based learning methods is that the former are not able to take background knowledge into account? Justify your answer.

(3)   In its original implementation, LEX was used to learn heuristics for symbolic integration. Would it be possible to use the LEX approach for learning in a different domain? What information would be required in order to develop a LEX-type system for a new domain?

(4)   What are version-space hypotheses and how are they used in LEX? Provide a version-space representation for a heuristic that might be used in a blocksworld, problem-solving (i.e. planning) system.

(5)   What are the main steps in explanation-based generalization (EBG) and what advantages does it have as a learning technique?

(6)   What types of information are required in explanation-based generalization? And what is involved in processing a single training pair?

(7)   What sort of output does EBG produce and in what sense does it 'explain' the input?

(8)   Consider an example in which EBG is used to discover a definition for the goal concept:

```
can_bully(X,Y)
```

The domain theory (expressed in standard Prolog) is as follows:

```
can_bully(X,Y) :- bigger(X,Y), not(neurotic Y).

bigger(X,Y) :- weight(X,S1), weight(Y,S2), S1 > S2.

weight(P1,S1) :- height(P1,H1), thigh(P1,C1), S1 is H1 * C1.

weight(P1,140) :- isa(P1,student).
```

The training input is made up of the following six facts:

```
isa(fred,student).

isa(bruno,heavyweight_boxer).

hair(fred,pink).

hair(bruno,black).

height(bruno,11).

thigh(bruno,20).
```

Show how EBG would process this input. Draw the proof tree which would be constructed and write out the definition (representation) which would be derived. What would the result be if the **isa(fred, student)** fact were removed from the training input? What would the result be if the **isa(bruno, heavyweight_boxer)** fact were removed? Justify your answers.

9

Introduction to connectionism

9.1. Neural networks versus conventional computers

At this point in the book we make the transition from the domain of symbolic learning algorithms to the domain of connectionist learning algorithms. In the present chapter we will examine the origins of the ideas which underlie the connectionist paradigm and we will see how the framework of basic concepts introduced in Chapter 1 applies to connectionist algorithms. All the algorithms we will look at make use of architectures called *artificial neural networks* or just *neural networks* for short.[1] Before anything else, then, we must look at the neural network and see how it is constructed.

A neural net[2] is essentially a type of computer. But it does not work in the same way as the conventional computer. Furthermore, it has very different computational properties. The conventional computer has two main components: a memory and some kind of processing device (e.g., a CPU). Information is represented in terms of structures of symbols and the way in which this information is processed all depends on the way in which the processing device manipulates the symbol structures stored in the memory.[3]

The neural network on the other hand is made up of a set of simple processing units connected together in a network. The connections between the units can be thought of

---

[1] In principle, a connectionist mechanism might involve some other type of architecture, but this is not common.

[2] The term 'net' is used synonymously with 'network'.

[3] If the computer is to produce useful behaviour, the processing device must manipulate symbols in a way that is compatible with the relationships between the items of information represented.

as wires which carry electrical activation from one unit to another. The units themselves are like biological neurons. They store and pass on a certain amount of electrical activation and this is related to the amount of activation that they receive via their input connections. Information is represented in terms of levels of activation and the way in which it is 'processed' all depends on the way in which activation propagates through the network; i.e. it all depends on the connections between the units.[4]

Of course, this way of characterizing the two types of computer glosses over many important details. It also tends to give the impression that the difference between the conventional and the neural computer is all to do with the physical components from which they are made. In reality this is not the case. The fact that we can simulate any mechanism whatsoever in a conventional computer means that we can build a neural network (or, for that matter, a conventional computer) out of simulated rather than physical components.[5] Surprisingly enough, in a great many cases, neural networks *are* built this way — as virtual machines running in conventional computers. The details of the simulation vary from case to case. But very often the activation storing units are represented as record fields, connections are represented as pointers from one field to another and activation levels are represented as real numbers between 0 and 1.

9.2. The neuron as a computational device

The idea that a network of simple activation-storing units might form an effective basis for computation came out of research on human and animal brains. An early milestone in this research was Cajal's work in the late 1880s. Cajal developed a modification of Golgi's *staining* method which enabled him to trace out the paths of nerve fibres in brain tissue in much greater detail than had previously been possible.[6] In particular, it enabled him to show that the nervous material in the brain is not one huge, connected mass of fibres, but rather is broken up into *neurons*.

Cajal showed that a biological neuron has a cell body and makes connections to other neurons via *synaptic junctions*. The simplest model of this structure is known as the *classical neuron*. This is an assembly comprising a single *cell body* with a number of

---

[4] Hence the name *connectionism*.

[5] The resulting device is called a *virtual machine* since it exists only in the sense that it can be used *as if* it were a machine.

[6] Cajal and Golgi argued intensely over the interpretation of their findings and criticised each other's work in their acceptance speeches for the Nobel Prize they shared in 1906.

attached fibres. One of these fibres is the *axon* and all the rest are *dendrites*. The axon branches and forms synaptic junctions (or 'synapses') with the dendrites of other neurons (see Figure 9.1).

In practice a biological neuron may depart from the classical picture in a number of ways. For example:

•   It may have no axon.

•   Axons/dendrites may have synaptic junctions on other axons/dendrites.

•   An axon may produce a graded potential rather than a spike. This can happen, for example if the axon is very short.

The neuron has a tendency to produce regular, electrical impulses called *spikes*. These travel down the axon and across the synapses. If the amount of activation (i.e. the number of spikes) which the neuron receives via the synaptic junctions at the end of its dendrites increases then the rate at which it sends out spikes (its *firing rate*) also increases, i.e. it sends out more activation. If the amount of activation decreases, then the firing rate decreases. Thus the firing rate reflects the amount of activation that the cell receives and its current internal state. To a crude approximation, the neuron

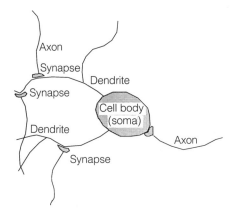

Figure 9.1. The basic structure of the neuron (after Beale and Jackson, 1990).

behaves as an activation-summing device.

9.3. The McCulloch-Pitts neuron

The mapping out of the basic morphology and physiology of the biological neuron —
while being a major step forward — raised the difficult question of how networks of
such neurons (i.e. brains) might carry out the information-processing tasks that they
were clearly responsible for. Some light was cast on this difficult question by
McCulloch and Pitts in the early 1940s. In a classic work, these two researchers
showed how neuron-like *threshold units* or TUs might represent logical expressions.
From this starting point they went on to show how networks of such units might
effectively carry out computations.

In the simplest case, the threshold unit is capable of being either on or off. It has
several input connections and, in a given time step, receives an input via each connection. The input can be a 1 or 0. If the number of 1s received exceeds some threshold, then the unit's activation is set to 1; otherwise it is set to 0. In a network of such
units the state of one unit becomes an input to another. McCulloch and Pitts suggested that networks of TUs provided a good model for biological neural functioning.

> Because of the 'all-or-none' character of nervous activity, neural events and the
> relations between them can be treated by means of propositional logic. It is
> found that the behaviour of every net can be described in these terms . . . and
> that for any logical expression satisfying certain conditions, one can find a net
> behaving in the fashion it describes. (McCulloch and Pitts, 1943, p. 115)

From this observation we can see that for any computation that can be viewed as a
'logical expression' one should be able to produce a network of units that implements
that computation. Of course the notion of 'implementing' a computation has a special
meaning here. Implementing a computation using a network of TUs involves (1)
representing the inputs and outputs using 1s and 0s (i.e. as *boolean vectors*) and (2)
finding a way to present the input to the network and to read off the output. As we
will see, in most connectionist work, presenting the input is typically done by setting
certain *input units* to have a given activation level (i.e. 1 or 0), while obtaining the
output involves reading off the states of certain *output units*.

9.4. Hand-coding a connectionist adder

Let us look at a concrete example of computation using a network of TUs. We will consider the task of constructing a network which will function as a simple adder. We imagine that we have an infinite stock of TUs and an infinite stock of links. Each unit has a threshold associated with it and stores a 1 or a 0 (i.e. its activation is 1 or 0). Following the usual conventions, a unit storing a 1 is said to be *on* or *active*. A unit storing a 0 is *off* or *inactive*. Links are directed: they lead from one unit to another and are able to propagate activation in that direction only. In a given time step, a unit propagates its current activation down all output links.

Given these components we can configure a simple network adder for a small range of integers as follows. We have two sets of 4 input units and one set of 8 output units arranged as an ordered sequence. We set the links such that each output unit has a link running to it from each input unit. The arrangement is shown in Figure 9.2. Here and in all other figures representing networks, the circles represent the units and the lines represent connections between them. Circles in the lower part of the figure represent input units. Circles in the upper part of the figure represent output units. Thus activation flows upwards in these diagrams.

Adding two numbers n and m (where $n < 5$ and $m < 5$) using this network will involve (1) setting the leftmost n units on in the left-hand group of input units and the leftmost m units on in the right-hand group of input units and then (2) finding the

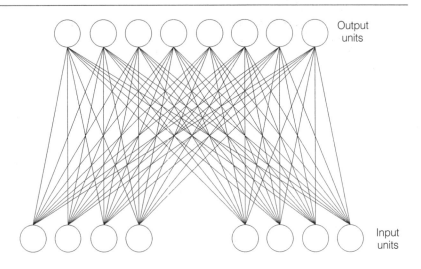

Figure 9.2. Structure of a connectionist adder.

highest (rightmost) active output unit. To get sensible addition behaviour we should set the thresholds in the output units so that the kth output unit only comes on if the total number of input units turned on is greater than or equal to k. Performing addition with the final network is simply a matter of turning on the appropriate input units and then finding the highest activated output unit.

9.5. Localized representation

Obviously, in practice, we would like to be able to construct networks with more powerful computational properties than the one described above. But although the McCulloch-Pitts proof showed that we can do this in principle, it did not explain how to do it in practice. So the question of how neural networks in general, and brains in particular, might compute complex functions remained open. Historically, research on this issue has tended to organize itself around two basic models: the *localized representation* model and the *distributed representation* model. These models provide an abstract picture of two ways in which a network of simple units might represent information in the form of concepts.

In the localized representation model, brains are construed as representing concepts in terms of the states of a small number of physically proximate neurons. In a very simple version of this model, any given entity or concept is assumed to be represented by the state of a single neuron. The receipt of stimuli (e.g., retinal inputs) indicating the presence of the entity is assumed to trigger high activation levels in that neuron. This version of the model sometimes goes under the name of the *grandmother-cell hypothesis*, since it seems to suggest that a human will have one neuron (cell) solely devoted to representing his/her grandmother.

Although this extreme variant of the localized representation model seems a bit absurd, the general form of the model has considerable plausibility and is supported by a large body of empirical work. Hubel and Wiesel, for example, have carried out studies which show how neurons in the visual cortex of monkeys can respond selectively to particular types of visual input. They discovered neurons whose firing rate was closely correlated with the presence of high-level features, e.g., the presence of a line at a certain orientation. Other studies have shown that electrical stimulation of various areas of the human cortex can produce very specific types of subjective experience, e.g., the experience of a particular memory or the pronunciation of a particular word.

However, we need to be careful in interpreting these results. A cautionary (and probably apocryphal) tale concerns the electronic engineer who, having found that a radio emitted a howl when a certain component was removed, concluded that the component must be a 'howl-suppressor'. The lesson we are supposed to deduce from this is that, even though the behaviour of a particular component seems to be related in a very simple way to a behaviour of the overall mechanism, it is not necessarily functionally *responsible* for that behaviour. The component may be just one part of a complex system that happens to generate a particular behaviour when the component is perturbed or removed.[7]

9.6. Distributed representation

The second model exerting a major influence on studies of brain function is the distributed representation model. This is often associated with Karl Lashley, a psychologist of major importance in the earlier part of this century. Lashley performed experiments on rats to test the localized representation model. He hypothesized that if the model was correct he should be able to eradicate a rat's memory of the structure of a maze by removing (*ablating*) the relevant brain material. He discovered that maze memories seem to be quite robust against such experiments. He found that he could remove surprisingly large amounts of brain matter without, apparently, obliterating the rat's memory of the structure of the maze.[8] He concluded that memories could not possibly be stored at any particular location in the brain, but rather that they must be distributed throughout its entire structure. From this he inferred that learning could not be based on localized, physiological changes.

> The capacity to learn the maze is dependent upon the amount of functional cortical tissue and not upon its anatomical specialization . . . The results are incompatible with theories of learning by changes in synaptic structure, or with any theories which assume that particular neural integrations are dependent upon definite anatomical paths specialized for them . . . The mechanisms of integration are to be sought in the dynamic relations among the parts of the nervous system rather than in details of structural differentiation (Lashley, 1929, p. 3).

The distributed representation model and the localized representation model represent two polar extremes. Each suggests a quite distinct way in which the brain might

---

[7] It is interesting to consider the relevance of this to John Searle's (1980; 1984) famous *Chinese room* argument against strong AI. In Searle's argument, the lack of a certain property (language understanding) in a component of a system is used as evidence in favour of the conclusion that the property must be lacking in the system as a whole.

[8] Memory retention was relatively good even in the case where the ablations had seriously impaired the rat's motor abilities and therefore its ability to run the maze.

represent information. However, it is not necessary for us to choose one model over the other as the preferred explanation for biological networks. As we will see, it is quite possible for artificial neural mechanisms to make use of both distributed and localized representations. Thus it may be that the two models provide complementary rather than contradictory accounts of the way in which information is represented and processed in biological neural networks.

9.7. Connectionist-style computational learning

In the ensuing chapters we will look at a wide range of learning algorithms that operate on and within neural networks. On the surface, these algorithms seem quite different in character from the symbolic algorithms that we have looked at previously. However, we can find considerable commonality if we adopt an abstract perspective. The basic framework of ideas introduced in Chapter 1 is still relevant, though in need of a little qualification. Recall that in the simplest model, computational learning is viewed as the process in which a learner generates a representation for, or implementation of, a target mapping using a training set of examples as a source of information. In carrying out this task the learner is viewed as exploring a space of hypotheses with a bias which may vary between strong and weak, and between correct and incorrect.

In connectionist learning we have the problem that there is often no clean separation between the learner and the representation (i.e. hypothesis) being produced. Connectionist learning typically involves the manipulation of connection 'weights' in a single network of units (see Chapter 10). The aim of the learning is to reach a point where the network produces certain types of input/output behaviour. This normally involves systematically updating the weights on possible connections between units. Thus, in the connectionist learning scenario, the learner is the weight updating procedure and the target mechanism (or representation) is the network with a certain configuration of weights. If the architecture of the network is fixed the hypothesis space is the space of possible weight configurations and a single hypothesis is a particular configuration of weights. If the architecture is not fixed, the hypothesis space is made up of all possible architecture/weight-configuration combinations.

In assessing the bias of a connectionist learner we need to discover to what degree the space of possible weight configurations is explored exhaustively. If the search is exhaustive then the bias is weak. If, on the other hand, weights are updated in a knowledge-driven fashion, then the bias is comparatively strong. If the architecture of the network is not fixed by the algorithm (and it very rarely is) then the selection of a particular architecture constitutes an additional source of bias that should be taken into account.

Apart from these minor caveats, our basic framework transfers from the symbolic to the connectionist domain largely unchanged. Some minor differences in language may be noticed. These include the following:

- The input part of a training pair which is called an *instance* in symbolic learning is just an *input* or a *pattern* in connectionist learning.

- Target-mapping representations are not usually called hypotheses since there is something unnatural about referring to a configuration of weight values as a hypothesis. They may be called *representations*, *weight configurations* or possibly just *states*.

- Since the target mapping in connectionist learning is always expressed — ultimately — in terms of numeric vectors, it is sometimes called the *target function*.

- And finally, the hypothesis space tends to be referred to as the *weight space*.

9.8. Further reading

For further reading on the topic of the biological neuron see Dayhoff (1990, Chapters 7 & 8), Wasserman (1989, Appendix A), Crick and Asanuma (1986) or Luria (1973). The historical perspective on the neuron is dealt with in Johnson and Brown (1988, Chapter 2) but see also the article on Cajal in Bullock and Wooding (1983). Hubel (1979) provides an accessible introduction to the work which demonstrated that neurons in the visual cortex may respond selectively to visual stimuli; see also Hubel and Wiesel (1962). Aleksander and Burnett (1987, pp. 140-9) provide a simplified account of Hubel and Wiesel's work with monkey brains and discuss the implications that follow from them. For a novel introduction to the entire structure of the human brain see Diamond *et al.* (1985).

Gardner's (1985) introduction to cognitive science gives excellent coverage of the tension between localized and distributed models of memory. His treatment of Lashley's work makes fascinating reading (pp. 260-71). See also the primary sources for this work; e.g., Lashley (1929; 1950). Penfield and Jasper (1954) deal with the tendency for electrical stimulation to trigger specific, subjective experiences.

9.9. Problems

(1)   Characterize the differences between the traditional computer and the neural network.

(2)   What are the components of the classical neuron? How would you describe its behaviour?

(3)   In what ways may a real neuron differ from the classical model?

(4)   What did McCulloch and Pitts prove could be done with networks of binary-threshold units?

(5)   Give an informal argument showing why it should be possible to compute any desired function using a network of threshold units.

(6)   Design a network of threshold units which computes the exclusive-OR logic function: $[0\ 0] \rightarrow [0]$, $[0\ 1] \rightarrow [1]$, $[1\ 0] \rightarrow [1]$, $[1\ 1] \rightarrow [0]$.

(7)   What is localized representation usually contrasted with? What is the nature of the difference and how does equipotentiality come into it?

(8)   Why does one need to be careful when interpreting results which show that neuron firing rates are related systematically to certain types of environmental cue?

(9)   Imagine that we have a dynamic system comprising a large number of components (e.g., a motor car engine). If we discover that the behaviour of one of the components (e.g., the fan belt) is systematically related to a particular behaviour of the system (e.g., engine overheating), can we conclude that the component is responsible for the behaviour? If not, why not? What does this have to do with John Searle's 'Chinese room' argument?

10

The linear threshold unit

10.1. Introduction

In the previous chapter we looked at the classical neuron and the simple, on/off threshold unit. As McCulloch and Pitts had demonstrated in the early 1940s, to a first approximation, networks of such units can perform arbitrary computations. However, this proof is of limited value for the purposes of constructing networks that perform useful computations. It does not tell us *how* to obtain specific computations from networks. It only tells us that it can be done.

Given the difficulty of constructing useful networks using TUs it is not surprising that, in the 1950s, researchers began experimenting with networks based on a different type of unit, namely, the *linear threshold unit* or LTU. This unit is slightly more complex than the TU but it is also more powerful from the computational viewpoint. More importantly, it turns out that there is a simple learning strategy that allows LTUs to be automatically configured for certain tasks. In the present chapter we will concentrate on the computational properties of LTUs. The learning strategy will be dealt with in Chapter 11.

10.2. Basic behaviour

The LTU is much like the TU except for the fact that it can accept real- rather than just binary-valued inputs and it has real-valued *weights* associated with its input connections. These affect the amount of activation that reaches the unit. Whereas the activation of the TU is derived by summing the inputs, the activation of the LTU is derived by summing the products of the inputs and the weights attached to the relevant connections, and then testing this sum against the unit's threshold. If the sum exceeds the threshold, the unit's activation is set to 1; otherwise it is set to 0. Thus, the LTU computes a linear function of the n-dimensional input vector and applies a threshold to the result.[1]

A network comprising a single LTU is shown in Figure 10.1. The LTU has three input connections and, for consistency with later diagrams, these are shown as connections from three *input units*. In this context the LTU becomes the *output unit* and the activation it receives is simply the activation of the input units to which it is connected. Thus, the activation of the leftmost unit is multiplied by **W1**. The activation of the middle input unit is multiplied by **W2** and the input from the rightmost input unit is multiplied by **W3**. The sum of these products is then compared against the LTU's threshold and its activation level set to 1 or 0 accordingly.

10.3. Input and output vectors

The weights on the input connections of a given unit form the unit's *weight vector*. The set of input-unit activation levels is its *input vector*. Normally, weight vectors and input vectors are written out working from left to right across the network. Thus if **W1** is 0.2, **W2** is -0.3 and **W3** is 0.9, the unit's weight vector would be [0.2 -0.3 0.9].[2] If the activations of the input units are 0.7, 0.3 and 0.1 then the input vector is [0.7 0.3 0.1]. The sum of products formed by multiplying two vectors of values

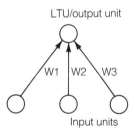

Figure 10.1. Simple linear-threshold unit.

---

[1] For present purposes, LTUs are assumed to have no bias value.

[2] The usual convention in connectionism is to use w_1, w_2, w_3, etc. to denote weight values. However, the conventions we are using here make more sense from the point of view of the programmer.

together is called the *inner product* of the vectors. Thus, LTUs may be viewed as devices that test whether the inner product of the input vector and the weight vector exceeds a given threshold.

10.4. Geometric interpretation of the inner product

Note that any input vector or weight vector with n components specifies a point in n-dimensional space. On this view, the components of the vector are the coordinates of the point. The advantage of viewing vectors as points or rays in an n-dimensional space is that we can then understand the behaviour of the LTU in terms of the way in which it divides the input space into two regions: a region containing all the input vectors that turn the LTU on (i.e. cause it to have an activation level of 1), and a region containing all the input vectors that turn it off (i.e. cause it to have an activation level of 0).

We can best see what this means by reducing the number of input units to two. This ensures that the input vectors and weight vectors are all 2-dimensional and can be drawn out in a diagram. If activation levels range between 0 and 1, and weights between -1 and 1, then we can draw out both spaces with one superimposed over the other. The general effect is shown in Figure 10.2. The origin of the space (i.e. [0 0]) is at the centre and coordinate values are assumed to increase up and to the right and decrease down and to the left. Thus the input space corresponds to the positive, top-right quadrant only. Any given point in the space may represent a weight vector or, if the point is in the positive quadrant, an input vector. In the diagram two points are shown: a weight vector **w** with components [0.11 0.6] and an input vector **L** with components [0.7 0.7].

In order to decide whether an LTU with weight vector **w** will return a 1 or a 0 when presented with input vector **L** we have to find out the inner product of **L** and **w**. As we have said, the inner product of two vectors is derived by summing the products of pairwise components. However, if **L** happens to be *normalized* (i.e. its length is exactly 1) then the inner product of **L** and **w** is just **w**'s *projection* on **L**, and can be derived geometrically.

Deriving the length of a vector V is a straightforward procedure involving the application of Pythagoras' theorem. We compute the square root of the sum of the squares of the corresponding values, i.e. we find the value of:

$$\sqrt{\sum_i V_i^2}^d$$

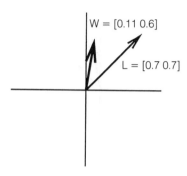

Figure 10.2. Sample vectors.

where V_i is the ith component of the vector V, whose length we want to find. If we want to normalize V, i.e. scale it so that its length is exactly 1, we divide each element of the vector by its original length. For example, assume V is the following 2-dimensional vector:

[0.9 0.8]

The length of this vector is 1.2. To normalize it we divide each element to 1.2. This gives us the vector

[0.74 0.66]

whose length is 1.

As noted, if vector V's length is exactly 1, the inner product of V and some other vector W is identical to the projection of W on V. The projection is the length of that portion of V that falls 'below' the perpendicular dropped on to V by W. If V is not normalized then the inner product will not be the same as the length of the shadow.

The length of the input vector **L** from the example above ([0.74 0.66]) is (approximately) 1. So the inner product of **L** and **W** is **W**'s projection on **L**. The inner product of **L** and **W** is 0.5. This means that the perpendicular dropped by **W** on to **L** will strike **L** exactly half way along its length. This is confirmed geometrically in Figure 10.3.

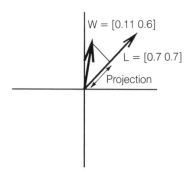

W = [0.11 0.6]

L = [0.7 0.7]

Projection

Figure 10.3. Projection of one vector on to another.

10.5. Computing boolean functions with linear threshold units

LTUs return a 1 or a 0 and these outputs can be thought of as the positive and negative (or [yes] and [no]) that we have in symbolic learning. We can try to train an
LTU to discriminate between two different classes of input, e.g., compute a simple
logic function. For example, consider the logic function AND. This implements the
following input/output mapping:

$$
\begin{array}{ccc}
[1\ 0] & \rightarrow & [0] \\
[0\ 0] & \rightarrow & [0] \\
[0\ 1] & \rightarrow & [0] \\
[1\ 1] & \rightarrow & [1]
\end{array}
$$

An LTU that computes AND must turn on (i.e. return a 1) when given the input vector [1 1] and turn off (i.e. return a 0) in all other cases. To construct an LTU that
does this we need to make sure that it returns the right output for each input. But the
output we get for a particular input depends on the inner product of the weight vector
and the input vector. Only if the inner product is greater than the threshold will we
get a 1 output. Geometrically (assuming input vectors are normalized), the outcome
all depends on whether the projection cast by the weight vector on the input vector
falls beyond the point corresponding to the threshold value.

What this means is that once we have picked a threshold value we can derive a satisfactory weight vector. We draw out each input vector with a perpendicular passing
through the threshold point. This perpendicular divides the input space into two

regions. If we put a weight vector in the region beyond the perpendicular then we know that it will make a projection on the input vector that is above the threshold. The output obtained will therefore be 1. Conversely, if we put the weight vector in the region behind the perpendicular then we know that it will make a projection on the input vector that is below the threshold point. The output will therefore be 0. Thus, to obtain a particular output we know that the weight vector must go on the right side of the perpendicular. The perpendicular passing through the threshold point on the input vector effectively forms a *constraint line* (or more generally a *constraint plane*) for the weight vector. In the situation depicted in Figure 10.4 we have an input vector of [0.9 0.3] and a threshold of 0.5. This gives us the constraint line shown.

To derive the weight vector that will give satisfactory behaviour for all the input vectors we have to draw in all the constraint lines. Once we have done this there may be a region that is on the satisfactory side of *all* the constraint lines. In this case, any weight vector positioned in the relevant region will give satisfactory behaviour. If there is no such region then we know that we cannot find a satisfactory weight vector.

In the case of the mapping:

```
<[0 0] [0]>
<[1 0] [0]>
<[0 1] [0]>
<[1 1] [1]>
```

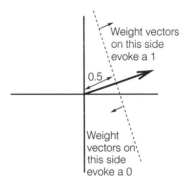

Figure 10.4. Constraint lines derived from a threshold value.

the input vectors are [1 0], [0 1], [0 0] and [1 1]. These input vectors are marked in Figure 10.5 with the outputs that they should evoke. The input vector [0 0] is a special case; its length is 0 and it will always have an inner product of 0 with any other vector. This is the output we want for [0 0] so we do not need to consider this case.

The remaining vectors are dealt with as follows. Since the threshold is 0.5, the critical point for any input containing a zero is exactly half way along the vector. The critical point for the input [1 1] is a quarter of the way along the vector. Thus the weight vector we want must cast a projection that is *below* the half-way mark on [1 0], [0 1] and [0 0] but *above* the quarter-way mark on [1 1]. These constraint lines give us a 'solution region' as shown in Figure 10.5.

10.6. Linear separability

As we noted, the fact that the LTU will return one of two outputs for any given input means that it will potentially discriminate between two classes of input. However, there is a severe restriction on the types of class that it can discriminate. We have seen that to obtain a particular output for a given input we have to ensure that the

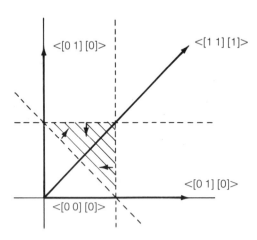

Figure 10.5. Solution region for AND problem.

weight vector has a certain projection on the input vector. But, assuming all vectors are normalized, projections work both ways. So, making sure that a weight vector has a certain projection on an input vector is the same thing as making sure that an input vector has a certain projection on a weight vector.

Imagine that we have fixed the position of the weight vector. To obtain an output of 1 we must present an input whose projection on the weight vector is greater than the threshold value (i.e. beyond the half-way mark). Conversely, to obtain a 0 we must present an input that has a projection less than the threshold value. Thus, all inputs that lie beyond a perpendicular passing through the threshold point on the weight vector will evoke a 1. Everything else will evoke a 0. This leads to the observation that the LTU discriminates between classes by separating them with a line — or more generally, a hyperplane — in the input space. This is a severe restriction since a great many classes cannot be separated this way, i.e. there are many classes that are not *linearly separable*.

Typically, the linear-separability constraint is illustrated by showing that LTUs cannot compute *exclusive-OR* (XOR). The situation is illustrated in Figure 10.6. Here

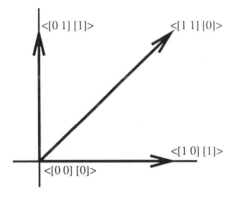

Figure 10.6. Hyperplane for XOR problem?.

we have drawn out the four vectors corresponding to the four possible binary pairs. It is easy to confirm that it is impossible to draw in a linear boundary separating the inputs that should evoke a 1 ([0 1] and [1 0]) from the inputs that should evoke a 0 ([1 1] and [0 0]).

10.7. Historical background: the rise and fall of the perceptron

The use of LTUs as a basic unit in neural networks was pioneered by Frank Rosenblatt. Rosenblatt headed a research group that constructed a mechanism called the *perceptron*. In contemporary literature, the architecture of the perceptron is often highly simplified. However, as Harry Barrow (1989, p. 8) notes,

> The Mark 1 perceptron is not quite as folk history remembers it. It had a 20 × 20 array of photocells to act as a retina, then a layer of 512 Association units. Each of the A-units [Association units] took input from a randomly selected subset of photocells, forming a simple logical combination of them. Their outputs were connected to 8 response units. The strengths of the connections between A- and *R*- units [Response units] were set by motor-driven potentiometers . . . The *R*-units could mutually interact so that they competed in a winner-take-all manner, eventually agreeing on a response. The whole machine occupied several full-height racks of electronics and mechanics.

The behaviour of the mechanism is primarily a function of the weights on the connections between the A-units and the *R*-units, and these were effectively LTUs. Thus, the mechanism was essentially an assembly of LTUs. But it seemed to possess some surprising computational properties and an ability to learn new concepts. Rosenblatt was not slow to make the most of these.[3]

Research on the general architecture by Rosenblatt and others continued into the late 1960s. During this period, Marvin Minsky and Seymour Papert became suspicious of the perceptron work and worried by the amount of attention it was receiving. They developed a mathematical analysis of the perceptron and related architectures that

---

[3] As McCorduck (1979, p. 87) notes: 'Rosenblatt was given to steady and extravagant statements about the performance of his machine. "He was a press agent's dream," one scientist says, "a real medicine man. To hear him tell it, the perceptron was capable of fantastic things. And maybe it was. But you couldn't prove it by the work that Frank did." '

went into print at the end of the 1960s.[4] (Minsky and Papert, 1969)

It was a central result of Minsky and Papert's work that since its basic computational element is the LTU, the perceptron can only discriminate between linearly separable classes. The fact that a large proportion of interesting classes of patterns (e.g., the class of all 'connected' patterns) are *not* linearly separable means that the general applicability of the method is rather restricted. For obvious reasons this result helped to accelerate the demise of the perceptron approach. Thus, Minsky and Papert's work dampened enthusiasm for neural networks and initiated a connectionist 'dark age'. This was something of an ironic outcome since Minsky had himself been an early pioneer in the field.[5] The general architecture of the Mark 1 perceptron is is visualized in Figure 10.7

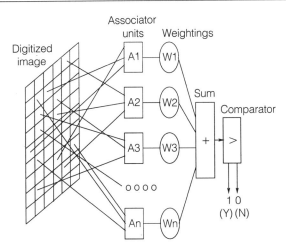

Figure 10.7. Mark 1 perceptron (after Forsyth and Rada, 1986).

---

[4] Publication was delayed for some time due to the authors' desire to tie up all the loose ends (i.e. prove all relevant results). Interestingly, Minsky now regrets doing such a good job. He feels that they should have left some easy problems unsolved to entice young researchers into doing more work in the area (McCorduck, 1979, p. 89).

[5] As an undergraduate student at Harvard he had used one of his three personal laboratories to construct an experimental network architecture (built using vacuum tubes and physical clutches) based on stochastic reinforcement learning.

10.8. Further reading

There is currently a first and a second edition of Minsky and Papert's book on Perceptrons (1969; 1988). The second edition benefits from the inclusion of an epilogue that deals quite pessimistically with the 'new connectionism'. The book makes extensive use of geometric figures and provides helpful visualizations for theoretical results (e.g., the linear-separability constraint in the 3-dimensional case; see p. 32). The introductory chapter of Hecht-Nielsen (1990) covers the perceptron in some depth and includes several pictures of the original Mark 1 implementation. Dayhoff (1990, Chapter 2) provides a less technical introduction. For more on the behaviour and geometric interpretation of LTUs see Anderson and Hinton (1981, p. 13). For an easygoing introduction to the perceptron see Forsyth and Rada (1986).

10.9. Problems

(1)   What are the functional properties of the LTU? What type of mathematical function is implemented by the LTU?

(2)   How would you represent the input vectors $[0.2 \ 0.5]$ and $[0.9 \ 0.1]$ geometrically?

(3)   Write down the principle steps in the vector normalization procedure described above and then use it to normalize the vector $[0.8 \ 0.34 \ -0.24 \ 0.1 \ 0.1 \ 0]$.

(4)   If vector V_1 is the normalized variant of vector V_2, what is the relationship between V_1 and V_2?

(5)   In what cases is the inner product of vectors V_1 and V_2 equal to the projection of V_1 on V_2? Provide an example to illustrate your answer.

(6)   Geometrically, how is the projection of one vector on to another derived?

(7)   What limitations are there on the computational properties of the LTU? Provide a geometric interpretation of this limitation.

(8)   Provide an example of a function — other than exclusive-OR — that cannot be computed by an LTU.

(9)   Explain why the constraint lines for boolean AND are where they are.

(10) Imagine that we would like to obtain an LTU that computes the boolean OR of two binary inputs. Show how we can geometrically derive a satisfactory weight vector and threshold for the unit. (Accuracy is not essential.)

(11) How many different types of unit does a perceptron have, and how many of each type can it have?

(12) What are the possible inputs to a perceptron? What are the possible outputs?

11

Learning by error-reduction

11.1. Introduction to the perceptron learning algorithm

We have seen that it is possible to obtain a linear threshold unit that implements a given input/output mapping by working out the constraints that are placed over the unit's weight vector by the training pairs. In the case of 2-dimensional input vectors we can draw in the constraint lines and determine where the weight vector must be in order to obtain satisfactory input/output behaviour. In the case of n-dimensional input vectors we cannot solve the problem geometrically but the underlying procedure remains the same. The important point is that there is a *systematic procedure* for discovering where to put the weight vector of an LTU in order to obtain particular input/output behaviour. This means that we can implement the placement of weight vectors computationally.

In principle it would be possible to implement the procedure directly, i.e. write a program that (1) worked out all the constraints imposed by all the pairs in the training set and then (2) identified the region of the weight space that satisfied those constraints. However, this procedure is complex to implement. And, in any case, there is a much easier way of achieving the same effect. This involves an iterative process of *error reduction*.

The basic idea is that we should take each training pair in turn and present the input vector to the unit. We then calculate the degree to which the activation of the unit differs from the desired activation (i.e. output) and adjust the weight vector so as to reduce this difference by a small, fixed amount. Let us see how this works in practice. Assume that we have a small network that comprises two input units and one output unit The output unit is an LTU with connections from both input units. Assume the current training pair is <[1 0] [1]>, the LTU's threshold is 0.5 and its current weight vector is [0.44 0.89]. If we present the input vector from the training pair, the inner product is 0.44. This is below the threshold so the output unit's new activation level is 0. The desired level was 1 so we have a difference of 1. This difference is referred to as the unit's *error* on the current training pair.

To correct the error we need to make sure that the inner product is greater than 0.5; this means that we should increase the weights. In particular we need to increase the weight on the line to the active input unit. If we add 0.1 to the weight on the first connection the new weight vector is [0.54 0.89], the inner product for the given training pair is 0.54 and the final output is 1.

If we find that we have a negative error (i.e. the output is 1 when it should be 0) then we have to reduce weights. The effect that changing weights has on the behaviour is shown in Figure 11.1. In fact it is not necessary to work out which connections lead to active input units. We can get the same effect by multiplying any weight change by the level of activation of the relevant input unit. This yields a procedure of three rules. Together they form a learning algorithm for the perceptron.

Perceptron learning algorithm[1]

First randomly initialize weights. Then cycle through the training set applying the following three rules to the weights on the connections to the output unit.

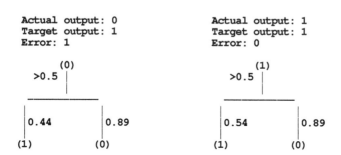

Figure 11.1. Basic error-reduction learning.

---

[1] The perceptron learning algorithm (PLA) is also known as the *perceptron convergence procedure.*

(1)   If the activation level of the output unit is 1 when it should be 0, reduce the weight on the link to the *i*th input unit by $r \times L_i$, where L_i is the activation level of the *i*th input unit and r is a fixed weight step.

(2)   If the activation level of the output unit is 0 when it should be 1, increase the weight on the link to the *i*th input unit by $r \times L_i$.

(3)   If the activation level of the output unit is the desired level do nothing.

After each presentation, the procedure either adds or subtracts a proportion of the input vector to the weight vector. This has the effect of moving the weight vector in the direction of the input vector, i.e. perpendicularly towards the constraint line that is, itself, perpendicular to the input vector. The amount of movement, which is proportional to the size of the weight step, is known as the *learning rate*.

If there exists a satisfactory weight vector for the training set, it must be the case that there is a region of the weight space that is associated with satisfactory behaviour. If there is such a region then the constraint lines must enclose a convex region. If the region is convex then the process of moving the weight vector by fixed steps perpendicularly towards constraint planes is guaranteed eventually to bring it into the satisfactory region, provided the weight step is not so large as to cause the weight vector to be moved right over the region back into the unsatisfactory region. Thus, if there is a satisfactory region the perceptron convergence procedure is guaranteed to find it. This result is called the *perceptron convergence theorem* and was originally proved by Rosenblatt in his work on perceptron learning.

11.2. Learning to compute boolean AND

We will now see how we can use the perceptron learning algorithm to obtain a linear threshold unit that computes the logical AND function. The network will have the same architecture as above. It will comprise two input units feeding into one output unit and a threshold of 0.5. We will use a weight step (learning rate) of 0.1. The training set — which is derived straightforwardly from the truth table for AND — is as follows. (We are ignoring the <[0 0] [0]> case here since its inclusion makes no difference to the learning. An LTU will always return the desired output of 0 for the input [0 0] regardless of its weight vector.)

```
<[1  0]    [0]>
<[0  1]    [0]>
<[1  1]    [1]>
```

We will show how the learning proceeds by tracing the progression of the weight vector. In Figure 11.2 we see the constraint lines imposed by the current training set. Each input vector is labelled with its corresponding training pair. The constraint lines define a central solution region — any weight vector in this region will produce the target behaviour. The initial (random) position of the weight vector is at the point marked **w**.

In epoch 1 the only violated constraint line is associated with input [1 1]. The weight vector is below threshold on this constraint line (causing the actual output to be [0]) whereas it should be above the threshold point. The learning therefore moves the weight vector perpendicularly towards the violated constraint line bringing it to the point marked **1**. In this position the weight vector is still on the wrong side of the constraint line for [1 1] so the error rate is 25% (i.e. 1/4). In the next epoch the learning moves the weight vector further to the north-east and this brings it to the point marked **2**. In this position the weight vector is on the wrong side of the constraint line for [1 0] so the error rate increases to 0.5.

In the next two epochs the learning initially moves the weight vector to the left to get it on the right side of the constraint line for [1 0]. Unfortunately, this puts it back on the wrong side of the constraint line for [1 1] so the learning then moves it north-east, thus putting it back on the wrong side of the constraint line for [1 0]. The overall effect is that the weight vector moves due north in small steps. After epoch 5 the weight vector is at the point marked **5**. From this position, the leftwards movement does not put it on the wrong side of the constraint line for [1 1]. Thus there is no further movement. Performance is now correct on all inputs, i.e. the error rate is zero.

11.3. Learning with linear units

One of the problems with the perceptron learning algorithm is the fact that it does not perform well in the case where there is no satisfactory set of weights. In this case we would like the learning algorithm to produce a reasonable compromise, i.e. produce behaviour that is as close as possible to the desired behaviour. In order to do this it is necessary to minimize the average distance between the weight vector and the violated constraint lines. However, since the PLA moves the weight vector a fixed distance towards a violated constraint line, there is no guarantee that a reasonable compromise will be achieved.

A learning algorithm that gets a little closer to the desired functionality is the *least mean squares* (LMS) procedure. This works in very much the same way as the PLA except that it changes weights in proportion to the current error. Thus it ensures that

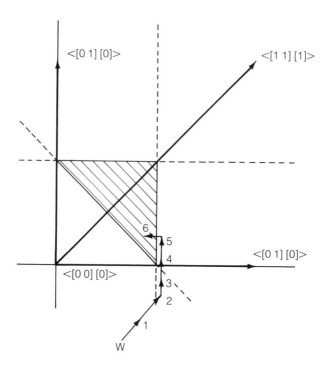

Figure 11.2. Perceptron learning boolean AND.

jumps of the weight vector become steadily smaller as the distance between it and the satisfactory region is reduced. This does not guarantee a perfect compromise since the problem may be such that the weight vector is always very distant from a violated constraint line. In this case, the weight vector will continue to make large jumps and may therefore deviate markedly from the ideal position.

The LMS procedure works with linear units rather than linear threshold units. The difference between these units and LTUs is that their activation is derived directly as a linear function of the relevant inputs, i.e. there is no thresholding. The usual way of putting this is to say that the units have a linear *activation function* rather than a non-linear one. The distinction between units with linear and non-linear activation functions is an important one. *Semi-linear* activation functions play an important role in learning mechanisms for more complex networks, as we will see later on.

The least mean squares procedure is defined in terms of the following weight-update rule that is applied to all weights in each iteration of the learning process:

- Set W_i equal to $W_i + (T_k - L_k) L_i \, r$

Here T_k is the target output, L_k is the actual output, L_i is the state of the ith unit, W_i is the weight on the link to that unit, and r is the learning rate.[2] The rule is often called the *delta rule* since it updates weights by an amount proportional to the difference between the actual and desired output. If the error is very small, the change in the weight will be very small. In the limit, the error vanishes and the weight is not changed at all.

The presence of the learning rate r in this rule might appear to be redundant since the size of the weight change is scaled automatically. However, by including a learning rate in the formula we ensure that weight changes are *proportional* to the current error rather than identically equal to it. This gives us an extra handle on the dynamics of the learning. By varying the learning rate we can vary the proportionality and thus speed up or slow down the learning.

The delta rule says that we should increment the weight on the link to the ith unit by an amount proportional to the product of the ith unit's activation and the difference between the desired and actual output. This neatly takes care of all possible cases. If the actual output is less than the desired output, the difference will be positive and the weight will be increased. If the actual output is greater than the desired output, the difference will be negative and the weight will be decreased.[3]

11.4. Gradient descent on error surfaces

When using the LMS to train units to produce certain behaviour, we need a measure of how well we are doing, i.e. a measure of how well the current behaviour approximates the desired behaviour. As we have noted, overall performance is usually quantified in terms of *mean error*. This is the average difference between actual and target outputs taken over all output units and all training pairs. Alternatively, we can sub-

---

[2] In connectionism, α often denotes the learning rate.

[3] Mathematically, the delta rule has the effect of changing each weight by an amount proportional to the derivative of the weight with respect to the mean sum-of-squares error for the unit.

tract the actual output from the target output and square the result.[4] The sum of these values taken over all training pairs is called the *sum-squared error* and is defined as follows:

$$E = \Sigma \, (L_{kp} - T_{kp})^2$$

Here L_{kp} is the activation level of the kth output unit when the network is presented with the pth training pair, and T_{kp} is the target activation level of that unit on that training input. The variables k and p iterate over the indexes of all output units and of all training pairs, respectively. To obtain the mean error we simply divide the sum-squared error by the number of training pairs. Sometimes, overall error is measured in terms of *root mean-squared error* (RMSE). This is derived by taking the square root of the mean of the squared differences.

Having a measure of mean error allows us to envisage the space of possible weights in terms of a surface of error values. To visualize this surface, imagine that we take the weight space (which has one dimension for each weight) and add one dimension to represent the current level of error. If we think of the values on this dimension as measuring height, then we have a picture in which each possible configuration of weights is associated with a point at a certain height. If we put all these points together we have a surface. Higher points on the surface represent weight configurations that give higher levels of error. Lower points are configurations that give lower error. A sample surface is visualized in Figure 11.3.

Now, the aim in learning is to reduce the error to an absolute minimum. This means moving 'downhill' on the error surface until the lowest point is reached. But this strategy — called *gradient descent* — is simply the upside-down complement of *hill climbing* in heuristic search. And just as hill climbing suffers from the problem of foothills so gradient descent suffers from the problem of *local minima*. Since a gradient descent process always tries to move downhill, it is possible for it to get stuck in a shallow dip before it ever reaches the absolute lowest point, called the *global minimum*. Thus, to show that the delta rule is guaranteed to solve a given learning problem, we need to show that the error surface for the problem has no local minima. And, allowing for certain assumptions concerning the learning rate, this can be done using geometric reasoning (see Section 11.9).

---

[4] A squared value is always positive.

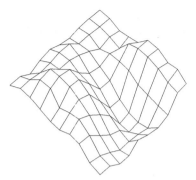

Figure 11.3. Example error surface.

11.5. Batch and online processing

We should note in passing that there are two possible ways to implement error-reduction learning strategies such as the LMS. Either we can cycle through all the input/output pairs in the training set applying the weight-change rule after each cycle according to the relevant error for that cycle; or we can cycle through the whole training set accumulating the required weight changes (i.e. the weight/error derivatives) for each weight in an array, and change the weights at the end of the epoch.

The first strategy is called *online* learning. The second is called *batch* learning. Batch learning uses more memory since it entails using an array of required weight changes but it guarantees that the weight vector will be moved in the direction of steepest descent on the error surface.[5] In online learning, individual movements of the weight vector may not be in the direction of steepest descent. But this does not matter provided that the learning rate is set sufficiently low to ensure that these do not move the weight vector too far from its current position.

---

[5] Note that this does not guarantee that the mean error will be reduced. If the learning rate is too high, moving the weight vector in the direction of steepest descent may actually move it to a higher point on the error surface.

11.6. The limitations of linear units

We have been focussing on the case of training a single linear unit and have noted that, using the LMS, we can train the unit to produce the best possible performance for a given set of input/output associations. There is nothing to stop us applying the LMS to more than one unit at a time. So, by implication, we can use the LMS to train networks involving any number of output units. But although we know that the LMS will — given certain architectural restrictions — give us the best possible performance, we would like to know how good that performance is likely to be. We will begin to form an answer to this question by seeing how many input/output associations can be learned by a single linear unit with just two input connections.

In Figure 11.4 we see a single, normalized input vector in the positive quadrant of a 2-dimensional space. The vector is labelled **1**. If we want to obtain a linear unit that will have a certain activation level for this input we have to position its weight vector so that it produces a projection of *exactly* this length on the input vector. For example, if we want the unit's activation level to be 0.5 we have to position the weight vector on a perpendicular that passes through the half-way point on the input vector. This perpendicular is shown as a dashed line in the diagram. Note that this procedure differs from the one which we use when dealing with threshold units. With TUs we only have to ensure that the projection is on the right side of the constraint line. Now that we are dealing with linear units, we have to ensure that the projection is right on the constraint line to get the output we want.

The case where we want to obtain outputs for two different input vectors is shown in Figure 11.5. One input vector is labelled **1**; the other is labelled **2**. Let us say that we want the first input vector to produce an output of 0.5 and the second input to produce an output of 0.6. From these target outputs we can derive two constraint lines in the usual way. One passes through a point 0.5 of the distance along vector **1**. The other passes through a point 0.6 of the distance along vector **2**. A weight vector that falls on the first line will produce the correct behaviour for input vector **1** and a vector that falls on the second line will produce correct behaviour for input vector **2**. A weight vector that falls on both lines will produce correct behaviour for both inputs. So we know that a satisfactory weight vector in this instance must fall on the *intersection* of the two lines. This weight vector is shown as the point marked **w** in Figure 11.5.

If we have more than two input vectors in our 2-dimensional input space then we will have more than two constraint lines and a low a priori probability of there being an intersection. (Three constraint lines drawn in at random will almost certainly not intersect at a unique point.) However, provided that we are careful in choosing target output values, we can produce constraints that do intersect.

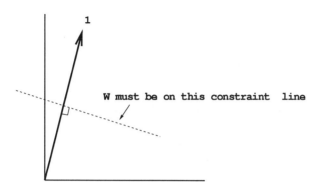

Figure 11.4. Constraint line for linear unit.

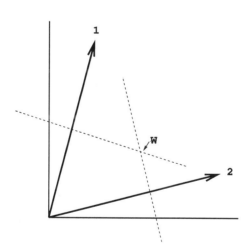

Figure 11.5. Two, intersecting constraint lines.

The diagram shown in Figure 11.6 has been constructed on the basis that the target output for input **1** is 0.5, while the target output for **2** and **3** is 0.6. The constraint lines that we get for these values just happen[6] to intersect at a unique point. Therefore we know that these input/output associations could be implemented by a single weight vector.

Of course, in general we cannot choose output vectors. They are fixed by the context. So it is most unlikely that constraint lines will intersect and therefore most unlikely that there will be a single weight vector that will reproduce the target mapping. The general conclusion is that, except in special, contrived cases, weight vectors in a 2-dimensional input space can map no more than two inputs on to two outputs. This follows from our observation that (1) in a 2-dimensional input space, constraints are always lines and (2) more than two lines are unlikely to have an intersection. The reasoning works for spaces of arbitrary dimensionality. For example, in a 3-dimensional input space constraints are always planes and more than three 3-dimensional planes are unlikely to intersect.

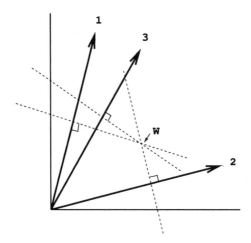

Figure 11.6. Three, intersecting constraint lines.

---

[6] They 'just happen' to intersect because the target outputs were carefully chosen to ensure that they would!

Since the delta rule updates weights in the same way as the PLA — by adding in a proportion of the relevant input vector — we know that it will move the weight vector perpendicularly towards violated constraint lines. Moreover, the fact that the size of the move is proportional to the error for the current pair means that the learning is guaranteed to slow down as the error approaches zero. Thus we can infer that, given a sufficiently small learning rate, the LMS will minimize the mean error. In the case depicted in Figure 11.7, where the output for input vector **1** is 0.6, the output for input vector **3** is 0.4 and the output for input vector **2** is 0.7, application of the LMS might result in the weight vector being placed near **w**.

11.7. Orthogonality and linear independence

Mathematically, the fact that a single *n*-dimensional weight vector is able to implement no more than *n* input/output associations stems from the fact that simple, linear networks involving input units and output units can only represent a set of input/output associations if the input vectors are *linearly independent*. Linear independence is related to *orthogonality*. Two 2-dimensional input vectors are orthogonal if they are at right angles to each other. For instance, if two vectors in a

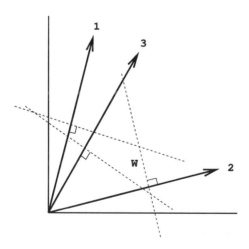

Figure 11.7. Three, non-intersecting constraint lines.

2-dimensional space are pointing due north and due east, then the vectors are orthogonal. If vectors are orthogonal then it is possible to travel along one without making any progress in the direction of the other. Thus, the fact that north and east are orthogonal vectors means that you can walk as far north as you like without ever getting any further east.

Any set of inputs that are orthogonal are linearly independent, but linearly independent inputs may not be orthogonal. Formally, a set of vectors are linearly independent if not a single one of them can be derived as a linear combination of any two others.[7] In an n-dimensional space, a set of linearly independent vectors contains no more than n elements. This gives us a result closely related to the one that we derived informally for single units. A linear network with m output units and n input units (i.e. an n-dimensional input space) can normally represent no more than n distinct input/output associations.

11.8. Summary and concluding comments

In the present chapter we have looked at learning algorithms for linear units and linear threshold units. Both the perceptron learning algorithm and the least mean squares procedure are based on the same idea — that once we have worked out the error of the unit in a given case, we can then reduce that error by changing the weights so as either to increase the net input if the unit's activation is too low or to decrease the net input if the unit's activation is too high. Of course, simple methods cannot be expected to produce startling performance. But these two are in fact surprisingly robust. Moreover, their very simplicity is a significant advantage since it enables us to see clearly what the limitations of the method actually are. With more complex learning algorithms such as back-propagation (see Chapter 13) we very often have to determine the limitations empirically, using time-consuming trial and error.

11.9. Further reading

Rosenblatt's (1962) book is the original reference for the perceptron learning algorithm but Hinton's (1989) survey paper provides all the essential details and a great deal more; see pp. 195-6 regarding the PLA and perceptron convergence theorem,

---

[7] A linear combination of the vectors X and Y is the sum of $X \times c_1 + Y \times c_2$ where c_1 and c_2 are coefficients.

and p. 194 regarding the significance of the error derivative in the LMS. Hinton also provides further details concerning the proof that the LMS is guaranteed to find a global minimum. This proof relies on geometric reasoning. As Hinton (1989, p. 194) notes:

> For networks with linear output units and no hidden units, the error surface always forms a bowl whose horizontal cross-sections are ellipses and whose vertical cross-sections are parabolas. Since the bowl only has one minimum, gradient descent on the error surface is guaranteed to find it.

Hinton also shows that in the case where the states of the output units are related to the relevant inputs via a non-linear, monotonic activation function rather than a linear one, the delta rule is guaranteed to be successful provided that there exists a set of weights that give satisfactory performance.

An early formulation of the delta rule was provided in 1959 by Bernard Widrow working with his student Marcian Hoff. In their work, the units that we have been calling linear units were called *ADALINES*; thus the delta rule (or *Widrow-Hoff rule*, as it is sometimes called) was originally produced as a learning procedure for the ADALINE unit. See Dayhoff (1990, p. 37) and Hecht-Nielsen (1990, p. 57) for more on the ADALINE unit.

Another reference of relevance to the material presented in this chapter is Gallant's paper describing the *Pocket algorithm* (Gallant, 1986). In Gallant's variant of the PLA a record is kept of the set of weights that has survived longest without being changed during training. Gallant has shown that, given sufficient training time, this set of weights will yield the minimum number of incorrect outputs. Thus, the need to obtain graceful degradation need not necessarily force us to abandon the basic perceptron strategy.

Nilsson (1982) deals with the foothills problem in heuristic search while Jordan (1986) provides background material for the concept of linear independence.

11.10. Problems

(1)   Consider the case where we want to train an LTU to compute boolean AND for two inputs. Is it likely to make the learning easier or harder if we normalize the input vectors? Why?

(2)   In the case where we have an LTU with a normalized weight vector and a threshold of 0.5, we know that any input vectors whose projection on the weight vector falls beyond the half-way point will turn the unit on, and that all other input vectors will turn it off. How does the analysis change if we have a linear unit rather than a linear threshold unit?

(3)   Can we use a linear unit to map three 2-dimensional input vectors on to three distinct output values? How would we set the weights of the unit?

(4)   What can we expect the delta rule to achieve in the case where there is no satisfactory weight vector for a problem?

(5)   What does it mean to say that a set of input vectors are linearly independent? Why do you think this property is significant in the case of the single-layer net?

(6)   In what cases are linearly independent vectors also orthogonal?

(7)   What does the training set contain in the case where we train a linear threshold unit to compute boolean OR?

(8)   State the rules for the perceptron learning algorithm.

(9)   What geometric effect does an application of the perceptron weight update rule have on a weight vector?

(10)   What does the perceptron convergence theorem state?

(11)   Geometrically characterize the situation in which the perceptron learning algorithm is guaranteed to fail.

(12)   What is the difference between online and batch learning?

(13)   What is an error surface? How can we estimate the a priori probability of finding a local minimum in an error surface?

12

The pattern associator

12.1. Introduction: connectionism in the dark age

In the 1970s, after Minsky and Papert's analysis had dampened the initial enthusiasm for the perceptron, connectionism went into a lull. Classical artificial intelligence was in its ascendancy with programs such as SHRDLU (Winograd, 1972) making a dramatic impact and convincing many of the long-term potential of the AI approach. However, some connectionist research did continue. For example, at Edinburgh in the UK a group led by Christopher Longuet-Higgins continued working on a family of architectures related to but more complex than the perceptron. Mathematical analysis was used extensively in this work. David Willshaw, for example, was able to determine the information-theoretic storage capacity of the *associative net* (now called the *Willshaw net*). This work was partly inspired by the invention of holography. This had shown how Lashley's idea of equipotentiality could be applied in a practical way and thus helped to revive the tradition that the brain might use distributed representation. As Willshaw (1981, pp. 83-84) notes:

> The technological advances made in the development of the hologram . . . had led people to suggest that the brain functioned on holographic principles. It had long been thought that the brain might store information in a manner resistant to local damage and that allowed for correct retrieval even when an inaccurate cue was presented, and the hologram seemed to possess these properties.

The properties of the hologram derive from the way in which it is constructed. A hologram is essentially a kind of photograph. But whereas a photograph is constructed by recording the pattern of light intensities produced by a given visual image, a hologram is constructed by recording the patterns of interference caused when two sources of coherent light are reflected off an object on to the same surface. The hologram is of interest from the practical point of view since, in certain optical circumstances, it yields a 3-dimensional rather than a 2-dimensional image. Its theoretical interest stems from the fact that it provides a practical demonstration of the power of distributed representation. The fact that the hologram is an explicit representation of an interference pattern means that any given point on the surface of a hologram stores information about the whole represented image. Thus, if the hologram is damaged at a particular location, the reproduced image degrades relatively evenly. The underlying representation is therefore distributed rather than localized.

12.2. Single-layer nets

The work at Edinburgh concentrated on what are now called *pattern associators*. These are networks in which we have several input units all with connections to a number of output units. Some of the properties and limitations of these networks can be derived by generalizing the results for networks with a single output unit. For example, the result that the delta rule is guaranteed to minimize the overall error of a single linear unit (applied to a given training set) applies equally well to the case where we have several linear units connected to several input units. Clearly, we can always minimize the overall error by minimizing the errors of the individual units.

Following the usual convention we will refer to a network that has one layer of input units and one layer of output units as a *single-layer network*. This is not as counter-intuitive as it sounds. In nearly all cases, the input units are just convenient vehicles for feeding activation into the input connections of the output units. They have no other functional role and can therefore be discounted in characterizing the architecture of the network.

Single-layer nets with multiple output units turn out to have quite severe theoretical limitations. However, they also exhibit some of the generic properties that make connectionist systems interesting from the computational viewpoint. McClelland and Rumelhart (1988, pp. 83-84) note the following properties of single-layer nets of the 'pattern-associator' family:

> They can act as content-addressable memories; they generalize the responses they make to novel inputs that are similar to the inputs that they have been trained on; they learn to extract the prototype of a set of repeated experiences in ways that are very similar to the concept-learning characteristics seen in human cognitive processes; and they degrade gracefully with damage and noise.

In the present chapter we will see how the single-layer net can be used in conjunction with error-reduction learning algorithms to produce pattern-associator mechanisms, and we will look at an experiment in which a large single-layer net was used in the modeling of human linguistic development.

12.3. Representations for single-layer networks

Single-layer networks are represented visually in several different ways. Most commonly, the representation that we have used for single units is used, i.e. units are represented as circles and connections as connecting lines. By convention, the flow of activation is assumed to be upwards or rightwards. Thus the input units in the network are typically represented by the leftmost or lower layer of circles. The network shown in Figure 12.1 is a single-layer network with three input units and three output units. The network features *complete inter-layer connectivity*. This means that every input unit is connected to every output unit.

In another common representation, the network is drawn as a grid with vertical lines corresponding to components of the input and horizontal lines corresponding to weight vectors. The point where a vertical line crosses a horizontal line corresponds to a specific weight and is often called the *synaptic junction* (by analogy with biological neural networks). Matrix representations are popular among researchers interested in making links between connectionist architectures and biological neural networks, or in understanding the computations performed by the pattern associator in terms of matrix algebra. A matrix representation for the network shown in Figure 12.1 is shown in Figure 12.2.

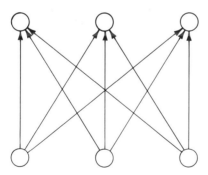

Figure 12.1. Simple pattern associator network.

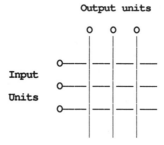

Figure 12.2. Matrix representation of a network.

12.4. A learning problem for the pattern associator

Let us now look at how a pattern associator (i.e. single-layer network) of *n* input units and *m* linear output units tackles a particular learning problem. We will first look at how the pattern associator deals with a learning problem involving linearly independent inputs. Then we will see how it copes with linearly dependent inputs. In both cases we will use an architecture with two input units only. In this scenario the input vectors are 2-dimensional and can be represented geometrically.

For the first experiment we use randomly initialized weight vectors, a learning rate of 0.9 and a training set as follows:

<[0.9 0.3] [0 1]>
<[0.7 0.7] [1 0]>

The learning is shown in Figure 12.3. The two weight vectors of interest belong to units 3 and 4. The initial positions of these weight vectors (i.e. their states in epoch 0) are shown as **W3** and **W4**. Movements of the weight vectors (i.e. changes in the weights) are indicated with arrows. As the text shows, in epoch 0, the outputs produced for the two inputs diverge markedly from the target outputs. For example, the output required for input 1 is [0 1]. The output actually produced is [0.83

0.23].[1] After epoch 3, **w3** and **w4** have moved relative to the input vectors, changing the projections on the input vectors and therefore the outputs produced. Note that, to achieve satisfactory performance, **w3** must move towards a position where it has a maximum projection on 2 and a minimum projection on 1. Unit **w4** must move towards a complementary position where it has a maximum projection on 1 and a minimum projection on 2. (The relevant constraint lines are shown as dashed lines in the figure.) Geometrically, this means **w3** must move up and to the left while **w4** must move down and to the right.

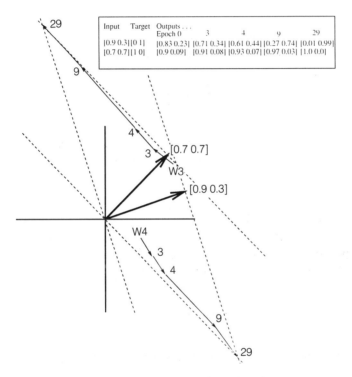

Figure 12.3. Pattern-associator learning.

---

[1] In this diagram **w3** provides the first component of the output vector and **w4** provides the second.

After epoch 4 we see that the two weight vectors have moved further in the appropriate directions. At this point the mean error is 0.33,[2] and the actual outputs are better approximations of the desired outputs. After epoch 9 the mean error is down to 0.15. w3 is moving towards the ideal position where it has a maximum projection on 2 and a minimum projection on 1. w4 is also approaching its ideal position. After twenty more epochs (i.e. by epoch 29) of training the mean error is less than 0.01 and w3 and w4 are very close to their ideal positions. The actual outputs are very close to the target outputs.

12.5. Learning with linearly dependent inputs

For contrast, consider a learning problem involving inputs that are *not* linearly independent. The training set for the problem we will look at is:

```
<[0.9 0.1] [0.8]>
<[0.7 0.7] [0]>
<[0.1 0.9] [1]>
```

We know these inputs cannot be linearly independent for the simple reason that there are three of them. In an input space of two dimensions we can have only two linearly independent vectors.

In this problem — which involves a single output unit — the pattern associator reduces the error to a minimum of 0.48, with the worst-case error being 0.63. In this particular case the constraint lines for the first and third input vectors are perpendiculars that pass through points close to the tips of the relevant vectors. The line for the second input vector is a perpendicular that passes through the origin. These three lines enclose a convex region, as shown in Figure 12.4. The output unit's weight vector (w3) is in the middle of this region, i.e. in a position where the average distance to a constraint line is (approximately) minimized.

12.6. Using the Hebb learning rule with the pattern associator

When we are dealing with a pattern-associator architecture it is possible to use a learning rule based on the synaptic modification scheme suggested by Donald Hebb (1949). This rule is simpler to implement than the delta rule and does not require the

---

[2] This is a root-mean-squared error value.

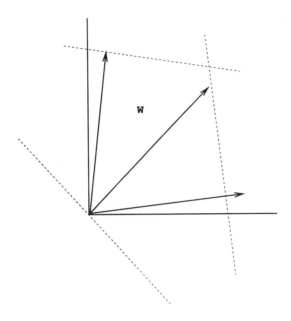

Figure 12.4. Pattern-associator learning with linearly independent inputs.

computation of explicit error information. The basic idea is that weight vectors are modified so as to increase weights on links connecting units that tend to be simultaneously active. The simplest implementation of the Hebb rule involves updating a given weight by an amount equal to the product of the activations of the two units involved. To apply this version of the rule to weight W_{ij} we

Set W_{ij} equal to $W_{ij} + L_i\,L_j$

Use of this Hebbian learning rule[3] ensures that the size of the weight on the link between input unit i and output unit j will correspond to the degree to which the ith component of training inputs tends to be correlated with the jth component of target

---

[3] There are in fact many variants of Hebb's rule. However in what follows we will take the 'Hebb rule' to be the one shown above.

outputs.[4]

If the input vectors are orthogonal the Hebb rule will produce perfect behaviour. This follows straightforwardly from the observation that the Hebb rule, like the delta rule, updates weight vectors by adding in or subtracting a proportion of the input vector. This moves the weight vector in the direction of the relevant input vector. If input vectors are always orthogonal then weight vectors will always be moved in a direction that is orthogonal to all other input vectors. Thus when a weight vector is moved so as to alter its projection on one input vector, its projection on all other input vectors will not change. In effect, then, in the case of orthogonal inputs, weight changes can never interfere with one another. In the situation where the input vectors are not orthogonal but merely linearly independent, use of the Hebb rule will not obtain perfect performance even though use of the LMS (with the delta rule) will do so.

12.7. The Willshaw net

The Willshaw net is an architecture that can, in some cases, deal with non-orthogonal input vectors. It allows use of a form of the Hebb learning rule but can only accept binary input vectors. This architecture, which is also called the *non-linear associative net*, is a single-layer network. Units are simple threshold units and weights can be set to 1 or 0. All weights are initially set to 0 and learning is achieved by cycling through the training set, clamping[5] inputs and outputs and setting all weights on links between simultaneously active units to 1. Note that the learning mechanism here is 'one-shot' — a particular input/output pair need only be presented once.

In Figure 12.5 we see a matrix representation of a network of six input units and six output units with complete connectivity. As a result of the presentation of the training pair `<[0 1 1 0 0 1]  [1 1 0 0 0 0]>` several weights have been set to 1 (i.e. on) as shown.

To produce an output vector from an input vector we set all the thresholds in the output units to a mean value which is identical to the number of ones in the input vector. In the present case this would mean setting the mean threshold to 3. Having done

---

[4] Technically, one full pass through the training set (applying the rule above to each weight after each iteration) sets the weight matrix to be the *outer product sum* of the input/output vectors. That is to say, it is the sum of outer products produced when we multiply each given input vector with its target output vector. The final weight matrix is also the *cross-correlation matrix* of the input vectors and the output vectors.

[5] The process of fixing the activation of a certain unit to a certain level is referred to as 'clamping'.

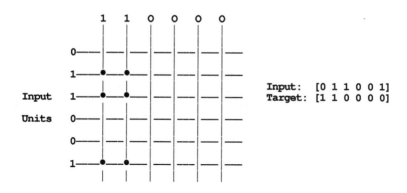

Figure 12.5. Learning in a Willshaw net.

this, presentating the original input vector will produce the desired output vector exactly, since the way in which we have set the thresholds ensures that output units which turn on are precisely those whose input lines connect with three active input units.

This method of setting thresholds is intended to ensure that an output unit will come on only if it has been explicitly trained to do so. If an output unit that has not been trained to turn on does turn on (for a given input) then it must be the case that every single weight from an active input unit must have been set to 1 by some *other* training pair. Provided the chances of this happening are relatively small — and if there are relatively few training pairs they should be — the network should exhibit perfect performance.

As noted, the efficiency of this form of Hebbian learning has been analysed in information-theoretic terms by Willshaw. He showed that, even in the case where the network is storing close to 70% of its information-theoretic capacity, the probability of perfect performance on tractable memory tasks is high provided the number of active input units (per input pattern) is logarithmically related to the total number of input units.

12.8. Learning past tenses

In the remainder of the chapter we will look at some experimental work by two major figures in the connectionist world: Rumelhart and McClelland. This work aimed to provide a connectionist model for certain phenomena in language learning. It is of relevance here since it involved use of a pattern-associator architecture. The phenomena that Rumelhart and McClelland wanted to model related to the development of linguistic abilities in children. Empirical evidence has shown that children learning English tend to pass through three, fairly distinct stages in learning past forms of verbs. In the first stage they use the past forms of verbs infrequently but where they do use a past form, they tend to give it the correct ending. In the second stage children catch on to the general rule that the past form of a verb can normally be constructed by attaching 'ed' to the end of the present form (e.g., that the past of 'look' must be 'looked'). The acquisition of this rule appears to eradicate their original knowledge of past forms and they will produce regularizations of irregular forms such as 'swimmed' and 'see-ed'. In the final phase children learn the special cases, i.e. they remember to use the correct form in the past even where the past form is formed in an irregular way. The learning curve here is roughly U-shaped. An initial sharp improvement in performance is followed first by a sudden deterioration, then by a more even rate of development.

Language phenomena such as the above are often explained in terms of the development of internal representations of linguistic rules, e.g., the rule that past-forms can often be generated by adding 'ed' to the present-form. However, Rumelhart and McClelland's thesis — stated very briefly — is that language learning in general, and learning past-tense forms in particular, may not involve the construction of explicit rules, as is usually assumed, but merely the evolution of rule-like behaviour. They are essentially questioning the assumption that rule-like behaviour implies the existence of *explicit* rules.

The authors hoped to support this view by constructing a variant of the pattern associator network that, while being trained on verb/past-form input/output pairs, would exhibit the same U-shaped learning curve. In some sense, they succeeded. However, they had to solve a number of implementational problems first. In particular, they had to find a suitable way to encode inputs (verbs) and outputs (past forms).

12.8.1. Input/output encodings

An example of a present-tense/past-tense association is:

pull → pulled

One way to encode such associations as training pairs would be to represent each word in the association by a set of real numbers representing the relative alphabetic positions of the component letters. For instance, we might represent 'p' by 16/26, 'u' by 21/26 and 'l' by 12/26. This would give us, as a representation for 'pull', the vector of real numbers:

[0.62 0.81 0.46 0.46]

We could then construct training pairs for the present-tense/past-tense mappings by putting together suitably encoded associations; e.g., the association:

pull → pulled

would be presented as the following training pair:

<[0.62 0.81 0.46 0.46] [0.62 0.81 0.46 0.46 0.19 0.15]>

This scheme has the advantage of simplicity. But the experimenters decided that a more sophisticated coding scheme was required. They say that:

> The input and target patterns--the base forms of the verbs and the correct past tenses of these verbs--must be presented to the model in such a way that the features provide a convenient basis for capturing the regularities embodied in the past-tense forms of English verbs. (Rumelhart and McClelland, 1986, p. 233)

They wanted an encoding scheme that would (1) permit a differentiation of all of the root forms of English and their past tenses and (2) provide a natural basis for generalizations about the correspondence between present and past-tense forms. In effect, they had to ensure that the representation made the significant similarities between inputs accessible. They therefore used a scheme that, unlike the one suggested above, takes account of the phonemic structure of words.[6]

----

[6] The discussion in Chapter 21 suggests that this strategy is not always feasible.

12.8.2. Phoneme encodings: wickelphones and wickelfeatures

A simplified feature space (i.e. description language) for phonemes is based on the following four dimensions:

1: interrupted, continuous-consonant, vowel
2: stop, fricative, high,nasal, liquid, low
3: front, middle, back
4: voiced, unvoiced, long, short

The values here denote features of phoneme pronunciation. These four sequences of features define a 4-dimensional feature space. Each point in this space corresponds to a possible phoneme, e.g., [vowel nasal middle voiced]. However, quite a large number of points correspond to phonemes that are never observed in practice. For example, if a phoneme is interrupted it can be either stopped or nasal but not liquid, fricative, high or low.

We can therefore use a cut-down version of the space in which dimensions 2 and 4 have just two values each, namely 0 and 1. A value of 1 in dimension 2 represents one of {stop, fricative, high} depending what the value is in dimension 1. A value of 0 in dimension 2 represents one of {interrupted, continuous-consonant, vowel}, depending what the values is in dimension 1. And so on. In the cut-down space we have ten possible feature values. If we encode each possible feature value in terms of a single binary digit, then we can encode a phoneme using a binary word of ten digits. For example, if we map feature values on to positions working left to right, [1 0 0 1 0 1 0 0 0 1] would represent the combination of features [interrupted stop front long].

Rumelhart and McClelland realized that the input encoding should make the phonemic *context* explicit. They therefore chose to encode inputs as feature triples, called *wickelfeatures*. Each of these specifies features for a sequence of three phonemes, i.e. it gives a feature of the previous phoneme, a feature of the current phoneme and a feature of the following phoneme.[7]

Unfortunately, there are 1000 (10^3) different wickelfeatures in all. So use of an encoding in which each binary digit represented the presence of a given wickelfeature would have resulted in input vectors with 1000 components, i.e. it would have entailed using a network with 1000 input units. The researchers therefore chose to

---

[7] Wickelfeatures are named after *wickelphones*, which are phoneme representations explicitly specifying a current, preceding and succeeding phoneme (Rumelhart and McClelland, 1986).

trim down the total set of wickelfeatures. This trimming knocked out all feature triplets whose first and third features were chosen from different phonetic dimensions.[8] The set was further trimmed so as to include only those wickelfeatures having *different* values (in the same dimension) for the predecessor and successor phonemes. The cut-down set contains just 460 elements. This enabled a given wickelphone to be encoded as a vector of 460 binary values, each of which represents a particular wickelfeature.[9]

A particular triple of phoneme features (a *wickelphone*) corresponds to ('activates') 16 wickelfeatures. Thus a verb with three phonemes/wickelphones (e.g., 'came') is encoded as at most 48 wickelfeatures (16 × 3). This, however, is a worst-case figure. Normally, the fact that a given wickelfeature may be activated by more than one phoneme in a given word means that the total number of activated wickelfeatures is less than this. Thus input vectors tended to contain less than the maximum number of 48 1s.

12.8.3. The architecture

The architecture used was based on a variant of the pattern-associator network. The units in the network were stochastic linear threshold units. The behaviour of these units is identical to that of units in the Boltzmann machine, described in detail in Chapter 20. For present purposes it is enough to know that these units behave like 'buggy' linear threshold units, i.e. units which occasionally turn off when they should have turned on, and vice versa. The learning rule used was the perceptron learning rule.

Inputs and outputs were wickelfeature representations of words. However, since the authors wanted an architecture that mapped phonemic representations of verbs on to phonemic representations of past tenses they added, at the front end, an encoding network (that consisted essentially of 460 'wickelfeature detectors') and, at the back end, a kind of competitive learning network (see Chapter 18) that effectively translated wickelfeature representations back into phonemic representations. The overall architecture is visualized in Figure 12.6.

---

[8] See Pinker & Prince (1988, p. 92) for further details.

[9] In fact, the final encoding scheme was even more elaborate than this. It involved a 'blurring' stage in which, for each set of 16 activated wickelfeatures, 16 extra wickelfeatures were also activated — these being randomly selected but similar to the original 16.

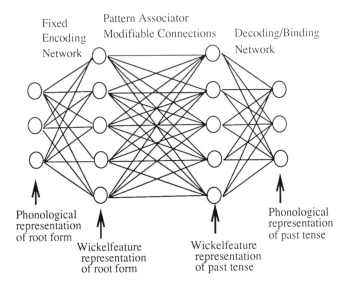

Figure 12.6. Past-tense network (after Rumelhart and McClelland, 1986).

12.9. Results

The experiment was successful in the sense that the researchers were able to obtain performance from the network that approximated the empirical data for the past-tense learning problem. Unfortunately, it was not entirely successful in establishing the credibility of the underlying idea that learning past-tense forms involves learning explicit rules. There is still a good deal of contention about the status of the model as a justification of this thesis.

Many of the criticisms of Rumelhart and McClelland's model are developed in detail in Pinker & Prince (1988). This book-length article is reminiscent of Minsky and

Papert's exhaustive examination of the perceptron. Surprisingly, it does not primarily seek to show that, in using such a contrived input encoding, the authors trivialized the computational task in question. Rather it shows that the encoding scheme is totally *inadequate* in general and could not play any role in an explanation of the linguistic phenomena in question. It also shows that some of the reported performance was due to the way in which the researchers handled the presentation of the training set.

The final conclusion of Pinker and Prince's article is that McClelland and Rumelhart's work does not justify dispensing with the notion of explicit rules in explanations of language acquisition. However, it is worth noting that this conclusion is drawn on the basis of arguments that undermine the credibility of Rumelhart and McClelland's thesis without actually showing that it must be wrong. There is, then, the possibility that new evidence in favour of the thesis may be provided, leading to an ultimate rejection of the notion of explicit linguistic rules.

12.10. Further reading

Rumelhart and McClelland (1986, pp. 219-20) provide further details on the past-tense work and references on the linguistic stages of development of relevance to the experiment described above. They also provide a general introduction to the features and limitations of the pattern associator and further details on the activation function employed in the pattern associator (see pp. 225-6).

Kohonen (1977; 1984) has provided the classic, formal analysis of pattern associator mechanisms; the essentials of this analysis are also to be found in Hecht-Nielsen (1990); see particularly pp. 50-6. Minsky and Papert (1988) also provide analytic material of relevance. Jordan (1986) provides a thorough analysis of pattern-associator-like mechanisms using linear algebra and some geometry. Hinton (1989, p. 191) provides an introduction to the Willshaw net but see also Willshaw (1981). For background reading on the Hebb's learning rule see Hebb (1949). For an implementation of the pattern associator mechanism, see McClelland and Rumelhart (1988).

12.11. Problems

(1)   Train a pattern associator to associate identical patterns of activation, i.e. train it to implement a mapping of the form:

```
<[0.5  0.41 0.51 0.67]  [0.5  0.41 0.51 0.67]>
<[0.91 0.46 0.94 0.94]  [0.91 0.46 0.94 0.94]>
<[0.97 0.31 0.71 0.23]  [0.97 0.31 0.71 0.23]>
<[0.65 0.61 0.89 0.33]  [0.65 0.61 0.89 0.33]>
<[0.03 0.11 0.22 0.22]  [0.03 0.11 0.22 0.22]>
<[0.28 0.25 0.84 0.54]  [0.28 0.25 0.84 0.54]>
<[0.34 0.56 0.94 0.84]  [0.34 0.56 0.94 0.84]>
<[0.3  0.74 0.98 0.58]  [0.3  0.74 0.98 0.58]>
<[0.63 0.56 0.78 0.87]  [0.63 0.56 0.78 0.87]>
<[0.11 0.47 0.34 0.95]  [0.11 0.47 0.34 0.95]>
```

Would you say that the learning produces a distributed representation for the mapping or a localized representation? Why? Justify your answer.

(2)   Derive and test the performance of a Willshaw net that implements the following mapping:

```
<[1 1 1 0]  [1 1 1 0]>
<[1 1 0 1]  [1 1 0 1]>
<[0 0 0 1]  [0 0 0 1]>
<[0 1 0 1]  [0 1 0 1]>
<[0 1 0 0]  [0 1 0 0]>
<[0 1 1 0]  [0 1 1 0]>
<[0 1 1 1]  [0 1 1 1]>
<[0 1 0 1]  [0 1 0 1]>
<[0 1 1 0]  [0 1 1 0]>
<[0 1 1 1]  [0 1 1 1]>
```

(3)   What is the relationship between the pattern associator and the perceptron?

(4)   How many input and output units can the pattern associator have? Can there be more output units than input units? If so, how would you expect them to be connected to the input units?

(5)   How can we represent a pattern associator with three input units and five output units as a matrix? Use a special symbol to denote synaptic junctions.

(6)   In what ways does a Willshaw net differ from a pattern associator? In what sense does the Willshaw net use a Hebbian learning rule?

13

Back-propagation

13.1. Supervised learning in complex networks

We have seen how we can use error-reduction methods to obtain supervised learning in single-layer networks but we have found that the performance of such mechanisms is quite limited. The perceptron convergence algorithm is only effective if the input classes are linearly separable. And the LMS procedure (using the delta rule) is only effective if the input patterns are linearly independent.

To achieve more powerful performance it is necessary to look at more complex networks — networks which, in addition to the input units and the output units, contain *hidden units*. In the simplest case these units accept activation from input units and feed it on into output units, as shown in Figure 13.1. In general, hidden units accept activation from either input units or other hidden units and feed it to hidden units or output units.

13.2. Feed-forward nets, hidden units and activation vectors

Before dealing with learning in the context of this more complex architecture, we should introduce some terminology. Firstly, a network containing a layer of input units, a layer of hidden units and a layer of output units is a *two-layer network*. A network with two layers of hidden units would be a *three-layer network*, and so on. As before, the justification for this is that the layer of input units is used only as an input channel and can therefore be discounted. If activation always flows forwards from the input units, through the hidden units to the output units then we have a *feed-forward network*. If every unit in every layer receives input from every unit in the layer below, the network is *completely connected* between layers. A network which only has connections between units in adjacent layers is *strictly layered*.

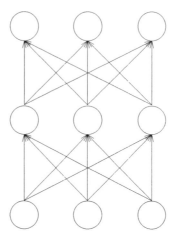

Figure 13.1. Simple two-layer network.

The terms *input vector* and *output vector* have the same interpretation in the case of the multi-layer network. An input vector is just a vector of input unit activations and an output vector is a vector of output unit activations. A vector of hidden unit activations is a *hidden vector* while the term *activation vector* can be used for input, output or hidden vectors. To identify the activation vector for a particular layer of the network we simply give the index of the layer, i.e. we can talk about the activation vector for the first layer of the network, meaning the activation vector for the first layer of hidden units. An input vector is the zeroth layer activation vector and an output vector is the nth-layer activation vector in an n-layer network.

13.3. Making use of hidden units

In trying to obtain more powerful behaviour through the use of hidden units we encounter two main problems. Firstly, if we are using networks of linear units, we have the problem that the addition of hidden *linear* units obtains no advantage whatsoever. A single-layer network of linear units defines a linear mapping. A two-layer network of linear units defines a sequence of two linear mappings. Since any sequence of linear mappings can be reduced to a single mapping we know that any n-layer network of linear units can be reduced to a single-layer network. Thus all the limitations which apply to single-layer networks of linear units apply to *n*-layer networks of linear units. If the introduction of hidden units is to achieve anything, then, it is essential for the units to have *non-linear* activation functions. That is to say, it is necessary for the activation of a unit to be a non-linear function of its inputs.

But which activation function should we use? One possibility would be to use a threshold (step) function as in the perceptron convergence algorithm. However, the most common approach involves using an activation function which is intermediate between the linear function and the step function. This function has a sigmoid shape and is sometimes called the *logistic function*. It is defined as follows (*x* is the total input to the unit):

$$\frac{1}{1 + e^{-x}}$$

Units which use this function to compute their activation levels are called *sigmoidal units*. Since the effect of the logistic function is to squash a signed number into the range 0-1, it is also sometimes called the *squashing function*. Its curve is shown in Figure 13.2. Using the squashing function for computing unit activations has a number of advantages. First of all, unlike a threshold function, it has a smoothly

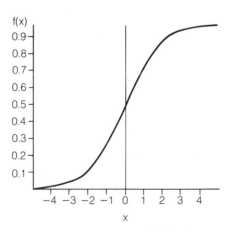

Figure 13.2. The sigmoid function.

varying first derivative.[1] Being able to compute the first derivative of the activation function is important, as we shall see. Second, it enables units to take on a large range of states (in principle, an infinite range of states). Finally, the function roughly approximates the relationship between the firing rate of a neuron and its summed inputs. This is of relevance to the physiological validity of connectionist models.

The second problem that we face in making the transition to complex networks is the fact that there is no straightforward way to apply the error-reducing rule to a hidden unit. Recall that computing the error of output units is trivial — the error is just the difference between the actual and target activation level. But how should we compute the error of a unit which is not an output unit? That is to say, how should we apportion blame (error) for a bad output among all the units which have played some role in producing that output?

In some sense, this problem is a connectionist variant of the AI *credit-assignment problem*. That problem is encountered whenever we have to decide which rule(s) in a production system make an important contribution to some particular piece of useful behaviour. In the present case the problem is encountered when we have to decide which hidden units have been (most) responsible for the generation of error at the output units.

13.4. Error-propagation

Back-propagation provides us with an answer to the problem. Formally, it gives us an easy way of computing the derivative of each weight with respect to the mean error. Informally, we can view it as a way of deriving error values for hidden units. Being able to do this means that we can use a variant of the usual error-reduction process to obtain learning in networks with hidden units.

The basic observation underlying back-propagation is that, although we cannot assign the errors of hidden units directly, we can *deduce* their level of error by computing the error of the output units and propagating this error backwards through the network. In a two-layer, feed-forward network, the contribution that a hidden unit makes to the error of an output unit to which it is connected is simply the degree to which the hidden unit was responsible for giving the output unit the *wrong* level of activation. The size of the contribution depends on two factors: (1) the weight on the link which connects the two units and (2) the activation of the hidden unit. Thus we can arrive at an estimated error value for an arbitrary hidden unit by summing all the

---

[1] The first derivative of a threshold function is infinite at the step and zero elsewhere.

'contributions' that it makes to the errors of the units to which it is connected.

Obviously, the procedure generalizes to *n*-layer networks. If we can derive error values for fourth-layer units we can derive error values for third-layer units. If we can derive error values for third-layer units we can derive error values for second-layer units and so on. This process of chaining backwards through the layers of the network is what puts the 'back' in back-propagation.

13.5. Error signals and error values

Let us look at this propagation mechanism in more detail. As we noted, the degree to which a hidden unit is responsible for the error of a unit into which it feeds activation is a function of (1) the weight on the relevant link and (2) its activation level. In back-propagation we take account of these two components of the responsibility in two steps. First we compute what is called the *error signal* by finding the sum of the products of relevant error and weight values. Assuming that the weight between non-connected units is 0, we can compute the initial error signal of a hidden unit *i* as follows:

$$S_i = \sum_j E_j \, W_{ij}$$

where E_j is the error value of the *j*th unit. Next we have to take account of the level of activation of the unit in question. The more extreme the activation level the greater the contribution to error. So we might therefore multiply the current error signal for the *i*th unit by its level of activation. However, in back-propagation the initial error is, in fact, multiplied by the derivative of the activation. This is necessary to ensure that the way in which we change a given weight will reflect the derivative of the weight with respect to the mean error.

There is also an intuitive justification. This is simply the idea that we would like back-propagation of error to have the greatest effect on units which are not yet committed to playing any particular role (i.e. being in any particular state) in the target computation. By multiplying the error signal by the first derivative of the activation — which is high for intermediate activation values like 0.5 but low for extreme values such as 0.9 and 0.1 — we effectively ensure that the error signal of uncommitted units (i.e. units that have a medium level of activation) is high. This in turn ensures that they will be the units that are most affected by the learning process. If L_i is the activation level of unit *i*, the final error of unit *i* is:

$$E_i = S_i \ d(L_i)$$

where S_i is the initial error signal and the function d returns the first derivative of the logistic function. In the case of output units, the error signal is just $T_o - L_o$; i.e. the result of subtracting the actual activation level of the output unit from the target activation level.

As we mentioned, the derivative of the logistic function is easily computed. If L_i is the current activation of unit i, the first derivative is just:

$$L_i(1 - L_i)$$

Once we have derived final error values for all the units in the network, we can then update weights by applying the error-reduction rule in the same way as in the LMS procedure. We update the weight on the connection which feeds activation from unit i to unit j by an amount proportional to the product of E_j and L_i (where E_j is the error of unit j and L_i is the activation level of unit i):

$$\Delta \ W_{ij} = E_j \ L_i$$

This method for updating weights in networks with hidden units is called the *generalized delta rule* or the *back-propagation procedure*. Application of the procedure minimizes the sum-squared error of the output of the network, i.e. the overall degree to which activations of the output units differ from the target activations. Multilayered, feed-forward networks using this learning rule are sometimes called *Rumelhart networks* or *multi-layered perceptrons*.

13.6. Local and quasi-local minima

Applying the generalized delta rule to a network ensures that the network will reduce the mean squared error (i.e. will improve its performance). However, as with all gradient descent (hill-climbing) methods, there is always the chance of getting stuck in local minima (on foothills). However, it is claimed that, in practice, back-propagation rarely gets stuck in local minima. One explanation that has been proposed is that, in many problems, there are many equivalent global minima, i.e. many different solution states for the network. Thus the gradient descent is not searching for a single global minimum but rather for one of a whole set of minima.[2]

Other explanations have been put forward. One example notes that where a high-dimensional input space is used there is reason to expect that genuine local minima will be quite rare. In order for a local minima to exist it must be the case that there is a coincident minimum in each dimension of the space in question. The more dimensions, the greater, and therefore the less probable, the coincidence. The conclusion is thus that genuine local minima will occur infrequently in high-dimensional input spaces.

Determining whether or not a given error surface contains a genuine local minimum is a difficult task requiring exhaustive exploration of the error surface. At the time of writing, only one genuine global minimum has been identified in a back-propagation error surface. Finding this minimum required 12 hours of processing on a Cray-2 supercomputer! (McInerney *et al.*, 1989) Of course, *quasi-local minima*, i.e. regions of the error surface where there is very little gradient, may trap the back-propagation procedure for an unacceptably long period of time and therefore be just as troublesome as genuine local minima.

13.7. Additional features of back-propagation

13.7.1. Bias

In back-propagation and the other connectionist learning mechanisms we have looked at, the activation level of a unit has always been produced by applying the activation function to the inputs to the unit. In the simplest case this involves finding the inner product of the weight vector with the (unit's) input vector. However, to obtain satisfactory performance from back-propagation we have to allow units to have some given level of activation independently of their inputs.

This activation is called a *bias* (not to be confused with *inductive bias*). It is typically implemented by connecting all units to a dummy unit which is always on (i.e. always has an activation level of 1). This unit is sometimes called the *true unit* by analogy with networks of logical propositions. The advantage of this scheme is that biases can then be learned just like ordinary weights.

---

[2] Unfortunately, this explanation seems to suggest that there will be many equivalent local minima too.

13.7.2. Momentum

As we have noted, back-propagation performs gradient descent in squared error. In effect, it tries to find a global minimum of the error surface by repeatedly making jumps in the downhill direction.[3] Unfortunately, this approach can lead to various forms of disadvantageous behaviour. In particular, consider what will happen when the weight configuration corresponds to a point high up, on one side of a long, thin valley in the error surface. If back-propagation makes a sufficiently large jump in the downhill direction it will move to a position high up on the other side of the valley! In the next iteration it will jump back to the original side, and so on. This phenomenon is known as *sloshing* and it can substantially slow down the learning process. The general effect is illustrated in Figure 13.3.

There are a number of potential solutions to the problem of sloshing. However, a long-standing method is to amend the weight-updating process so that the gradient descent process is able to build up some *momentum* along the valley floor. The most convenient way of doing this involves changing the weight-update rule so that, at each weight change, the value of the change is some combination of the current

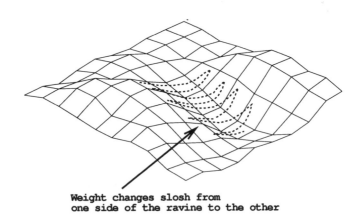

**Weight changes slosh from
one side of the ravine to the other**

Figure 13.3. The sloshing problem.

---

[3] Of course, it is the weight configuration, rather than back-propagation itself, which does the jumping.

change and the change last applied to the weight. The general effect is to smooth out the weight changes and thus to prevent the gradient descent process from oscillating wildly between the two sides of a valley.

Momentum is typically implemented using a numeric parameter, i.e. a number between 0 and 1. To compute a given weight change we first find the product of the previous weight change and the momentum parameter. We then add this to the product of the desired weight change and the complement of the momentum parameter.[4] The result is the weight change to be applied. A typical value for the momentum parameter is 0.9. In this case, direction of movement over the error surface remains fairly constant from iteration to iteration.

13.7.3. Symmetry-breaking

A final problem that we have to solve when using back-propagation is that of *symmetry breakage*. This problem occurs when all weights are initialized to the same value (e.g., 0). Because error values of hidden units are derived from weight values, setting all weights to the same value means that hidden units will be assigned identical error values.[5] This will cause all weights to be revised in an identical manner and thus prevent the mean error ever being reduced. When we set all weights to the same value we place the network at a local maximum of the error function from which it cannot escape. To solve the problem we should initialize the weights to small random values. This ensures that there are some initial non-symmetries upon which the error-reduction process can build.

13.8. Theoretical properties of multi-layer networks

The theoretical properties of multi-layer networks are a subject of active research at the present time. An initial breakthrough was made in 1986 when Hecht-Nielsen used Kolmogorov's mapping theorem to show that any mapping (subject to certain constraints) from n-dimensional binary vectors to m-dimensional activation vectors can be represented in a network which has $2n+1$ hidden units.[6] The drawback with this demonstration was the fact that, in the context of the proof, the hidden units were assumed to be able to adopt arbitrary activation functions, i.e. they were not assumed

---

[4] That is, 1 - momentum.

[5] We are assuming complete within-layer connectivity here.

[6] Hecht-Nielsen calls this *Kolmogorov's Mapping Neural Network Existence Theorem*.

to use the familiar sigmoid function.

More recently, various researchers have argued that two-layer networks of sigmoidal units (i.e. units using the logistic activation function) are also able to implement virtually any mapping, provided that the number of hidden units is assumed to be unlimited.[7] In contrast to these positive results, we also have the recent result by Judd (1990) that network learning is an NP-complete problem, which is to say it is, in general, computationally intractable. The theoretical picture, then, is still developing and may change substantially in the next few years.

13.9. Example

We now turn to a worked example of back-propagation. We will concentrate on the exclusive-OR task, which is a simple but interesting problem. In particular, we will look at the case where back-propagation is applied to a strictly layered network with two input units, two hidden units, one output unit and complete inter-layer connectivity. This network with randomly initialized weights is shown below.

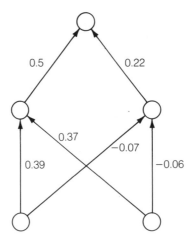

---

[7] Of course we should not be misled by this into thinking that one layer of hidden units will always be the correct architecture for any problem. In many cases a network using more than one layer of hidden units will be much more efficient and effective than a network using an arbitrarily large single layer.

Example 181

Strictly layered architectures are typically labelled by a hyphenated string of integers corresponding to the number of units in each layer. Thus the present network would be labelled a *2-2-1* network. We will first work through one iteration in the learning procedure. Then we will look at a complete run from the point of view of the *error profile* generated. Finally, we will look at the learning behaviour geometrically.

13.10. Hand-simulation of one iteration

We begin the hand-simulation by selecting the training pair <[0 1] [1]>. The input vector in this pair is [0 1] so, adopting the convention that we set input unit activations working from left to right, we set the activation of the left input unit to 0 and that of the right input unit to 1. We then propagate the activation forwards through the network using the logistic function to compute new activations. This gives us activation values [8] for all the units in the network:

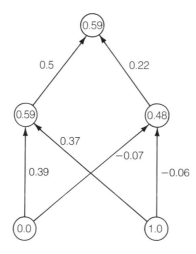

13.11. Back-propagation of error values

Once the activations of all the units have been set, back-propagation derives the error value for the output unit and then propagates this error back through the network. The

---

[8] In the trace, bias values are ignored and all activation/weight values are truncated to no more than two decimal places.

error signal for the output unit is derived by subtracting the actual output from the target output and multiplying the result by the derivative of the activation value. This error value can then be used to generate error signals for the two hidden units (the signal is derived by multiplying the error value by the relevant weight). Finally, the error values for the hidden units are derived in the same way as for the output unit:

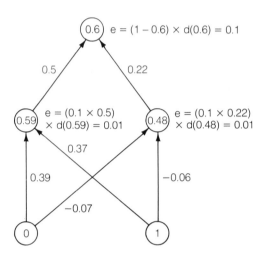

13.12. Weight updates

Now that the error values have been computed for all non-input units we can update the weights. This is done by applying the standard weight-update rule which changes the weight by an amount proportional to the product of the error value of the receiving unit and the activation of the sending unit.

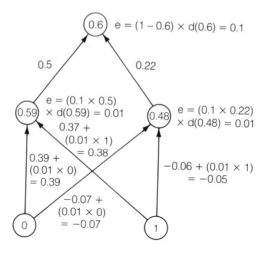

In fact, in this example the learning rate is assumed to be 1 so the weight change is identical to the product value. (For simplicity we assume that the momentum is 0. A non-zero momentum would mean that the real weight change would have to be a mix of the previous weight changes and the current change.) Once the weights have been updated, the next training pair in sequence the whole process is repeated.

13.13. The error profile

The complexity of the back-propagation procedure means that a hand-simulation of a complete run would be extremely long-winded. To get a picture of the behaviour of the mechanism in solving a problem we have to adopt a longer-term perspective. A simple approach involves mapping out the graph of mean error values which are passed through as back-propagation gradually develops the desired input/output behaviour. A graph of this type is an *error profile*.

In Figure 13.4 we see several error profiles for the XOR problem. Mean error values are shown on the vertical axis and epochs are shown on the horizontal axis. Each profile was generated during a different run of back-propagation. In all the runs, a learning rate of 1 and momentum of 0.9 were used. Note that with these values, it normally takes back-propagation less than 500 epochs to achieve good performance on the XOR problem but that in one case, the learning appears to have fallen into a local minimum or quasi-minimum.

Once the mean error has fallen below 0.05 the behaviour of the network is a close approximation of the desired behaviour. The output vectors actually produced by the

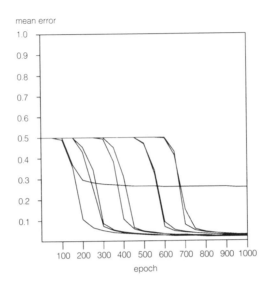

Figure 13.4. Error profiles of back-propagation learning XOR.

network for the various input cases are:

```
[input {0 0}] [target {0}] [output {0.02}]
[input {1 0}] [target {1}] [output {0.98}]
[input {1 1}] [target {0}] [output {0.02}]
[input {0 1}] [target {1}] [output {0.98}]
```

After one successful run of back-propagation on the XOR problem, the final weights were as shown in Figure 13.5. This is a weight configuration that is frequently produced by back-propagation when applied to this problem (given this architecture).

13.14. Hinton weight displays

In Figure 13.6 we see the learned weight vectors using a *Hinton diagram*. Each large rectangle in the diagram corresponds to a unit and the layout is the same as in the

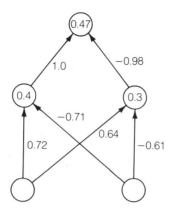

Figure 13.5. Weights for XOR learned by back-propagation.

figures above. The top rectangle represents the output unit, the middle two rectangles represent the hidden units and the lower two rectangles represent the input units. The boxes inside rectangles correspond in position, size and colour to its weights. If the unit has a strongly negative weight to the unit whose rectangle appears in, say, the bottom, left-hand corner of the display, then there will be a large, filled box in the bottom, left-hand corner of the rectangle. If the weight is positive, the box will be large but unfilled. The box which corresponds to the unit's own position in the network represents the unit's bias.

We can understand the weights by thinking of the way in which they enable the units to compute simple logical functions. The right hidden unit has a large positive bias and large negative weights to both input units. The strength of the positive bias means that the unit is normally on (i.e. has a high activation level). But its large negative weights mean that it will be turned off (i.e. set to a low activation level) if both input units are on together. Thus, this unit effectively computes the logical function NOT AND (i.e. NAND) of the two inputs.

The other hidden unit also has negative weights but it has a much smaller positive bias. It, too, will normally be on but it will be turned off whenever *either* of the two input units is on. Thus this unit effectively computes the logical function NOT OR (i.e. NOR) of the two inputs.

The output unit has a large positive weight to the right hidden unit and a large

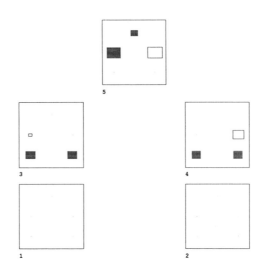

Figure 13.6. Hinton diagram of satisfactory weights for XOR.

negative weight to the left hidden unit. This means that it is turned on if the right hidden unit is on, and off if the left hidden unit is on. Thus this unit effectively computes the logical function NOT(NOR)) AND NAND, i.e. it is on provided that it is not the case that neither of the units are on and also not the case that both input units are on. Thus the output unit computes the XOR of the inputs.

13.15. Hyperplane analysis

Of course, since we are dealing with a network that has just two input units and two hidden units we can employ geometric analysis as we did in analysing the behaviour of the perceptron. The method of analysis we used with the perceptron exploited the fact that any linear threshold unit effectively defines a hyperplane in its input space. Inputs that fall to one side of this hyperplane turn the LTU on. Inputs that fall on the other side of the hyperplane turn it off. When we came to look at linear units and the LMS procedure the analysis had to be modified a little. For an LTU to return a particular output for a given input it must be the case that the input falls precisely on the constraint line. This is just the hyperplane that cuts the LTU's weight vector at a point corresponding to the desired output.

With back-propagation, of course, we are dealing with non-linear, *sigmoidal* units. However, in many cases, we can treat them — for purposes of analysis — as if they were threshold units. We can identify the inputs that will effectively turn a sigmoidal unit on (i.e. give it an activation value close to 1) and the inputs that will effectively turn it off (give it an activation close to 0). But, whereas with the LTU we were able to say that these two sets are separated by an infinitely thin hyperplane, with the sigmoidal unit we have to say that the two sets are separated by a fuzzy region in which the activation of the unit gradually changes from one state to the other.

With sigmoidal units, the region in which a unit is neither clearly on nor off is quite thin, as we can see if we map out activation values for all net inputs between -25 and 25 (see Figure 13.7).[9] As is clear, for all cases where the input value is below approximately -1 the unit is effectively off. For all cases where the input value is over approximately 1 the unit is effectively on. This unit thus defines a fuzzy hyperplane that lies over all inputs with the relevant component in the range -1 to 1.

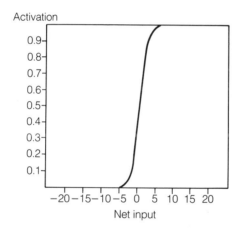

Figure 13.7. Activation values for a sigmoidal unit.

---

[9] Other things being equal, the larger a unit's weights, the bigger the net input and the thinner the fuzzy region.

If we map out the fuzzy hyperplanes defined by the two units in the 2-2-1 network shown in the Hinton diagram above (Figure 13-6) we can see that the learning has oriented the hyperplanes defined by the hidden units so as to make it easy for the output unit to produce the required behaviour. In Figure 13.8, inputs requiring a 0 output are shown as negatives and inputs requiring a 1 output are shown as positives. The weight vectors for the two hidden units are shown as the points marked **w3** and **w4**.[10] The numbers in parentheses are the corresponding bias values.

Note how unit 3's hyperplane separates off the input [0 0], while unit 4's

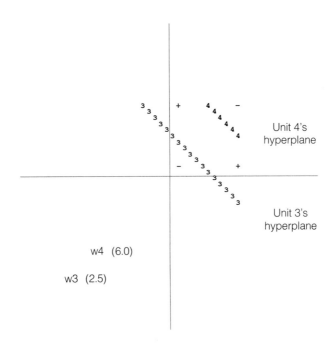

Figure 13.8. Hyperplanes defined by sigmoidal units.

---

[10] So as to show the figure at a reasonable scale, their coordinates are actually derived from the logarithms of the relevant weight values.

hyperplane separates off the input [1 1]. The net effect is that unit 3 is turned on by [0 0] and off by all other inputs while unit 4 is turned on by all inputs except [1 1]. Given these two units, the output unit will produce the desired behaviour if it is strongly excited by unit 4 but strongly inhibited by unit 3. And this is indeed the effect achieved by the weight values back-propagation has produced for the two connections into the output unit. There are at least two other ways in which the XOR mapping can be achieved in this architecture. There are also a number of local (or quasi-local) minima that the mechanism can become trapped in.

13.16. Concluding comments

Back-propagation is one of the most interesting and most powerful learning algorithms currently available. Its performance has been shown to be impressive on a wide range of difficult learning problems, although, as we noted, research into its theoretical properties and limitations is far from complete. From the historical point of view back-propagation has played a central role in the reversal of the fortunes of connectionism. Just as Minsky and Papert's analysis of the perceptron was perceived as a damning condemnation of the research on connectionist networks, so back-propagation has been perceived as providing some sort of 'refutation' of Minsky and Papert's anti-connectionist stance. Of course, these are extreme views, not to be taken too seriously. However, the importance of back-propagation as a central landmark in connectionist research should not be underestimated.

13.17. Further reading

The XOR problem (and its generalization, the *parity problem*) have been extensively studied in the connectionist literature. Again, some of the major theoretical work is to be found in Minsky and Papert (1988). There is also relevant material in Rumelhart *et al.* (1986b, pp. 332-334) and in Hinton (1986).

The back-propagation learning algorithm was first popularized by Rumelhart *et al.* (1986a). Earlier presentations include le Cun (1985), Parker (1982) and Werbos (1974). Hinton (1989, pp. 198-199) is, as ever, one of the best sources for the covered material particularly in its clarification of the way in which back-propagation computes the derivative of each weight with respect to the mean error. For the proof that the generalized delta rule minimizes the mean error see Rumelhart *et al.* (1986a). For more on the random initialization of weights, see Rumelhart *et al.* (1986b, pp. 330).

The fact that back-propagation is vulnerable to the problem of local minima forms a central point in Minsky and Papert's (1988) epilogue on connectionism, included in the second edition of *Perceptrons*. The question whether genuine global minima exist in back-propagation error surfaces is dealt with by Hecht-Nielsen (1990, p. 131). Hecht-Nielsen (1990, p. 122 and p. 132) also provides extensive coverage of the theoretical properties of back-propagation networks. For the original paper by Kolmogorov containing the theorem on which Hecht-Nielsen's existence theorem was based, see Kolmogorov (1957).

On the practical front, the PDP workbook (McClelland and Rumelhart, 1988) covers the computing of the derivative of the logistic function and provides sample code from a *C* implementation of back-propagation. It also provides a number of sample problems.

13.18. Problems

(1)   What is the difference between an activation vector, a hidden vector and an input vector?

(2)   What does it mean to say that a unit has a bias? How is unit bias typically implemented and why?

(3)   By introducing a momentum characteristic into the gradient descent process implemented by back-propagation it is possible to avoid certain problems which can arise with online processing. What are these problems? What alternative solution might we employ?

(4)   How is momentum usually implemented?

(5)   In what situation can back-propagation get trapped at a local maximum in the error surface?

(6)   What are the arguments against/in favour of the use of linear activation functions in multi-layered networks?

(7)   What is the form of the logistic function? What advantages does it provide when used with back-propagation?

(8)   How can we estimate the contribution made by a unit in the penultimate layer of a three-layer network to the error level of an output unit? How can we reduce it? Provide an example to illustrate your answer.

(9)   What is propagated in back-propagation?

(10) What is the formal basis of the back-propagation learning procedure?

(11) How is the error of a hidden unit computed in back-propagation? What impact does the activation of the unit have in the computation of error?

(12) In what sense is back-propagation a search procedure? Is it subject to the difficulties associated with conventional searching procedures? If so, what are they?

(13) The application of back-propagation to the XOR problem in a 2-2-1 network can encounter local minima (or quasi-minima) of various types. Explain why back-propagation finds it hard to escape from these weight configurations.

(14) Why does back-propagation build in negative biases to hidden units in the case where the first phase of learning has led to them to be positioned in the positive, north-east quadrant of the space?

14

Learning to diagnose heart disease

14.1. Introduction

How can we use back-propagation to solve practical problems? In this chapter we will return to the problem of diagnosing heart disease introduced in Chapter 1. However, this time around, we will take a more serious look at the problem. We will think about how one might set about achieving the goal of a satisfactory heart-disease diagnosis. We will look at some of the problems that are encountered along the way and how to go about solving them. As before, we will make use of the database of records provided by Robert Detrano at the V.A. Medical Center, Long Beach and Cleveland Clinic Foundation except that, in this case, we will use the records as provided with only minor modifications applied.[1]

The raw database we will be using contains just over 300 records. Each of these records lists attribute values for a single individual. Each record is made up of 15 fields and the value of each of these specifies an attribute of the relevant case. Some of these attributes are numerical (e.g., blood pressure) and some are symbolic (e.g., whether the individual was male or female — shown as 'fem' in the records). Each record is represented as an appropriate sequence of ASCII characters in an ordinary file. A subset of ten records is shown in Figure 14.1.

The possible attribute values are shown below. In most cases the interpretation is straightforward. Values of the age are integers. Values of the sex attribute are 'male' and 'fem'. And so on. Note that the word 'buff' here means 'healthy'.

---

[1] The database was acquired via the University of California at Irvine (UCI) repository of machine learning databases.

```
44.0 male asympt 112.0 290.0 fal   hyp 153.0 fal  0.0     up 1.0 norm sick
44.0 male notang 140.0 235.0 fal   hyp 180.0 fal  0.0     up 0.0 norm buff
41.0 male abnang 120.0 157.0 fal  norm 182.0 fal  0.0     up 0.0 norm buff
44.0 male notang 120.0 226.0 fal  norm 169.0 fal  0.0     up 0.0 norm buff
60.0 male asympt 117.0 230.0 true norm 160.0 true 1.4     up 2.0  rev sick
68.0 male notang 118.0 277.0 fal  norm 151.0 fal  1.0     up 1.0  rev buff
55.0  fem abnang 135.0 250.0 fal   hyp 161.0 fal  1.4 flat 0.0 norm buff
67.0  fem notang 115.0 564.0 fal   hyp 160.0 fal  1.6 flat 0.0  rev buff
45.0 male angina 110.0 264.0 fal  norm 132.0 fal  1.2 flat 0.0  rev sick
58.0 male abnang 125.0 220.0 fal  norm 144.0 fal  0.4 flat  ?   rev buff
```

Figure 14.1. Subset of the heart-disease training set.

1. age
2. sex: male, fem
3. chest pain type: angina, abnang, notang, asympt
4. resting blood pressure
5. cholesterol
6. fasting blood sugar < 120: true or false
7. resting ECG: norm, abn, hyper
8. maximum heart rate
9. exercise-induced angina: true or false
10. oldpeak
11. slope: up, flat, down
12. number of vessels coloured
13. thal: norm, fixed, rever
14. diagnosis: buff, sick

14.2. Using the database to specify a learning problem

Our aim is to use back-propagation to derive a configuration of weights that yields accurate diagnosis of the presence of heart disease. Since each record effectively describes a given case in terms of a set of attributes we can treat the whole database as a training set for a supervised learning problem. It would be feasible to treat the learning problem as a classification problem — this would mean we would be attempting to derive a mechanism that could classify descriptions of individual cases as being in the 'sick' class or the 'buff' class. Alternatively, since there are only two classes, we could treat the problem as a concept learning problem, i.e. do away with the class labels using 'yes' for 'buff' (i.e. healthy) and 'no' for 'sick'. From the practical point of view it makes no difference which strategy we adopt.

For present purposes we will treat the problem as a supervised classification problem. We therefore convert the database of records into training pairs which have, as output, the given classification:

```
<[44 male asympt 112 290 fal  hyp  153 fal  0    up   1 norm] [sick]>
<[44 male notang 140 235 fal  hyp  180 fal  0    up   0 norm] [buff]>
<[41 male abnang 120 157 fal  norm 182 fal  0    up   0 norm] [buff]>
<[44 male notang 120 226 fal  norm 169 fal  0    up   0 norm] [buff]>
<[60 male asympt 117 230 true norm 160 true 1.4 up   2 rev]  [sick]>
<[68 male notang 118 277 fal  norm 151 fal  1    up   1 rev]  [buff]>
<[55 fem  abnang 135 250 fal  hyp  161 fal  1.4 flat 0 norm] [buff]>
<[67 fem  notang 115 564 fal  hyp  160 fal  1.6 flat 0 rev]  [buff]>
<[45 male angina 110 264 fal  norm 132 fal  1.2 flat 0 rev]  [sick]>
<[58 male abnang 125 220 fal  norm 144 fal  0.4 flat ? rev]  [buff]>
```

14.3.   Turning the learning problem into a network learning problem

In back-propagation, inputs are presented by setting the activation levels of the input units of the network while outputs are read off as the final activation levels of output units. Thus in order to use the given training set with back-propagation it is essential for it to be preprocessed so that the components of input and output vectors are represented as (sets of) activation levels. Some of the attributes are indeed numeric and it is a fairly straightforward matter to normalize the attribute values into the range 0-1. But this still leaves us with the symbolic (*nominal*) attributes such as type of chest pain. A simple way to deal with these attributes is to map each value of each attribute into a unique integer, beginning with 0 and working upwards. We can then derive the activation value for a given symbol by dividing the relevant integer by the total number of distinct values.

If we process the training set using these two procedures we end up with pairs such as:

```
<[0.11 0 0.00 0.07 0.33 0 0 0.42 0 0 0 0.5 0]  [0]>
<[0.11 0 0.33 1.00 0.19 0 0 0.96 0 0 0 0.0 0]  [1]>
```

Note how **sick** is here represented by the output vector [0] while **buff** is represented by [1]. In fact, this approach is not entirely satisfactory since it obliterates much of the information which was implicitly captured in the symbolic attributes. Even worse, it creates phoney similarity relationships between them. For example, in the mapping **asympt** got mapped to 0, **abnang** got mapped to 0.67 and **notang** got mapped to 0.33. Since back-propagation treats these numbers purely as activation values, it will tend to assume that the difference between **notang** and **asympt** is double the difference between **abnang** and **notang**. But, looking solely at the training set we have no reason to suspect this is the case.

A better strategy involves mapping the values of the symbolic attributes into *sparse* binary vectors, i.e. binary vectors that have only one bit set. Applied to the third attribute from the training set (which has four possible values) this would give us the mapping:

$$\begin{aligned} \text{angina} &\rightarrow [1\ 0\ 0\ 0] \\ \text{abnang} &\rightarrow [0\ 1\ 0\ 0] \\ \text{notang} &\rightarrow [0\ 0\ 1\ 0] \\ \text{asympt} &\rightarrow [0\ 0\ 0\ 1] \end{aligned}$$

Once we have mapped specific values into such binary vectors, we can turn an input into a satisfactory activation vector by simply normalizing the numeric attribute values and replacing the symbolic attribute values with their given binary sequence. This approach produces training pairs such as the ones shown below. In generating this training set we ignored attribute 12 (number of coloured vessels) due to the fact that quite a large number of entries in the database have an unspecified value in this field. We also adopted the convention that any nominal attribute with just two values is mapped on to the two binary vectors **[1]** and **[0]** rather than the sparse vectors **[1 0]** and **[0 1]**. This enables us to have single-component outputs:

```
<[0.97 0 1 0 0 0 0.19 0.36 0 1 0 0 0.45 0 0.93 1 0 0 1 0 0] [0]>
<[0.28 0 0 1 0 0 0.35 0.45 0 0 1 0 1.0  1 0.0  0 1 0 0 1 0] [1]>
<[0.31 1 0 1 0 0 0.35 0.53 0 0 1 0 0.56 1 0.07 0 1 0 0 1 0] [1]>
<[0.52 1 0 0 1 0 0.39 0.57 1 1 0 0 0.78 0 0.0  0 1 0 0 1 0] [1]>
<[0.45 0 0 0 1 0 0.19 0.7  0 0 1 0 0.92 1 0.07 0 1 0 0 1 0] [1]>
<[0.34 1 1 0 0 0 0.35 0.51 0 0 1 0 0.82 1 0.0  0 1 0 0 1 0] [1]>
<[1.1  1 0 0 1 0 0.84 0.62 0 0 1 0 0.81 1 0.14 0 1 0 0 1 0] [1]>
<[0.52 0 1 0 0 0 0.03 0.4  0 0 1 0 0.42 0 1.0  1 0 0 1 0 0] [0]>
<[0.86 0 0 0 0 1 1.0  0.36 0 1 0 0 0.74 1 0.21 1 0 0 1 0 0] [1]>
<[0.17 0 1 0 0 0 0.19 0.15 0 0 1 0 0.62 0 1.0  0 0 1 0 0 1] [0]>
```

For the experiments described below we converted the whole database into training pairs. We then produced a training set by randomly selecting 250 pairs and a testing set by randomly selecting another 40 pairs. There was no overlap between the training set and the testing set. The aim in producing the testing set was to provide some way of testing the performance of the network on unseen cases, i.e. cases that had not been used as a part of the learning.

14.4. Configuring the network

Having derived a usable training set, we should decide what architecture we are going to use. The number of input units and output units is fixed by the form of the input and output vectors in the derived training set. The input vectors contain 21 components while the output vectors contain just one. Thus the network *must* have 21 input units and one output unit. We only have to choose its internal architecture.

At present there is no completely satisfactory technique for determining an appropriate internal architecture for an arbitrary problem. Even if we are committed to using a simple two-layer network with one layer of hidden units, there is still no way of determining *for sure* how many hidden units there should be. If we have too few hidden units the network may not have the capacity required to form satisfactory internal representations. On the other hand, if we have too many, the network may resort to using each hidden unit in an over-specific manner. This extreme situation is the connectionist version of the 'lookup table', in which the compression provided by the representation is negligible.

A rule of thumb that is occasionally used states that one should have approximately ten times as many training pairs as nodes in the network. We have a database of just over 300 pairs. We are already committed to using 22 units so, by the rule of thumb, we might try using eight hidden units. But it would be unwise to place too much reliance on this rule since the representational capacity of the network is clearly related to the number of weights rather than to the number of units. Suffice to say that there should ideally be several times as many pairs in the training set as there are weights in the network.[2] Thus if we have only 300 training pairs, 21 input units and one output unit, we should be wary of having more than about seven hidden units. (In the present case this yields a total of 148 weights.)

14.5. Determining the number of hidden units

In practice, trial and error can be used to determine a suitable internal architecture for the network. That is to say, we try learning with different numbers of hidden units and observe the performance obtained. For an initial test, a network with four hidden units was compared with one using no hidden units (i.e. using just 21 input units feeding into one output unit). The former architecture is shown in Figure 14.2.

---

[2] We can think of this requirement in terms of the placing of several 'constraints' on each weight.

Figure 14.2. The 21-4-1 network.

The performance of the two networks is shown in Figure 14.3. This shows *error pro-files* for a number of runs on the derived training set. There are four curves in all. The lower two curves show error rates (i.e. the proportion of inputs incorrectly classified) resulting from test made against the training set. The upper two curves show error rates resulting from tests against the testing set. The vertical axis ranges over error rates and the horizontal axis ranges over epoch numbers. In all cases the training was run over 5000 epochs using a learning rate of 0.1 and a momentum value of 0.5.

There are several points to note about the graph. A striking feature is the fact that all the error rate profiles drop sharply right at the beginning of the training. This quite common feature of back-propagation learning seems to indicate that there are typically a substantial number of 'accessible generalizations' that can be exploited fairly easily via the weight adjustment mechanism. Once these generalizations have been tapped, the learning has to concentrate on trying to form representations of the more inaccessible generalizations. This is a much slower process.

Looking at the curves for the case in which no hidden units are used we see that the performance of the network is actually surprisingly good. After about 200 epochs, the error rate on the training set is down to about 12%, that is, the network is producing nearly 90% correct diagnoses. The implication is that a substantial part of the problem is in fact linearly separable . Of course, the performance on the testing set is not so good — the network achieves only around 75% correct diagnoses (an error

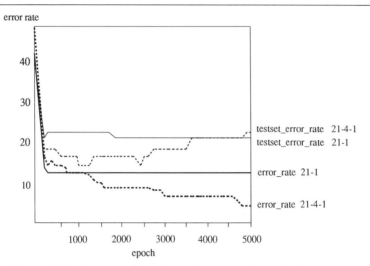

Figure 14.3. Error profiles for back-propagation with 0 and 4 units.

rate of about 25%).

Moving now to the case in which there are four hidden units we see that the error rate on the training set drops fairly smoothly throughout the training process. After 5000 epochs it is below 5%, i.e. the network is scoring over 95% correct diagnoses. The error rate on the testing set, on the other hand, drops initially to around 13% after 1000 epochs and then *increases* fairly consistently thereafter. This is a very common feature of back-propagation learning and crops up in nearly all types of computational learning. It is called *over training*, *over generalization* or *over fitting*.

The phenomenon of over generalization can be explained as follows. In the early stages of training, the learning algorithm is effectively exploiting the most overt and most accessible generalizations. These will tend to be common to all inputs from the domain and therefore will apply to pairs from the testing set as well as the training set. Hence the error rate on both the training set and the testing set falls. Subsequently, the learning algorithm begins to exploit and take account of properties that are specific to the training set. In the worst case, the training set contains some *noise*, i.e. some inputs that have an incorrect classification attached to them. In this case the learning algorithm will — in the later stages of training — attempt to take account of properties that are inevitably restricted to the training set. The overall result is plain to see. After a certain point, improvements in the performance on the training set are accompanied by a deterioration in the performance on the testing set.

In some cases it is possible to prevent over generalization by ensuring that the network does not have the capacity to generalize beyond a certain point, e.g., by limiting the amount of internal architecture. However in the present case this approach is not effective, possibly because the training set is too small relative to the number of weights in the network. As we can see from the graphs shown in Figure 14.3 the capacity of the network — in terms of the number of hidden units it has — does not seem to have any great impact on over generalization. In this situation the only recourse is to observe the point at which over generalization appears to begin and to terminate training at that point.

14.6. Testing the behaviour

The general implication of the tests described above was that the network was capable of producing good, overall performance with a small number of hidden units. Another run was therefore performed using just three hidden units and storing the weights in those epochs where the overall error rate (the summed training set and testing set rate) was at a minimum. This produced a set of weights that yielded even better performance.[3] The error rate on the training set was 7% while on the testing set it was 10%, i.e. the network achieved 90% correct diagnoses on unseen cases. The graph for this run is shown in Figure 14.4. The performance of the network on the first eight pairs from the testing set is shown by the following output. This is a listing produced by the implementation used that shows the behaviour on each pair. Note the incorrect classification of input 7:

```
pair 1
  input {52.0 male angina 152.0 298.0 true norm 178.0 fal 1.2 flat rev}
  target {buff}
  output {buff}
  learner_error 0.2928

pair 2
  input {44.0 male abnang 120.0 220.0 fal norm 170.0 fal 0.0 up norm}
  target {buff}
  output {buff}
```

---

[3] Runs with less than this number of hidden units failed to produce even reasonable performance.

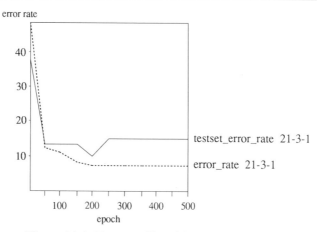

Figure 14.4. Error profile with three hidden units.

learner_error 0.0013

pair 3
  input {57.0 male asympt 152.0 274.0 fal norm 88.0 true 1.2 flat rev}
  target {sick}
  output {sick}
  learner_error 0.0667

pair 4
  input {42.0 male notang 130.0 180.0 fal norm 150.0 fal 0.0 up norm}
  target {buff}
  output {buff}
  learner_error 0.0004

pair 5
  input {57.0 male notang 150.0 126.0 true norm 173.0 fal 0.2 up rev}
  target {buff}
  output {buff}
  learner_error 0.043

pair 6
  input {62.0 fem asympt 124.0 209.0 fal norm 163.0 fal 0.0 up norm}
  target {buff}

output {buff}
learner_error 0.0381

pair 7
  input {64.0 male notang 140.0 335.0 fal norm 158.0 fal 0.0 up norm}
  target {sick}
  output {buff}
  learner_error 0.999

pair 8
  input {39.0 fem notang 138.0 220.0 fal norm 152.0 fal 0.0 flat norm}
  target {buff}
  output {buff}
  learner_error 0.0017

It is interesting to note that the overall error (i.e. the mean difference between desired output values and actual output values) on input 7 is very close to 1. An activation value at the output unit of 0 indicates **sick**, while an activation of 1 indicates **buff**. On input 7, the network produced an output activation very close to 1. In effect, the network has classified the input as a perfect example of the **buff** class, whereas the given classification is **sick**. Could it be that the network is right and the original database entry wrong? In other words, could it be that input 7 represents noise in the training set?

There is no way of telling for sure without going back to the original records. However, it is interesting to see how many other cases of 'perfectly incorrect' classifications there are. In Figure 14.5 we see a table showing the distribution of error values for cases in the testing set. This shows quite clearly that while there are relatively few cases with intermediate error values, there are in fact four cases with the maximum error value of 1. (Here we treat any error greater than 0.99 as an error of 1.) The relevant cases are:

pair 31
  input {47.0 male notang 108.0 243.0 fal norm 152.0 fal 0.0 up norm}
  target {sick}
  output {buff}
  learner_error 1.0

pair 17
  input {65.0 male angina 138.0 282.0 true hyp 174.0 fal 1.4 flat norm}
  target {sick}
  output {buff}
  learner_error 1.0

Error	Cases
0.0	25
0.1	6
0.2	1
0.3	2
0.4	1
0.5	1
1.0	4

Figure 14.5. Distribution of error values.

pair 9

    input `{53.0 male asympt 142.0 226.0 fal hyp 111.0 true 0.0 up rev}`
    target `{buff}`
    output `{sick}`
    learner_error 0.99

pair 7

    input `{64.0 male notang 140.0 335.0 fal norm 158.0 fal 0.0 up norm}`
    target `{sick}`
    output `{buff}`
    learner_error 0.999

If we derive a hierarchical clustering (Anderberg, 1973) of the input vectors in the testing set we produce the tree in Figure 14.6. The labels on the leaf nodes show the index number of the relevant training input and the associated target output (either 1 or 0) separated by a colon (e.g., 31:0 labels pair 31 whose target output is 0). From the dendrogram we can see that pair 4 is extremely similar to two pairs (31 and 7) that have the opposite classification. Similar comments apply to pairs 28 and 19. These cases then form what are known in statistics as *outliers*, i.e. cases that are classified differently to their nearest neighbours in the input space. Of course, the fact that these cases are outliers does not show that they have an incorrect classification. However, it does suggest that it might be worth checking their validity.

14.7. Inspecting the representation

Once a successful configuration of weights has been learned, as in the example described above, it is interesting to investigate the internal representation that has

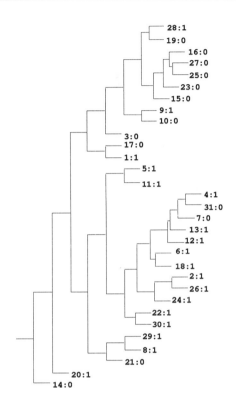

Figure 14.6. Dendrogram of instances.

been formed. There are various methods that can be employed, but for present purposes we will simply use a Hinton diagram to examine the weights in the hidden and output layers of the network. This diagram is shown in Figure 14.7. The diagram only includes representations for the non-input units but weights from the input units to the hidden units (units 22, 23 and 24) are shown. These appear as a layer at the bottom of the representations of hidden units. All the weights from the input units have single-character labels and these are explained in the key. In the case where a nominal attribute is represented in terms of a subsequence of input units, we see the label for the relevant attribute followed by a sequence of Xs marking the corresponding weights.

a = age   h = maximum heart rate

s = sex   i = induced angina

p = pain type (asymt, anang,   e = resting ECG
            notang, angina)   (norm, abnorm, hyper)

b = blood pressure   o = oldpeak

c = cholesterol   l = slope (flat, up, down)

f = low fasting blood sugar   t = thalamus (rev, norm, fixed)

Figure 14.7. Unit receptive fields.

Clearly the output unit is excited and inhibited by unit 24. In particular, it is strongly inhibited by unit 23. If we look at the hidden units we see that unit 23 is strongly inhibited by a pain type of **asympt** but excited by a normal resting ECG. Unit 23, on the other hand, is strongly excited by a pain-type of **notang** but strongly inhibited by an abnormal resting ECG. Unit 24 responds positively to high blood pressure but is strongly inhibited by a high value for the induced angina attribute. Putting this together we might say that the output unit will be turned on (i.e. will indicate a **healthy** result) if the patient has an **asympt** rather than an **notang** pain type, a normal resting ECG, and does not have high blood pressure.

14.8. Concluding comments

This chapter has shown how we can take a real-world diagnosis problem and use back-propagation to learn a representation that permits automatic diagnoses to be produced. The level of performance achieved by our network on this problem appears to be fairly good (90% accuracy on unseen cases) although, obviously, much more testing would be needed in order to confirm this evaluation. The results compare quite favourably with other results reported for this training set. For example, the CLASSIT conceptual clustering system achieved a 78.9% accuracy on the same training set (Gennari *et al.*, 1989). Other attempts have produced accuracy rates of 77% and 74.8%.[4]

The chapter has not attempted to show what one might *do* with the network after training since this is an issue which very much depends on the context in which the work is being done. If, in developing this network, our ultimate aim was to provide some sort of diagnosis support mechanism, then it would obviously be necessary to embed the network representation within an interactive environment. This would enable users to type in descriptions of cases and to obtain diagnoses in a comprehensible form. The environment might also provide the means of modifying the network representation by passing in particularly salient cases, or of generating prototypical examples of certain classes. Unfortunately, the investigation of such possibilities is beyond the scope of this book.

---

[4] As reported in the notes accompanying the database in the UCI repository.

15

Analysing internal representations

15.1. Introduction: looking for internal representations

In previous chapters we have seen how back-propagation manipulates weight vectors at different layers of the network so as to obtain desired behaviour. Where we have a multi-layered network the processing of any particular input leads to the production of activation vectors in the hidden layers (i.e. hidden vectors). These hidden vectors can be thought of as internal representations of the input. However, at first sight, such representations are very different from conventional representation structures. Typically, representation schemes are based on hierarchies of concepts and relationships rather than collections of activation values. The question is, then, how can we reconcile the conventional notion of symbolic representation with the notion presented to us by connectionist models such as back-propagation?

One way to proceed is to invoke the notion of the grandmother-cell. Recall, that a grandmother-cell is a neuron that responds very positively (i.e. becomes very active) when 'grandmother' enters the visual field. The point of the grandmother-cell idea is that it provides an illustrative example of *local* representation, i.e. a scheme in which real-world entities are represented by the state of — in the extreme case — a single neuron. The complementary scheme is *distributed representation*. In a distributed scheme, real-world entities and concepts are represented by patterns of activity across large numbers of physically disparate neurons.

The distributed versus localized distinction is a helpful guide when we come to analyse connectionist representations. To discover cases of localized representation we should look for units (or small numbers of closely connected units) whose behaviour seems to correlate well with a high-level feature of the problem domain. A good example of this sort of representation has been described by Hinton (1986). He discusses an experiment in which a four-layer network was trained to provide the third term from family-relationship triples such as **[Roberto Father-of Lucia]**. The training set was drawn up from the two, isomorphic family trees shown in Figure 15.1. The input in each training pair named an individual and a relationship. The output named the other party in the relationship. A sample of five training pairs is:

```
<[Gina      niece]   [Sophia]>
<[Alfonso   uncle]   [Emilio]>
<[Penelope  husband] [Christopher]>
<[Tomaso    nephew]  [Alfonso]>
<[Christine son]     [James]>
```

In the experiment the training inputs and outputs were converted into binary vectors.

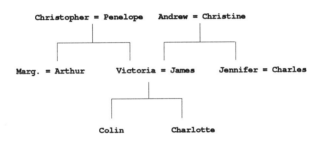

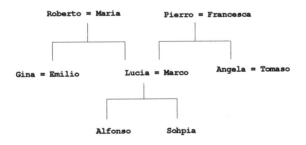

Figure 15.1. Two isomorphic family trees (after Hinton, 1989).

The inputs contained 36 bits each. The initial 24-bits in each input represented the 24 individuals and the final 12 bits represented the 12 possible relationships. Thus a training input such as [Gina niece] was represented as a 36 bit vector with a 1 in the position representing Gina, a 1 in the position representing niece and 0s elsewhere. A training output such as [Sophia] was represented by a 24-bit vector with a 1 in the position representing Sophia and 0s elsewhere. The architecture used in the experiment is shown in Figure 15.2. (The arrows denote complete connectivity between subnets.) Note how the input units and first layer of hidden units are divided up into two halves. The right-hand group of input units represents the 24 individuals. The left-hand group of input units represents the 12 relationships.

Hinton was able to show how the network developed localized representations for

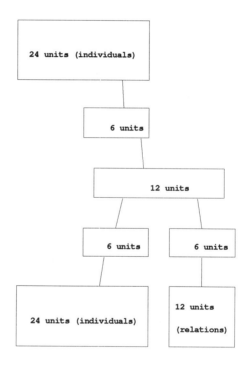

Figure 15.2. Kinship network structure.

various high-level features in the right-hand group of layer 1.[1] In particular, he demonstrated that one of the units learned to respond to the 'age' of the person represented by the first component of an input triple, even though nothing in the training set gave any explicit information about age. An example of such a unit appears in Figure 15.3. The hidden unit has 'discovered' that relatively older people are represented by input units that appear further to the right. Since the hidden unit's weights tend to increase from left to right we know that it will respond more positively to inputs representing older people. The unit has thus learned to respond selectively to the 'age' feature of the input. The unit that appears in Figure 15.4 has weighted its connections to input units in the upper row positively but its connections to input units in the lower row negatively. Again we can understand this by looking at the way in which the input units have been organized. The upper input units were, in fact, used to represent English people and the lower input units were used to represent Italian people so we know that this unit has learned to respond selectively

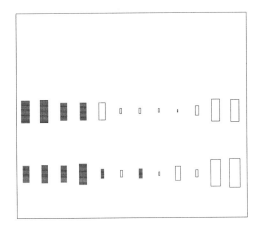

Figure 15.3. Kinship 'generation' node.

---

[1] In fact his preference was to say that the network developed *distributed* representations of the individuals expressed in terms of high-level features.

to 'nationality'.

15.2. Analysing distributed representations

To discover cases of distributed representation we have to take a very different approach. Rather than looking at the behaviour (or weight vectors) of individual units, we have to look for patterns of behaviour over sets of units. One approach to this task that has been particularly successful involves applying cluster analysis to the total set of hidden vectors (in a given layer) generated by a given training set. Recall that cluster analysis is a process which shows us how a set of vectors can be divided up into similarity groups. By applying cluster analysis to hidden vector sets we discover whether the hidden vectors fall into distinct classes. If we discover that they are structured in this way, we may be able to understand the representation by working out which high-level features correspond to which classes.

To demonstrate how this type of analysis works we will look at two recent pieces of

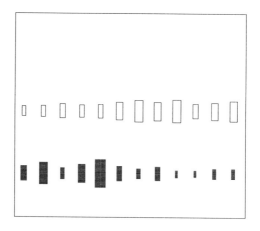

Figure 15.4. Kinship 'nationality' node.

empirical research. Both of these involved training feed-forward networks to produce certain linguistic competences. And in both cases cluster analysis was used to produce an interpretation of the distributed internal representations which were constructed during learning.

15.3. Elman's copy-back net

The first network we will examine was constructed by Elman (1989) as a part of his research on the representation of grammatical structure in neural networks. The network was constructed with the aim of finding out whether a connectionist learning algorithm might be able to produce representations of the structural properties of a lexicon and in particular the way in which words are arranged into grammatical categories. The training set was based on a corpus of 10 000 two- and three-word sentences. These sentences were grammatically very primitive. However, they were generated so as to reflect semantic properties of the component words. A sample sentence would be a triple such as 'man smash plate' — the conjunction of 'smash' and 'plate' here reflecting the semantic property that plates are things which can be smashed.

Elman arranged the training set into a stream of vectors representing sequences of words derived from linguistically permissible permutations of the original sentences. The network was then trained to respond to the presentation of a representation of a given word by producing the representation for the following word in the sequence; e.g., generating 'plate' given 'smash' as input. In trying to obtain a network for this task one might adopt a number of strategies. Elman utilized a two-layer network with 31 output units and 31 input units. The 31-dimensional input and output vectors provided a sparse coding of a single word.

So as to provide the network with information about the preceding words in a sequence, Elman arranged the training set so that the sequence of training inputs respected the sequence of words from the sentences.[2] And he configured the net so that, in addition to the 31 input units, there were 150 hidden units and 150 *context units* which behaved like ordinary input units except that their activations were always set to be copies of the activations of the hidden units in the *previous* iteration. The aim in adopting this approach was to ensure that information about previous words was available to the network in the current input. In Figure 15.5 we see a simplified version of Elman's network. The context units here are the units in a separate

---

[2] The network was not given any explicit information about sentence boundaries so it had no way of knowing the position of a given word in a sentence.

group on the right.

The performance obtained was fairly good although Elman's method of measuring error was, in this case, a non-standard one. However, the significant result from our point of view was the fact that Elman was able to analyse the hidden vectors and show that they collectively formed a distributed representation for high-level features of the problem domain.

15.3.1. Cluster analysis of the copy-back network

After the network had been trained to a satisfactory level of performance, Elman ran the training set through once more, keeping track of the hidden vectors produced for each given training input. Having obtained this set of vectors, he then applied a hierarchical cluster analysis to discover how the vectors were organized in hidden-vector space. Recall that cluster analysis is a process which produces a tree summarizing the similarity relationships existing between a set of objects (see Chapter 7).

The clustering produced is shown in Figure 15.6.[3] Each tip node represents a particular class of similar hidden vectors (i.e. internal representations) and is labelled with the word which was responsible for producing that type of hidden vector. Following

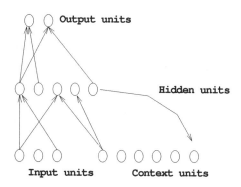

Figure 15.5. Elman's copy-back net (after Elman, 1989).

---

[3] This is an approximation of the dendrogram provided by Elman.

the usual convention for displaying dendrograms, node heights give the average similarity for subsumed nodes. Thus if we want to know the similarity of two vectors we have to find the height of the internal node which subsumes them both. The further the node is to the right, the more similar are the subsumed vectors (i.e. the vectors corresponding to the subsumed nodes).

The point to note is the way in which the similarity structure among the hidden vectors has captured linguistically meaningful features. For example, note that all the words in the upper main branch are verbs. All the words in the lower main branch are nouns. If we look at the structure in more detail we find groupings which correspond to animate nouns, inanimate nouns, and various semantic classes (e.g., the class of nouns labelling food).

As a representation scheme, this dendrogram of hidden vectors captures a hierarchy of syntactic features. Thus, in re-encoding a word as a hidden vector the network is effectively rerepresenting it in terms of syntactic features at various levels of generality. Access to this feature-based representation makes the task of guessing the next word easier, as can be confirmed intuitively. If we establish that the third word in a sentence is a non-abstract transitive verb, it is possible to guess that the next word is likely to be a non-abstract noun. By knowing what the features of the current word are we can make sensible inferences about the next word.[4]

Of course, it seems slightly unnatural to regard a pattern of activation values as encoding a set of high-level features. This is certainly not the conventional representation for a high-level feature. However, once the learning has configured the network weights so as to obtain the required structure in the hidden-vector space, there can be no doubt that a point in the space effectively encodes sets of features. The representation is implicit rather than explicit. But this does not at all affect its utility, as the performance of the network shows.

15.4. NETtalk

Let us now turn our attention to the NETtalk system. The construction of NETtalk formed part of a major case study in which cluster analysis was used to reveal the

---

[4] It is interesting to contrast this case with the case of the past-tense network discussed in Chapter 12. Recall that the *behaviour* of the past-tense network seemed implicitly to capture certain linguistically meaningful properties of words. Here we have a case where the network's internal *representation* can be shown implicitly to capture linguistically meaningful features.

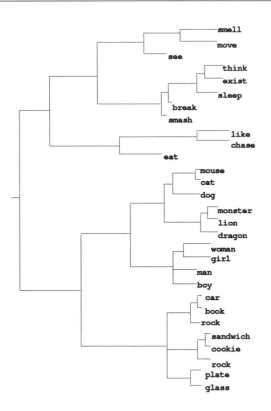

Figure 15.6. Copy-back net dendrogram (after Elman, 1989).

structure of internal representations (Sejnowski and Rosenberg, 1987). The ostensible aim of the study was to construct a network which would learn to pronounce words. 'Pronouncing words' in this case meant producing, as output, the right encodings of speech synthesizer inputs, when given particular encodings of textual items as input.

The architecture used for the network was a conventional two-layer, feed-forward configuration consisting of 203 input units, 80 hidden units and 26 output units. Two different training sets were used, one containing 1024 words derived from phonetic transcriptions of real speech, the other containing 1000 words derived from Miriam

Webster's *Pocket Dictionary*. Each input was an encoding of a string of seven letters.

The target output in each case was (an encoding of) the phoneme for the middle (i.e. fourth) letter in the string. By arranging for inputs to encode *seven* letters rather than just one, the authors hoped to provide the network with enough context to enable it to sort out phonemes for ambiguous letters (e.g., 'o' in 'go' and 'got'). Note how this approach contrasts with Elman's way of providing the network with contextual information. The authors describe the encoding scheme as follows:

> The letters and phonemes were represented in different ways. The letters were represented locally within each group of 29 units, one unit for each letter of the alphabet plus an additional 3 units to encode punctuation and word boundaries. Only one unit in each group was active for a given input. The phonemes, in contrast, were represented in terms of 21 articulatory features, such as point of articulation, voicing, vowel height and so on . . . Five additional units encoded stress and syllable boundaries, making a total of 26 units. This was a distributed representation since each output unit participates in the encoding of several phonemes. (Sejnowski and Rosenberg, 1987, p. 151)

In most cases, the system learned to pronounce words rather well, i.e. to generate output patterns which when interpreted in terms of articulatory features and fed into the DECtalk speech synthesis system sounded correct. The authors determined that the hidden units played a non-trivial role since performance with no hidden units reached only about 82% accuracy (versus over 95% using 120 hidden units).

The results of the cluster analysis showed that the structure of the hidden-vector space had effectively captured a hierarchy of phonetic categories in the same way that Elman's network had captured a hierarchy of syntactic categories. The researchers found that the cluster analysis of the system always turned out the same even when the configuration of (final) weights was different. Thus, in some sense, the network always produced the *same* internal representation for this task. The fundamental feature captured in the NETtalk internal representation was the distinction between consonants and vowels, as the dendrogram in Figure 15.7 shows.[5]

NETtalk exhibited many interesting properties such as rapid relearning after damage, and good generalization. The cluster analysis shows that it had formed a

---

[5] The dendrogram is an approximation of the original. It adopts the usual conventions, e.g., the height of a node gives the average similarity of subsumed nodes. Each tip node is labelled with a pair of characters separated by a hyphen. The character on the left is the character appearing in the text. The character on the right indicates the pronunciation.

Figure 15.7. NETtalk dendrogram (after Sejnowski and Rosenberg, 1987).

representation of the input patterns in hidden-vector space such that a point representing a given input is always close to the points representing inputs requiring similar
outputs (vowels are close to other vowels, etc.). This arrangement naturally leads to
sensible generalizations and approximations. If a particular textual context suggests a
vowel-like phoneme, then it is likely to produce a hidden vector in the 'vowel region'
of the representation and therefore evoke a vowel phoneme.

15.5. Comments

Cluster analysis is an effective and illuminating way of analysing distributed, internal representations. However, in using it we are assuming that the representations will be arranged such that the hidden vectors naturally fall into similarity groups corresponding to meaningful entities or concepts. There seems to be no a priori reason why distributed representations will be of this form. So it is possible that there will be cases where cluster analysis will be completely ineffective in revealing the meaning of the representations. For these cases we require other analytic techniques.

The general issue of the representational properties of connectionist networks is a contentious one at the present time. Fodor and Pylyshyn (1988) have presented a powerful critique that suggests that the representational properties of connectionist networks are fundamentally restricted since they are unable to exploit the benefits of structured representations fully. Elman's work seems to answer this criticism to a degree. However, there are still many difficult questions. Since this area is the subject of intense investigation at present there is the possibility that some of these will be resolved in the near future. But we should be wary of closing the book too soon.

15.6. Further reading

The detection and characterization of localized representations has been greatly facilitated by the development of Hinton's method for showing weights. There are many other examples of the use of this technique in the literature. Hinton's own use of this technique in the family-tree experiment is described in Hinton (1989, p. 199-202); see also Hinton and Sejnowski (1986, p. 301) Elman's work with lexical representations is described in Elman (1989) while the original reference for Sejnowski and Rosenberg's work on the NETtalk system is Sejnowski and Rosenberg (1987).

For a general introduction to cluster analysis, see Anderberg (1973) or Chatfield and Collins (1980).

15.7. Problems

(1)   What alternative input-encoding strategies might Elman have adopted in developing the copy-back net?

(2)   In what sense does the structure of the hidden-vector space in networks like NETtalk form a 'representation'? Could this sort of representation be used in the way that symbolic representations are typically used (e.g., for capturing relationships)? If so, how?

(3)   How many linguistically meaningful features does the dendrogram produced by Elman's cluster analysis represent? What are they?

16

Constructive learning procedures

16.1. Introduction: problems with back-propagation

The emergence of back-propagation as an effective learning procedure for multi-layered networks was a major breakthrough in connectionist computing. More than anything else, it demonstrated that connectionism was capable of supplying mechanisms with powerful learning abilities and interesting psychological implications. And it was a major ingredient stimulating the recent, rapid growth of activity taking place under the general headings of parallel distributed processing, neural networks and connectionism.

But while back-propagation was quickly shown to be an effective learning procedure for complex networks, it was also shown to be heavily dependent on skilful, human manipulation. In applying back-propagation to a learning problem we have to ensure that we are using an appropriate architecture (e.g., the right number of hidden units). We also have to set the learning rate and the momentum to values which ensure that the learning (1) does not take an unreasonable length of time and (2) does not become bogged down in unfruitful oscillations on those parts of the error surface where the local curvature gives a misleading indication of where the global minimum is to be found.

In the worst case, back-propagation's reliance on human intervention can cause applications work to degenerate into a long-winded process of trial and error, i.e. an exhaustive   search   through   the   whole   space   of   possible architecture/momentum/learning-rate combinations.[1] Even in the case where the right architecture and momentum have been established, the learning process may well take a quite unreasonable length of time (of the order of several months). These basic difficulties have led researchers to look for ways of speeding up back-propagation and for ways in which the internal architecture of the network can be automatically derived as a part of the learning process. The present chapter will look at two techniques for automatically deriving an appropriate architecture.

16.2. Cascade-correlation

Algorithms that create new network structure are called *constructive algorithms*. They address what is, perhaps, the most serious problem to afflict standard back-propagation, namely, the fact that it requires the internal architecture of the network to be prespecified. In practice, carrying out trial and error experiments to determine an appropriate architecture is extremely costly in time. Whereas, a value of the momentum or learning-rate parameter can be experimented with during a run of the algorithm, the internal architecture cannot be explicitly altered — except in the sense that the algorithm is capable of effectively 'deleting' units by setting all relevant connections to zero.

Fahlman and Lebiere (1990) have described a learning algorithm called *cascade-correlation* that dynamically constructs new internal units and connects them into an existing network while learning is taking place. The algorithm starts out with an initial architecture involving several input units and a single output unit[2] and then adds new units to it one at a time. Each new unit is given input connections from all the input units and a single connection to the output unit. Each unit is also given an input connection from any previously constructed hidden units.

When a new unit is added in to the network it is trained to produce a certain type of response and then its weights are frozen and not altered again. The new unit is trained so that its activation level is maximally correlated with the error profile for the output unit. If the output unit had an error of 0.2 on the first training pair, 0.6 on the second training pair, 0.4 on the third, etc., then the new unit will be trained so that its responses are maximally correlated with these values (e.g., so that its responses are

---

[1] These problems may be compounded if the implementation being used always initializes weights to different random values. This ensures that the behaviour of the mechanism will vary from run to run even where the basic parameters are fixed.

[2] In fact the algorithm can be applied to networks involving more than one output unit but the description is more complex in this case.

0.4 on the first pair, 1.2 on the second and 0.8 on the third). The correlation can be positive or negative. If it is negative then its response profile will be the opposite of the output unit's error profile.

Once the unit has been trained to respond in this way, all the weights on the links to the output unit are retrained. If the correlation of the new hidden unit is large and positive (as it is in the example above) then the new unit will develop a negative weight on its connection to the output unit, i.e. it will attempt to smooth out some of the error. If the correlation is large but negative, the weight will be positive for the same reason.

In the diagrams below we see a network of three input units and one output unit. Underneath this we see the same network after a single new unit has been added by cascade-correlation. Note that the new unit has an input connection from all the input units and an output connection to the single output unit. Since learning only needs to be applied to the input connections of new units, we can use a learning rule for single-layer networks if we like (e.g., the delta rule).

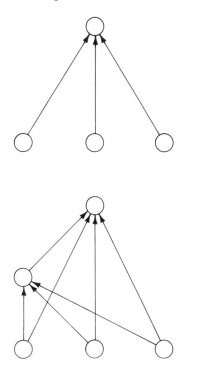

If a second new unit is added to the network it will have input connections from all the input units and one from the previously added unit; see below. The process of adding new units continues until the mean error of the output unit is below some minimum threshold.

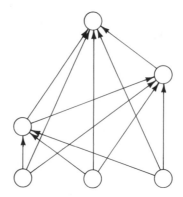

16.2.1. Performance of cascade-correlation

The inventors of cascade-correlation claim that it performs very well on classic learning problems for feed-forward networks. For example, they say that it usually requires approximately 24 epochs of training to solve the 2-dimensional XOR problem (Fahlman and Lebiere, 1990, p. 10). This is substantially less than the 100-500 epochs required by conventional back-propagation. They also show that it develops an interesting internal representation when applied to the *two-spirals* problem. In this problem the training set is made up of 2-dimensional vectors representing points in a real-valued space. The points in the training set represent two interlocking spirals. There are only two target outputs: 1 and 0. Points on one spiral should evoke a 1; points on the other should evoke a 0. The training set is shown geometrically in Figure 16.1.

The problem is exceedingly hard due to the fact that, just as with XOR, training inputs that are supposed to evoke *different* outputs are often very similar. Since back-propagation, like virtually all learning algorithms, tries to exploit input-class similarities, it performs very badly on this problem. The cascade-correlation algorithm, on the other hand, performs relatively well. In solving the problem it 'discovers' the structure of the training data by constructing a superposition of n hyperplanes that collectively track the boundary between the two spirals.

Figure 16.1. Two-spirals training set.

16.3. Upstart

In adding new units into the network, the cascade-correlation algorithm trains them to produce a response profile that will enable some or all of the error of the main output unit to be soaked up. This error-soaking strategy is used in several constructive learning algorithms including the *upstart* algorithm developed by Marcus Frean (1989). This algorithm constructs networks of perceptrons rather than *sigmoidal* units.[3] As with cascade-correlation, the algorithm is most easily described in the case where we assume there is a single output unit; however it can easily be adapted for use with several output units.

At the beginning of training, we have a simple network of n input units and a single linear threshold output unit that has input connections from all the input units. The algorithm trains this unit using a stochastic variant of the perceptron learning rule, continuing until the error has been minimized.[4] At this point, if the classes are not linearly separable, the output unit will classify some inputs incorrectly, i.e. it will be on for certain inputs for which it is supposed to be off, and off for inputs for which it

---

[3] A sigmoidal unit is a unit that uses the sigmoid activation function.

[4] If the error does not fall in a time period fixed by a 'patience' parameter, then it is assumed to have been minimized.

is supposed to be on. The upstart algorithm responds to this by generating two *daughter* units. These are called the *X upstart* and the *Y upstart*. Both of these units have connections from all the input units and one connection to the output unit.

The *X* upstart is trained to respond positively to (i.e. return a 1 for) those inputs that the output unit incorrectly returned a 1 for. The *Y* upstart is trained to respond positively to those inputs that the output unit incorrectly returned a 0 for. The behaviour of the output unit can then be corrected by setting a connection with a large negative weight that feeds activation from the *X* upstart to the output unit, and a similar connection with a large negative weight from the *Y* upstart to the output unit.

If the behaviour of the network is still not perfect, the procedure can be applied recursively to the two daughter units. The general effect is that the network expands downwards as a binary tree. At the top level we have the output unit. At the next level we have the daughter units, then the granddaughter units, then the great-granddaughter units, and so on. If each child unit is guaranteed to make fewer errors than its parent, we are guaranteed convergence since we will eventually reach a situation in which the daughter make no errors.[5] Thus, given this condition, it is guaranteed that the procedure will eventually produce a feed-forward network with perfect performance.

Unfortunately, if the upstart convergence criterion is not met, the algorithm may produce long branches of *redundant* units, i.e. units that correct no errors in the parent. However, its general performance on problems that can be represented using binary vectors seems to be quite impressive. The diagrams below shows a feed-forward network as it is dynamically constructed by the upstart algorithm. Initially (top network) we have a simple, one-layer net with three input units and one output unit. Next (middle network) we have the generation of two daughters. These form the new first layer of the network. Finally (bottom network) we have the generation of two more sets of daughters. These feed into the original daughter that now form the second layer of a three-layer network:

---

[5] One situation in which this is ensured is where any input from the training set can be separated off from all the other inputs by a hyperplane. In this case, each upstart is guaranteed to correct at least one error in each iteration. In fact, with binary input vectors, the criterion is always met. Any such vector forms one corner of a hypercube. And one can always separate off a corner with a hyperplane.

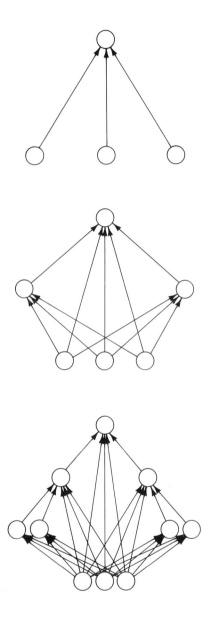

16.4. Comments

The approach we have looked at in this chapter is a relatively recent development in connectionism. At the present time it is difficult to evaluate the long-term potential of algorithms such as upstart and cascade-correlation or the error-reducing strategy that they use. But we can be fairly certain that they have paved the way for a whole generation of techniques in which the architecture of the network is just as much under the control of the learning algorithm as are the weight and activation values.

Of course, in experimenting with algorithms that manipulate representation spaces we are brought back to the thorny question that permeates all computation-based research, namely, what *is* the best representation for a given problem or mapping? We know that algorithms such as upstart and cascade-correlation improve their performance at each step but, of course, this does not guarantee that they produce an optimal representation (i.e. an optimal architecture). Just as the process of gradient descent can get stuck in a local minimum, so the process of improving the quality of a representation can get stuck on a 'foothill'. To produce an algorithm that does not get stuck on foothills we have to make sure that it optimizes rather than merely improves the representation space. But how can we do this if we cannot determine what the optimal representation is in any given case? The situation is somewhat vexing. But we can hope that connectionist research such as that described above is bringing a satisfactory theory of representation (and an answer to our question) a little nearer.

16.5. Further reading

The algorithms described in this chapter are of relatively recent origin. The main sources are therefore conference papers and technical reports. The original report for cascade-correlation is Fahlman and Lebiere (1990) while an early paper describing upstart is Frean (1989). A related algorithm called the tiling algorithm is described in Mezard and Nadal (1989). Sutton (1986) discusses the problem of unsmooth error surfaces in back-propagation.

16.6. Problems

(1)   Is the upstart algorithm likely to converge when presented with the two-spirals problem? If not, how could we transform the input representation so as to obtain convergence?

(2)   Implement Fahlman and Lebiere's cascade-correlation algorithm and try to replicate their results on learning problems such as two-spirals and *n*-bit parity. Try the algorithm on a range of problems and see whether you can identify a class of problems on which the algorithm's performance is no better than back-propagation's.

17

The WISARD net

17.1. Introduction: the 'silicon neuron'

The WISARD net is named after its principal developers: Wilkie, Stoneham and Aleksander. The name is, in fact, an acronym for 'Wilkie, Stoneham and Aleksander's Recognition Device.' Developed in the UK, this network architecture has shown itself capable of performing a number of interesting learning tasks. For example, in one case it has been trained to discriminate correctly between images of smiling and non-smiling faces. It has also been used in commercial applications.

The main difference between the WISARD architecture and the conventional neural network architecture is that WISARD uses small random access memories (RAMs) as its basic units. These units take as input a vector of binary values. This is treated as an address of a cell in the RAM; and the output of the unit is just the content of the memory cell, which is usually a binary digit. This arrangement is illustrated figuratively in Figure 17.1. It shows a single RAM with three input units. The current input vector (i.e. layer-zero activation vector) is [0 1 0]. This addresses the second memory cell from the left which contains a 1. Thus the output from the RAM is 1.

There are several advantages of using RAMs rather than, e.g., LTUs as the basic network unit. First, they have a very simple training procedure. To train a RAM to produce a certain output given a particular input vector, we simply write the output value into the cell in the RAM which is addressed by the input vector. Second, RAMs are readily available and steadily decreasing in cost. This means that the construction of large, experimental networks in hardware is a much more practical proposition. Third, RAMs can implement arbitrary 'activation functions'. That is to say, depending on how we store values in the memory, arbitrary input/output behaviour can be achieved. The main drawback is that since RAM units effectively treat each input as a special case, they do not naturally provide any generalization effects. However, it turns out, as we shall see, that this limitation can be overcome by employing multiple

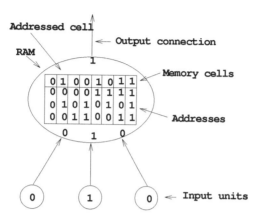

Figure 17.1. WISARD 'silicon neuron'.

RAM units, each of which is connected to a small subset of randomly chosen input units.

17.2. RAM units

In WISARD parlance, a RAM unit is a *silicon neuron*. But it is important to note that these 'neurons' do not behave in the standard manner. Once the contents of the cells in the RAM unit have been initialized, the unit's behaviour is fixed; it functions as a lookup table. The output returned is just the content of the cell addressed by the input vector. With this arrangement there can be no generalization beyond the training set. If we want a particular output for a particular input, we have to train the unit explicitly to produce it (i.e. we have to store the relevant value in the appropriate memory cell). In some cases, this is a serious drawback. For example, if the mapping we are seeking to represent is infinitely large, we cannot hope to cover all the individual cases and therefore will not be able to obtain perfect performance.

The solution adopted in the WISARD architecture involves a departure from the standard network configuration featuring complete first-layer connectivity. Rather than connect each unit in layer 1 to all the input units, we connect each one up to a subset of the input units, as shown in Figure 17.2. As we will see, this arrangement provides

the basis for generalization effects. Conveniently enough, it also obviates the techno-
logical constraint imposed by the fact that current RAM chips have a relatively small
number of address lines and therefore can only be connected to a limited number of
input units.

17.3. Generalization effects

The generalization effects obtained are most easily illustrated with a visual learning
problem.[1] Consider the case where we have a 25 × 9 array of pixels and we would
like to construct a WISARD network that will respond positively to the presence of
the word 'ANT' in the image (see Figure 17.3). We would like the network to generalize over noisy instances of this word, i.e. respond positively to ANT images in
which up to 15 pixels are flipped from black to white or vice versa.

One approach to this problem would be to use a network of 225 input units and one
RAM output unit with each input unit being connected to a unique pixel. We could
arrange things such that the unit is on if the pixel is black, and off otherwise. To train
the network to respond positively to instances of 'ANT' in the image we need to
present all the different, noisy images to the network and to write a 1 into the cell

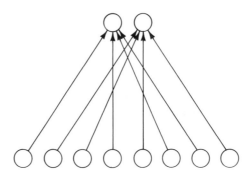

Figure 17.2. Simple WISARD network.

---

[1] The problem is based on the 'T' problem described in Aleksander and Burnett (1987).

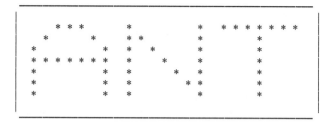

Figure 17.3. Visual array showing the word 'ANT'.

addressed in each case (see Figure 17.4).

One problem with this is that there are over 10^{35} different instances involving up to 15 flipped pixels. We have one training pair for each different case so the training process is going to be extremely time-consuming. A second problem is the fact that, as yet, RAM units with a capacity of 2^{225} are not available. A better approach is to use a *series* of RAM units. For example, we could use 15 RAMs with each one connected to a random subset of 15 input units — given the constraint that a single input unit is only ever connected to one RAM. In this situation the pixels responsible for the inputs received by a given RAM are the unit's *receptive field*.

If we 'train' each RAM to respond to the perfect 'ANT' and the 15 variants in which just one pixel is flipped we obtain a network which will respond to instances with up to 15 flipped pixels provided that there is only one flipped pixel in each unit's receptive field. Thus we find that by using a set of RAM units rather than just one we can obtain a certain degree of generalization.

Unfortunately, this approach relies on a sensible choice being made for the number of input units to connect to each RAM (known as the choice of *n-tuple*). The larger we make the receptive fields the more likely it is that each input unit will encode a meaningful image feature; e.g., the presence of a line in a certain orientation. On the other hand, as we make the receptive fields larger we increase the probability that the relevant unit will not have been trained to respond to (its sector of) a previously unseen variant of the image. In practice we have to use our judgement to make a sensible choice.

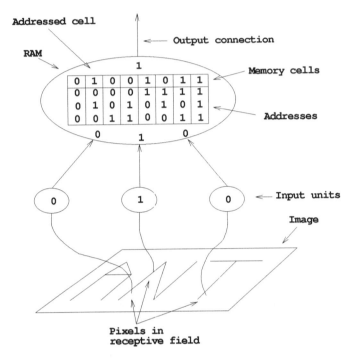

Figure 17.4. WISARD unit being trained to respond to 'ANT'.

17.4. Discriminator units

In principle, the RAM units in a one-layer network such as the one described above can form the output units of the network. However, in the standard WISARD architecture, the RAM units are divided up into assemblies called *discriminators*. These are effectively higher-level units which accept inputs from subsets of RAMS (see Figure 17.5). The output from a discriminator is usually just the number of 1s generated by the RAMs that it contains.

In the case where we want to train the network to discriminate between one of *n* different classes we proceed as follows. We take each class in turn and train one of the discriminators to respond positively to members of that class. This involves repeatedly presenting members of the class and writing 1s into the memory cells addressed

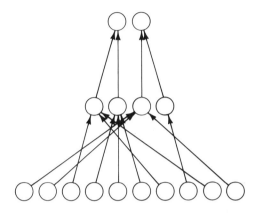

Figure 17.5. Two-level WISARD network.

in the relevant RAMs. Once we have all the discriminators trained up we can produce classifications by presenting an input and then comparing the relative strengths of the discriminator responses. The class of the input can then be inferred from the discriminator which yields the highest relative response.

17.5. Use of feedback mechanisms

In the simplest case the WISARD net is used in a purely feed-forward fashion. Inputs are presented, certain RAMS fire (i.e. return 1s) and the output from the discriminator units is read off. However, it is possible to use feedback mechanisms to obtain other types of behaviour. An approach that has been extensively investigated involves laying out a series of RAM units in a 2-dimensional array, such that each pixel in the input image has a corresponding RAM in the 2-dimensional array. With this arrangement we can view a particular collection of firing RAMs as an 'image' made up of black pixels (the firing RAMs) and white pixels (non-firing RAMS). We can then train the network to map input images on to internal images.

If we feed the internal image back into the network as an input image we obtain a network with a feedback loop. This type of network can be used for a variety of purposes. For example, we might train the network to implement an identity function for a set of images, i.e. to map images on to copies of themselves. If we feed in a noisy image to such a network we will expect the internal image to be slightly closer to the original. If we repeatedly feed the internal image back into the network, we should eventually obtain a perfect reproduction of the original. We could also train the network to cycle through a set of images, i.e. train it to respond to image 1 by producing image 2; to respond to image 2 by producing image 3, and so on. This sequential behaviour might be useful in the case where the network is used to classify sequences of objects.

17.6. Comments

The WISARD net represents a radical departure from the standard connectionist approach in which the basic network units have continuous activation functions. The basic idea in WISARD (that we can produce desired responses by counting up the votes cast by a large number of low-level feature detectors) would seem to be somewhat problem-specific. Problems which are largely decomposable, i.e. which can be represented in terms of large numbers of local features, are likely to be well suited to the WISARD approach. Problems which require global features to be taken into account are likely to be less well suited.[2] So in deciding whether or not the WISARD approach is likely to be successful we have to think carefully about the nature of the problem being addressed.

17.7. Further reading

An excellent introduction to WISARD is to be found in Aleksander and Burnett (1987). Colour illustrations are used extensively and greatly enhance the exposition. A more technical introduction is Stonham *et al.* (1982). The idea of using RAM units can be traced back at least to Samuel's (1959; 1967) checkers-learning program. This used a hierarchy of signature tables each one of which was similar to a single RAM unit. The idea of randomly wired receptive fields is closely related to the idea of coarse coding (Hinton *et al.*, 1986, p. 93).

---

[2] In a recent application, a WISARD net was successfully trained to map TV images of a certain London underground platform on to a count of the number of people standing on the platform.

17.8. Problems

(1)   In what cases might it be of benefit to wire up receptive fields in a non-random manner? In such cases, how could we decide on a suitable connectivity?

18

Competitive Learning and the Kohonen net

18.1. Introduction: discovering regularities

So far, in dealing with connectionist learning, we have concentrated on learning by the method of *error-reduction*. This is a *supervised* strategy which can only be used in the case where we have an explicit training set which gives us examples of target outputs. The advantage of the supervised approach is that it enables the learner to lock on to an effective representation for the target mapping more quickly. The disadvantage is that there has to be a teacher or oracle that provides the training pairs in the first place.

In this chapter we will look at an alternative learning strategy called *competitive learning*. This is an *unsupervised* regime which constructs a mapping from inputs to outputs without any direct guidance from the environment, i.e. without having access to a training set. In the absence of any target outputs the final form of the implemented mapping depends entirely on the interaction between the algorithm and the input data. The character of this interaction differs from case to case. However, as we will see, it very often produces a mapping which brings out regularities or patterns in the input data. Thus we can view competitive learning as a procedure for discovering regularities.

18.2. Simple competitive learning

Competitive learning is associated with Rosenblatt (1962), von der Malsburg (1973), Grossberg (1976), Willshaw (1981), Kohonen (1984) and Rumelhart and Zipser (1986) among others. In the simplest form of the process we have a network made up of a single layer of input units completely connected to a single layer of output units.

The algorithm is as follows:

Competitive Learning algorithm

Initialize the units to have random weights. Then repeatedly iterate through the training set executing the following two steps with each training pair.

(1)   Find the weight vector which is closest to the presented input vector. Call this the *winner* or the *winning vector*.

(2)   Modify the winner so as to move it closer to the input vector.[1]

Over time, application of this procedure tends to move the weight vectors towards the centres of clusters of input vectors. Thus, in a final state we might expect to find one weight vector over the centre of each cluster of input vectors. In locating clusters of input vectors, the algorithm is essentially performing a type of *cluster analysis* (see Chapter 7).

There are various ways in which we might measure the distance between weight vectors and input vectors but the simplest method involves computing the inner product of the two vectors; recall that this involves multiplying together the corresponding vector components and then summing the products. The method works well provided that the two vectors being compared are of the same *length*. If the lengths are not standardized then the distance measures we obtain will be misleading. A weight vector with very large components will be computed as being very close to an input vector even if that input vector is pointing in a very different direction.

The best solution to the problem is to ensure that weight vectors always have the same length. We can ensure that weight vectors are of a standard length by normalizing them after each weight change. This is done by dividing all the components of the vector by the original length of the vector. The vector of values produced is of *unit length* (i.e. its length is 1).

18.3. The dynamics of competitive learning

In describing the algorithm we have said that the central operation is to move the

---

[1] Note that this step simply involves modifying the weights in the weight vector so as to make them more similar to the values in the input vector.

weight vector which is closest to the current input vector *closer* to that input vector. This operation can be easily understood by visualizing the vectors as points in space. When we apply the competitive learning rule we effectively move the winning vector a little closer to the current input vector. If we have a set of input vectors gathered together in a clump, they are likely to share a single nearest weight vector. This weight vector will thus be gradually attracted towards the centre of the clump. Once it has reached this position, weight changes will tend to be small. Thus the weight vector will tend to stay in position.

In Figure 18.1 we see a simple characterization of competitive learning. The diagram represents a flat, 2-dimensional projection of a spherical or hyperspherical surface on which three weight vectors (**W1**, **W2** and **W3**) and a number of input vectors (represented as dots) are shown.[2] Competitive learning results in weight vectors being moved towards those input vectors from which they are the least distant. Thus, given sufficient training, **W1** will tend to move towards the centre of the upper left-hand group of input vectors. **W2** will tend to move towards the centre of the rightmost group of inputs; and **W3** will tend to move towards the centre of the bottommost group of inputs. Once the weight vectors have reached the centres of the input groups they will tend to stay in position.

18.4. Example: using competitive learning to clean up noisy images

Although the general aim in competitive learning is to discover regularities in the input data, the achieved goal may be more prosaic. In the simplest case the algorithm's behaviour tends to do little more than identify the way in which the input data are arranged into similarity classes. However, in the case where the inputs in a given group are well spaced out, the placing of a weight vector in the group centre effectively produces a *prototype* for the group, i.e. an exemplar which captures the central tendency of the group without necessarily being a member of it. There are a number of ways in which we might make use of this prototype-producing behaviour. For example, consider the case where we have a series of noisy variants of a visual image. By finding the prototype underlying the noisy variants we can recover the original image.

To demonstrate this we will look at an example in which competitive learning is applied to a series of noisy images of the three-letter words 'BIG' and 'ANT'. The input vectors in this example are linearized 25 × 9 binary images, i.e. binary vectors in which 1s represent black pixels and 0s represent white pixels. The network used

---

[2] The tips of all unit-length, *n*-dimensional vectors fall on the surface of a hypersphere.

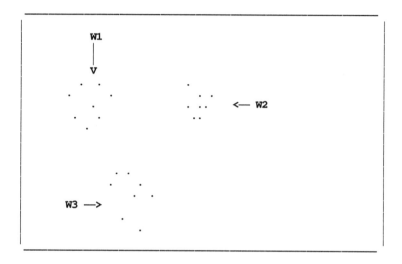

Figure 18.1. Basic competitive learning.

has $25 \times 9 = 225$ input units and two output units.

We will portray the learning using a representation scheme introduced by Rumelhart and Zipser (1986). In this scheme, the weights for a particular unit are shown as a 2-dimensional image which mirrors the original image array. If the unit has a large weight[3] to a given unit, then the weight image has a star at the corresponding point. If the weight is small then the weight image is blank at that point. The overall pattern thus shows the unit's *receptive field*, that is to say, the pattern to which it responds most strongly.

18.4.1. Noisy images

Before showing how competitive learning behaves in this example, let us look at some examples of noisy images. In Figure 18.2 we see four input images displayed as

---

[3] A large weight is a weight whose value exceeds the mean weight value and a small weight is a weight whose value is less than the mean weight value.

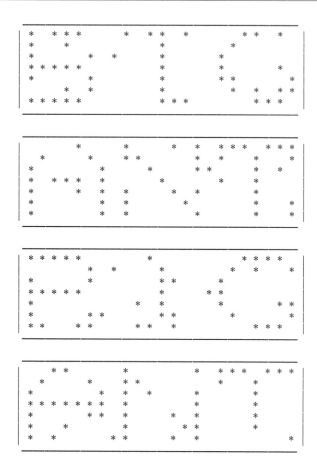

Figure 18.2. Noisy versions of 'BIG' and 'ANT'.

weight vectors using the conventions described above. Two images are noisy variants of the word 'BIG' and two are noisy variants of the word 'ANT'. The noise level in all four images (i.e. the probability that a pixel is flipped from black to white or vice versa) is 5%.

By presenting noisy images such as those shown above to competitive learning we obtain the following behaviour. All weights are randomly initialized but the total amount of weight in any one vector is always equal to 1. This does not ensure that the length of input vectors is always the same. But it does keep the lengths roughly equal and thus enables the algorithm to work effectively.

In the diagram below we see the weight vectors for the two output units after the first epoch of learning (i.e. the first pass through all the input vectors). Note that at this point the weight vectors show no particular resemblance to either of the two underlying images:

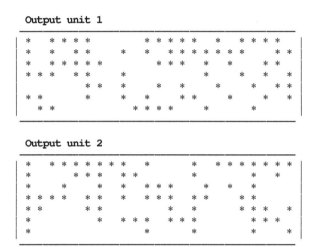

After epoch 2 we see the prototypical images beginning to emerge. Output unit 1 is beginning to move towards a prototype for the 'BIG' images while output unit 2 is moving towards a prototype for the 'ANT' images:

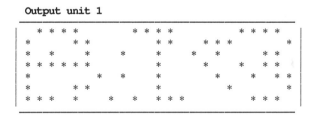

Output unit 2

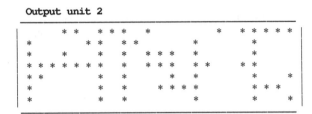

The trend is continued in epoch 3. At the end of this epoch it is quite clear that output unit 1 has now captured the input group corresponding to the 'BIG' images while output unit 2 has captured the group for the 'ANT' images:

Output unit 1

Output unit 2

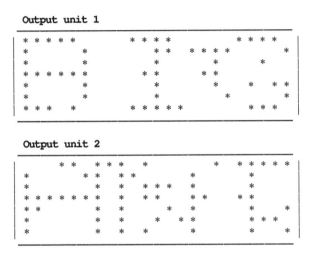

By epoch 16, the process is complete and the prototypes provide a perfect recovery of the two underlying images:

Output unit 1

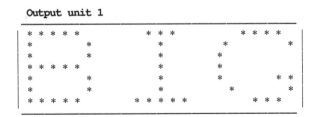

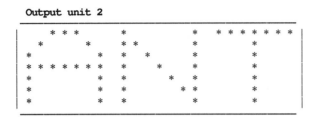

Obviously, this is only an illustrative example. Using competitive learning for the purposes of cleaning up noisy images might be quite impractical in a realistic case since we cannot normally guarantee that a given image feature will correspond to a given pixel. A more appropriate application of competitive learning would be a task that involves finding the basic partitions (groupings) of a body of data. An example of this is seen in Rumelhart and McClelland's work on the past-tense network (see Chapter 12). In their work the outputs produced by the main network tended to be quite noisy (i.e. to exhibit a lot of spurious variability). Competitive learning was used to sort outputs into basic classes, i.e. to clean them up.

18.5. Competitive learning instabilities

The ideal situation in a competitive learning experiment can be described as follows. The input vectors should fall into m groups (classes), where m is exactly equal to the number of output units. The perfect match between the number of input groups and the number of output units means that learning should produce an ideal end result with each weight vector positioned over a unique group of inputs. The resulting network will 'classify' inputs perfectly: the presentation of an input in a given group (class) will always cause the same output unit to become active.

Unfortunately, it is quite possible to produce training sets that cause the learning process to oscillate in an uncontrolled fashion. Geometrically, this can happen when we have, say, one group on either side of a weight vector. As training pairs are presented, the learning mechanism first attempts to move the weight vector towards the first group, then towards the second group, then towards the first group, and so on. Each time it moves it towards the second group it moves it directly away from the first group, and vice versa. Thus it continually undoes what it has just done.

A slightly more complex example is depicted in Figure 18.3. This shows inputs as dots and three weight vectors **W1**, **W2** and **W3** in the usual fashion. Given the relative positions of the input groups and the weight vectors we would expect **W1** to continue oscillating between the two upper clumps of inputs while **W2** and **W3** continue to compete for inputs in the lower clump. If **W1** is still the closest weight vector to the top right-hand clump even after it has moved some way towards the top left-hand clump (and vice versa) then neither **W2** nor **W3** will ever win a competition involving an input vector from an upper clump.

In the instability described above, all the units will tend to win some of the time. However, consider Figure 18.4. Here we have one unit (**W3**) that is very distant from all the inputs. This unit will never win a competition and will therefore never move at all.

18.6. Non-uniform input distributions

The two situations described above are examples of the sort of problem that results when the distribution of inputs within the input space is non-uniform in a way that does not match the initial (random) distribution of the weight vectors. This difficulty has been intensively investigated and various solutions have been identified. We will

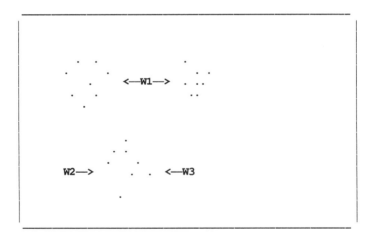

Figure 18.3. Mismatch between instance/unit distributions.

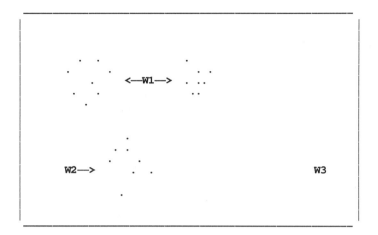

Figure 18.4. The problem of 'outlier' weight vectors.

consider just two.[4]

18.6.1. Leaky learning and the Conscience method

A very simple approach to the problem of non-uniform input distribution is known as *leaky learning*. In leaky learning, *all* the units in a cluster have their weight vector modified so as to bring them closer to the relevant activation vector but the winner's weight vector is modified to a much greater degree. The intended result of using a leaky rule is that units that are initially very distant from all inputs gradually get pulled into the region of the input space where they can capture an input group. However, it can also cause problems in cases where the input clumps are crowded together.

A more robust method is to make use of what is known as unit *conscience*. In this method each output unit is modified so that it maintains an internal record of how frequently it wins the competition for an input vector. If it turns out that the unit is winning more than its fair share (i.e. substantially more than n/m times per epoch, where

---

[4] For a longer list see Hertz *et al.* (1991, p.221).

n is the number of output units and m is the number of training pairs), then the unit is temporarily removed from the competition process. This allows 'lost' units to move in towards dense regions of the input space.

18.7. The Rumelhart-Zipser model

Rumelhart and Zipser have presented a model of competitive learning which extends the simple model described above. It can be used with networks involving several layers of units and it incorporates a simple method for modifying weights which satisfies the constraint that weight vector lengths must be standardized but without using a costly renormalization step. The basic idea is that all weight vectors are initialized to have the same total amount of weight (i.e. to sum to the same value). Then, during learning, weight vectors are modified so as to *shift* weight from connections to inactive input units to connections from active input units. Note that changing weights by *redistribution* from inactive to active links has two implications. First, it means that the total amount of weight on the links to a unit (i.e. the result of simply adding all the unit's weights together) will always remain constant. Second, it means that the similarity between a unit's weight vector and its 'captured' input vectors will tend to increase. Clearly, if we always increase the weight on active links and decrease it on inactive links, then the weights on the links to units in the 1 state must get ever closer to 1 and the weights on the links to the units in the 0 state must get ever closer to 0.

The network in the Rumelhart-Zipser model is subdivided into one or more layers. The layers are then subdivided again into a set of mutually exclusive (i.e. non-overlapping) *clusters*. The connections between the layers are so arranged such that all the units in a cluster have connections to the same group of inputs at the layer below. Thus these networks are effectively feed-forward nets in which the non-input units are gathered together in clusters. An example network with two clusters of two hidden units and one cluster of two output units is shown in Figure 18.5.

18.8. The Kohonen net

A close relation of the competitive network that has been extensively studied by Tuevo Kohonen is called the *self-organizing topographic map* or *Kohonen net*.[5] This

---

[5] In fact, the term 'Kohonen net' is also often used to label the simple competitive learning scheme described above.

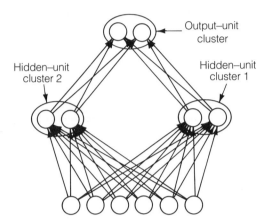

Figure 18.5. A Rumelhart-Zipser network.

mechanism relies on competition in much the same way that ordinary competitive learning does. However, whereas in ordinary competitive learning it is only the winning unit (in each cluster) that is trained in each iteration, in the self-organizing topographic map all the units in the 'neighbourhood' of the winning unit are trained.

In order to decide which output units are in a given neighbourhood we have to organize our output units into a grid. We can then define the neighbourhood of a given output unit as all the units which are within a certain distance (e.g., Euclidean distance) from the output unit's position in the grid. In Figure 18.6 a situation is visualized in which we have a set of input units and a set of output units both organized into 2-dimensional arrays. Every output unit receives a connection from every input unit. The neighbourhood of the central output unit would contain every output unit that was within a certain distance in the array (e.g., the area enclosed by the dashed line). In training a Kohonen net we initially use large neighbourhoods whose diameter is close to the maximum inter-unit distance in the array. As training progresses we gradually reduce the size of the neighbourhoods until eventually the only unit whose weights are modified in each iteration is the winner. Simultaneously with this gradual reduction in neighbourhood size we implement a gradual reduction in learning rate (i.e. the degree to which we move the winning unit (and its neighbours) closer to the input vector). Typically both the neighbourhood size and the learning rate are reduced linearly so that they both become zero at the end of the training period.

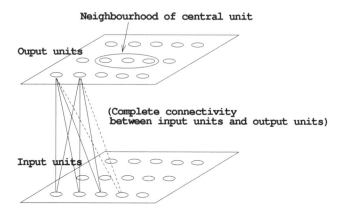

Figure 18.6. A Kohonen neighbourhood.

18.9. Example: recovering 2-dimensional structure from 4-dimensional inputs

We can illustrate the behaviour of the Kohonen net by showing how it can recover implicit 2-dimensional structure from 4-dimensional inputs. Let us imagine that we have some 2-dimensional surface and we construct a training set by repeatedly picking a point on the surface and then writing down the distances between the chosen point and four fixed landmarks in the space. This produces training inputs such as these:

```
<[0.442347 -0.237384 0.744212  1.02488]   []>
<[0.347878 0.148932  0.626645  0.679685]  []>
<[0.368051 0.611038  0.733276  0.343154]  []>
<[0.639993 -0.025265 0.392646  0.845507]  []>
<[0.41509  0.827624  0.857431  0.259564]  []>
<[0.491196 0.628569  0.624431  0.271868]  []>
<[0.758872 -0.22519  0.468937  1.07446]   []>
<[0.471506 0.100212  0.505508  0.696945]  []>
<[0.165789 0.560893  0.886421  0.537201]  []>
<[0.48475  0.721249  0.698922  0.215216]  []>
<[1.02681  0.463042  -0.056726 0.884723]  []>
<[0.061752 0.259076  0.967704  0.881603]  []>
<[0.263246 0.477349  0.758664  0.484391]  []>
```

If we feed this sort of training input to a Kohonen net comprising 64 output units arranged into an 8 × 8 array then the training gradually modifies the weight vectors so as to recover the original 2-dimensional surface from which the inputs were generated. What this means is that each output unit gradually acquires a weight vector which causes it to be maximally responsive to inputs that were generated from a point on the original 2-dimensional surface which corresponds to its own position in the output array. In effect, the output units self-organize so as to recover the 2-dimensional structure of the input data.

We can show how this works by drawing out the 'map' that the network has of the input space at various intervals during training. To draw out the map we simply draw lines connecting each output unit with its next-door neighbour above, below and to left and right. But when we draw a line to a particular output unit we do not draw a line to its position in the output array. Rather we draw a line to the position in the original 2-dimensional surface to which it is maximally responsive. This way we see the degree to which the output units have self-organized to form a topologically correct map of the input surface. The sequence of six maps shown in Figure 18.7 were produced by a Kohonen net being trained on data of the form shown above.

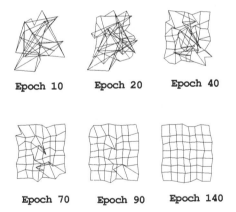

Epoch 10   Epoch 20   Epoch 40

Epoch 70   Epoch 90   Epoch 140

Figure 18.7. Developing a 2-dimensional map.

18.10. The phonetic typewriter

One of the experiments for which the Kohonen net is most famous is the *phonetic typewriter*. This was a text-generating mechanism that was driven by the output of a network trained using Kohonen's method. The input vectors for the learning were produced by recording the response of 15 acoustic filters to the pronunciation of a large number of Finnish phonemes. After training with the units arranged in a 2-dimensional map, Kohonen analysed the responses of the units to see which phoneme they responded most strongly to. The map that we see in Figure 18.8 shows the locations of maximal response for a selection of phonemes after a particular training sequence.

The use of this map for the purposes of generating speech is a fairly complex operation. However, to a first approximation the procedure involves (1) feeding the speech into the network via the acoustic filters and (2) generating text segments appropriate to the most strongly activated units in the network. Because the network has self-organized so that regions of the array correspond to particular classes of phoneme, the robustness of the performance is quite high. Provided that an input is fairly similar to the typical input for phoneme *P*, the output will be fairly close to *P*. The effect here is the same as was achieved in the NETtalk system except that here the representation is encapsulated in the organization of the 2-dimensional array rather than in the structure of the hidden-vector space.

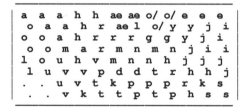

Figure 18.8. Phoneme map.

18.11. Comments

As we have seen in this chapter, competitive mechanisms such as the Kohonen net and competitive learning are capable of discovering statistical regularities in a body of data. Furthermore, the process by which competitive learning moves weight vectors towards the centres of input groups can, in certain situations, produce the sort of result that is obtained by carrying out a conventional clustering analysis, i.e. it can produce an implicit clustering of the input data. The Kohonen net also provides us with an implicit clustering of the data but in the case where we cause the units to self-organize within an n-dimensional array, we obtain not only an implicit clustering of the input data, but also a mapping of the original data into another, possibly lower-dimensional, space.[6]

18.12. Further reading

An accessible reference for competitive learning is the paper by Rumelhart and Zipser (1986). Further coverage of the algorithm can be found in McClelland and Rumelhart (1988, pp. 188-201). Grossberg has derived a variety of theoretical results for learning schemes closely related to competitive learning. In particular he has shown that a competitive network's tendency to produce oscillations depends on the relative sparseness of the input vectors in the input space. If a certain level of sparseness is not preserved oscillations inevitably result (Grossberg, 1976). For a description of the leaky learning rule see Rumelhart and Zipser (1986, p. 179)

Hecht-Nielsen (1990) gives an interesting history of the Kohonen learning mechanism. He also provides a more detailed description of the mechanism itself (pp. 65-70) and discusses a number of alternatives to the leaky learning modification (pp. 68-69). He also discusses a 'robot arm' example in which a Kohonen net is used to recover the structure of the space in which the robot arm is operating. For a case in which the robot arm has four degrees of freedom, see Barrow (1989).

The main source of further reading for the Kohonen net is Kohonen's own book on self-organization (Kohonen, 1988b) and his papers on the phonetic map work (Kohonen, 1988a; 1989). However, useful introductions are also provided by Barrow (1989) and by Wasserman (1989). Dayhoff (1990, pp. 188-90) and Beale and Jackson (1990, Chapter 5) provide introductions to the phonetic typewriter work. See also Kohonen's contribution to an early collection of papers on connectionist approaches

---

[6] As such it is comparable with statistical methods such as *principal components analysis.*

(Kohonen *et al.*, 1981).

For material on the topic of principal components analysis see Chatfield and Collins (1980).

18.13. Problems

(1)   What type of network architecture is used in competitive learning?

(2)   What happens in competitive learning when a unit wins a competition? How is the winning unit selected?

(3)   How are weight vectors modified in competitive learning? What effect does the modification procedure have on the length of a weight vector?

(4)   In the case where competitive learning is applied to an *n*-layered network ($n >$ 1) what similarity groupings can we expect to be identified?

(5)   Provide a geometric interpretation of competitive learning and detail the caveats which apply to it.

(6)   Describe an example in which unsupervised learning is successfully used to solve a supervised learning problem.

(7)   Characterize the relationship between competitive learning and cluster analysis. What advantages might cluster analysis have over competitive learning as a method of statistical analysis?

(8)   Could the delta rule be used as the weight-change procedure in competitive learning? If so, what extra actions would be required and how might they be implemented?

(9)   The Rumelhart-Zipser competitive learning algorithm ensures that the total sum of weight on any unit's input lines remains the same. Is this necessary? Why?

(10)   How can instabilities arise in competitive learning? Provide one example in which the instabilities arise contingently and one in which they arise

necessarily.

(11)   In what cases is it necessary to use the leaky learning method? Propose an alternative approach that might be used in such cases.

19

The Hopfield net

19.1. Introduction: recurrent networks

With the exception of our brief look at WISARD and at Elman's copy-back network, we have concentrated so far exclusively on *non-recurrent networks*. In these architectures activation is fed in via the input units and propagates through the network to the output units. There are no feedback loops via which activation at one layer can feed back into the units at a lower layer. Networks in which feedback does take place are known as *recurrent networks*. When presented with an input, such networks will cycle, perhaps indefinitely, through sequences of states. In these situations we cannot talk about the final output of the network since the states of the output units may be continually changing. To obtain an output we have to examine the instantaneous state of the output units.

In this chapter we will look at two examples of recurrent networks, namely Rumelhart and McClelland's *schema model* and Hopfield's energy minimizing network, known as the *Hopfield net*. These two architectures share many features. For example, they are typically constructed the same way, with complete connectivity between units, i.e. with every unit having a bi-directional connection with every other unit in the network (see Figure 19.1).[1] They also tend to be used in the same way. First the weights are configured by hand. Then the network is allowed to run until the unit activations settle down into a stable configuration. This settling process is the 'engine' that produces the computation in these networks. In the case of the Hopfield net the settling or *relaxation* process has a mathematical characterization that exploits an analogy with simple physical systems that gradually settle into a

---

[1] We have followed the usual convention of showing incoming connections arriving at the bottom of a unit and outgoing ones emerging from the top.

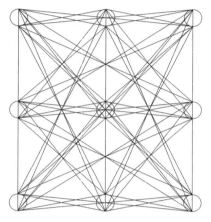

Figure 19.1. Hopfield network.

stable state in which their *global energy* is minimized.

19.2. Constraint satisfaction

We will begin by looking at the *schema model* of constraint satisfaction. This model is based on a method for implementing constraint satisfaction used by Hinton (1977) in his early work on connectionist systems. The idea is very simple. We conceptualize our constraint satisfaction problem as an attempt to find a set of mutually compatible hypotheses. For example, we might represent the problem of finding a satisfactory timetable for the following week in terms of 'hypotheses' such as 'meet John for lunch on Tuesday' and 'visit Aberdeen on Wednesday'.

Once we have couched the problem in these terms we configure the network so that we have one unit for each, distinct hypothesis. We set the weights so that they reflect the degree to which one hypothesis supports another. Thus if unit X represents 'meet John in London on Tuesday' and unit Y represents the hypothesis 'spend Tuesday in Glasgow' we would place a large, negative weight between X and Y so as to capture the fact that one hypothesis is incompatible with the other. If unit Z represents the hypothesis 'spend Monday night in Glasgow' then we would set a positive weight between units Y and Z.

To obtain constraint satisfaction from a network configured this way we have to make sure that units behave in a particular way. In the simplest case units can adopt any activation level between -1 and 1 and we set the activation updating function so that units tend to become more active if the amount of net activation they receive exceeds 0, and less active otherwise. It turns out that this gives us the behaviour we want (see below) but it leaves us with the problem of deciding *when* units should have their activation levels updated. Normally we update an activation level once all the inputs for the given unit are available. But in the present scenario all the inputs (for every unit) are available all the time. If we simply update units in a fixed sequence, units will tend to see a completely different set of states depending on when they are updated.

There are two main strategies for dealing with this problem. One strategy involves *synchronous updates*. This is a simple procedure but it imposes an extra memory cost. In each iteration we work through all the units finding out how much activation each one is receiving as input and store this net input value somewhere. Then we set the new states of units by looking at their stored net input value. The alternative strategy is *asynchronous updates*. This is just the obvious strategy of updating units in a sequence; but it avoids the problem mentioned above by selecting units at random.

Once we have the weights configured and the activation updating machinery working in the required manner (using either synchronous or asynchronous updates) we have a network that will tend to settle into a state in which the levels of activation are maximally compatible with the constraints, i.e. it will tend to settle into a state in which the units that are most strongly active will tend to have positive weights between them.

We can modulate the behaviour by *clamping* certain units on, i.e. by fixing them so that their activation level is always 1. In doing this, we upgrade the represented hypotheses to 'facts' — hypotheses that are defined as definitely true. In this case the network settles into a state that maximally satisfies (1) the constraints captured in the weights and (2) the constraints represented by the clamped units.

19.3. A simple example of schema representation

The process of finding a set of maximally compatible hypotheses can sometimes be viewed as a way of accessing a *schema* for the domain. We can demonstrate this using a simple example involving hypotheses about an item of fruit. Let us imagine that we have eleven numbered hypotheses as follows:

```
 1: toxic=yes
 2: skin=smooth
 3: size=small
 4: colour=red
 5: flesh=soft
 6: colour=green
 7: toxic=no
 8: flesh=hard
 9: size=large
10: colour=brown
11: skin=hairy
```

These hypotheses are made up of an attribute and a value, e.g., the attribute `colour` and the value `red`. One should read the hypothesis `colour=red` as 'the colour of the fruit is red'.

We construct a network of 11 units corresponding to our 11 hypotheses. Then we utilize our background knowledge of the domain (i.e. of items of fruit) to set the weights so as to reflect the degree to which one hypothesis supports another. A matrix of weights derived in this fashion is shown in Figure 19.2.[2] The names of the particular units (i.e. particular weight vectors) correspond to hypotheses in the obvious way: `W1` corresponds to hypothesis 1, `W2` to hypothesis 2, and so on. Note how the weights capture relationships between the features. For example, the strong weight between `W7` and `W11` represents the fact that a hairy skin usually means that

	W1	W2	W3	W4	W5	W6	W7	W8	W9	W10
W11	−0.39	−0.73	0.04	0.04	0.04	0.04	0.66	0.23	0.23	−0.39
W10	−0.54	−0.1	−0.16	−0.54	−0.16	−0.54	0.8	0.42	0.42	
W9	−0.22	0.06	−0.78	0.04	−0.04	0.01	0.49	0.3		
W8	−0.28	0.21	0.13	0.23	−0.83	0.01	0.54			
W7	−0.87	0.06	0.13	0.23	0.04	0.01				
W6	0.25	−0.28	0.25	−0.61	0.25					
W5	0.23	0.06	0.13	0.04						
W4	0.04	0.06	0.23							
W3	0.13	0.21								
W2	0.21									

Figure 19.2. Weight-matrix for fruit-attribute units.

---

[2] The use of a very simple weight-derivation rule has resulted in some slightly counter-intuitive weights here. For example, the weight between `toxic=yes` and `toxic=no` is only -0.87 rather than -1 as we might expect.

fruit is safe to eat (i.e. non-toxic).[3]

In Figure 19.3, the matrix of weights is shown using a Hinton diagram. Recall that in these diagrams each large rectangle corresponds to a unit and the boxes inside rectangles correspond — position-wise, size-wise and colour-wise — to its weights. If the unit has a strongly negative weight to the unit whose rectangle appears in, say, the bottom left-hand corner of the display, then there will be a large, filled box in the bottom left-hand corner of the rectangle. If the weight is positive, the box will be large

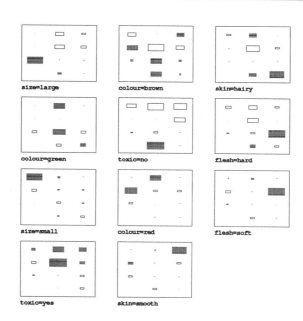

Figure 19.3. Unit receptive fields.

---

[3] The weights were actually derived from a Bayesian analysis of a small training set for toxic fruit classification.

but unfilled.

19.4. Running the network

Imagine that we clamp the unit representing `toxic=yes` on and then let the network run. How do the activations of the other units change? We can display the activation changes using a scheme in which each unit's activation levels are displayed as boxes running across the page. The unit names appear on the left. The activation for a unit is shown as a rectangle to the right of the unit's name. The size of the rectangle corresponds to the level of activation in the same way as in the weight representation used above. The position of the rectangle gives the cycle in which the activation level occurred. Rectangles further to the right represent activation levels in later cycles.[4]

The representation for a run of the network with the `toxic=yes` unit clamped on is shown below.

```
toxic=yes:        □□□□□□□□□□□□□□□□□□□□□□□□□□□□□□□
skin=smooth:      · · · · · · · · · · · · · · · · · · · · · · · · · · · ·
size=small:       · · · · · · · · · □ □ □ □ □ □ □ □ □ □ □ □ □ □ □ □
colour=red:       · · · · · · · · · · · · · · · · · · · · · · · · · · · ·
flesh=soft:       · · · · · · □ □ □ □ □ □ □ □ □ □ □ □ □ □ □ □ □ □ □ □
colour=green:     · · · · · □ □ □ □ □ □ □ □ □ □ □ □ □ □ □ □ □ □ □
toxic=no:         · · · · · · · · · · · · · · · · · · · · · · · · · · · ·
flesh=hard:       · · · · · · · · · · · · · · · · · · · · · · · · · · · ·
size=large:       · · · · · · · · · · · · · · · · · · · · · · · · · · · ·
colour=brown:     · · · · · · · · · · · · · · · · · · · · · · · · · · · ·
skin=hairy:       · · · · · · · · · · · · · · · · · · · · · · · · · · · ·
```

As we can see, clamping this unit on tends to produce a certain pattern of activation in which `flesh=soft`, `size=small` and `colour=green` are also active. Thus, clamping the `toxic=yes` unit on tends to evoke the toxic fruit schema — it tends to bring out the fact that an item of toxic fruit is likely to be small, soft and green:

An example in which the network performs something closer to constraint optimization is produced if we clamp on the units representing `colour=brown` and `flesh=hard`. The behaviour produced is shown below. The unit representing `toxic=no` develops a strong, positive level of activation while the one representing `toxic=yes` remains inactive. In some sense the network is showing that, other things being equal, a hard, brown fruit is likely to be safe to eat (as well as large and hairy):

---

[4] This scheme is used in Rumelhart *et al.* (1986c).

```
toxic=yes:        · · · · · · · · · · · · · · · · · · · · · · ·
skin=smooth:      · · · · · · · · · · · · · · · · · · · · · · ·
size=small:       · · · · · · · · · · · · · · · · · · · · · · ·
colour=red:       · · · · · · · · · · · · · · · · · · · · · · ·
flesh=soft:       · · · · · · · · · · · · · · · · · · · · · · ·
colour=green:     · · · · · · · · · · · · · · · · · · · · · · ·
toxic=no:         · □ □ □ □ □ □ □ □ □ □ □ □ □ □ □ □ □ □ □ □ □ □
flesh=hard:       □ □ □ □ □ □ □ □ □ □ □ □ □ □ □ □ □ □ □ □ □ □ □
size=large:       · · · □ □ □ □ □ □ □ □ □ □ □ □ □ □ □ □ □ □ □ □
colour=brown:     □ □ □ □ □ □ □ □ □ □ □ □ □ □ □ □ □ □ □ □ □ □ □
skin=hairy:       · · · · · · · · · □ □ □ □ □ □ □ □ □ □ □ □ □ □
```

19.5. Measuring mean compatibility

In setting up the network for constraint satisfaction we arranged for units to change their level of activation depending on the amount of activation they receive as input. Units receiving a net input exceeding zero increase their level of activation. Units receiving a net input of less than zero decrease their activation. There are good intuitive reasons for thinking this is an appropriate activation rule — the more support a given hypothesis has, the more we should believe it. But in addition there is a mathematical argument. To develop this argument we first have to think about the way in which we would measure the *compatibility* of a given configuration of hypotheses (i.e. the compatibility of a configuration of active units).

Consider a particular pair of units. The presence of a positive weight on the link between them indicates that the hypothesis represented by one unit *supports* the hypothesis represented by the other unit, and vice versa. In effect, it indicates that the states of the two units should be the same. The level of compatibility is increased if the two states *are* the same. Conversely, the presence of a negative weight on the link indicates that one hypothesis contradicts the other, i.e. that the states should be different. We see then that the overall level of compatibility is increased whenever we find positive weights between units that are in the same state, and is decreased in all other cases. Moreover, the degree to which compatibility is increased or decreased depends on the size of the weight, i.e. the strength of the relationship between the two hypotheses.

Thus, given a pair of units, we can measure their contribution to compatibility by taking the product of the two states and the relevant weight:[5]

$$L_i \, L_j \, W_{ij}$$

---

[5] Remember that the connection is bidirectional.

Here L_i and L_j are the activation levels of units i and j while W_{ij} is the weight between them. Note how this rule neatly takes care of all possible cases, even where units are allowed to take on negative activation levels. If both L_i and L_j are positive and the weight is positive then we have a positive product, i.e. a positive contribution to compatibility. This is what we want since the positive weight says that the two hypotheses should be in the same state. If, on the other hand, the weight is negative we have a negative product and a decrease in the overall level of compatibility. Again, this is what we want since the negative weight indicates the fact that the two hypotheses contradict one another.

If the signs of the activation levels are different and the weight is positive, then the contribution is negative (the positive weight says that the two hypotheses *should* be in the same state). If, on the other hand, the weight is negative then the contribution is positive (the negative weight says that the two hypotheses *should* be in different states).

To work out the total contribution to compatibility made by a single unit i we multiply the unit's activation level by the sum of the contributions associated with each individual weight:

$$L_i \ \Sigma_j L_j \ W_{ij}$$

To work out the total level of compatibility for the whole network we iterate over all the units and all the weights, summing the relevant contributions:

$$\Sigma_i \ \Sigma_{j<i} \ L_i \ L_j \ W_{ij}$$

This measure of global compatibility is a simplified version of the *goodness* measure defined in the PDP workbook (McClelland and Rumelhart, 1988, p. 51).

19.6. Unit updates

Clearly, the correct rule for updating unit activation levels will be one that ensures that the compatibility level of the network is increased as a result of the update. If the unit's contribution to compatibility is positive, then by increasing its activation level in absolute terms (i.e. making it more negative if it is negative and more positive if it is positive) we will increase the overall level of compatibility. On the other hand, if the unit's contribution to compatibility is negative (i.e. if its current state detracts from global compatibility) then we will achieve the same thing by decreasing its absolute activation level.

Now, the point to note is this. Because of the symmetrical weights, a unit's contribution to compatibility is *always the same* as its net input. That is to say, it is always computed by summing up the products of all the weights to, and activations of, the units to which it is connected. Thus, to increase overall compatibility we should increase the activation level of any units whose net input is positive and decrease the activation level of any unit whose net input is negative. This, of course, is precisely the updating function that we chose on intuitive grounds.

19.7. Global energy in Hopfield nets

John Hopfield has popularized a framework for these ideas that is firmly embedded in a mathematical context. He has in fact experimented with a number of different network mechanisms. But in his original work he described a fully connected network of binary threshold units, i.e. units whose activation level was always either 1 or 0. He visualized his network as a content-addressable memory device. This type of memory is essentially a type of pattern-completion device. Presented with some parts of a stored memory, it should return the complete item.

Hopfield realized that the process by which a neural network settles into a state of maximum compatibility is similar to the way in which a simple physical system settles into an energy minimum. This led him to measure the *in*compatibility of unit states rather than their compatibility and to call his measure *global energy*. The equations that define this measure are similar to the ones used above except that they are preceded with a minus sign. For example, the contribution to global energy associated with a single unit *i* is:

$$- L_i \sum_j L_j W_{ij}$$

And the global energy (incompatibility) of the whole network is:

$$- \sum_i \sum_{j<i} L_i L_j W_{ij}$$

In fact, in most formulations (including the original one) the inner summation iterates over every unit *j* where *j* is not equal to *i*, and the total value is multiplied by ½ to compensate for the fact that (in this arrangement) all the weights are counted twice.

We can derive the update rule for units from this measure in the same way that we derived it above. The argument is simplest if we assume that units can be either on or off. In this case turning a unit off (i.e. resetting its activation to 0) effectively cancels its contribution to global energy. Thus, the change in global energy obtained when we change the state of a unit is equal to the unit's contribution to global energy when it is turned on. In order to increase the level of compatibility in the network we obviously have to change the states of units so as to decrease the global energy. This means that we should turn the unit on if its contribution to global energy is negative (i.e. if turning it on will reduce global energy) and off otherwise.

In Hopfield's formulation the change in the contribution made by a single unit as a result of a change in state is defined as the *energy gap* of the unit. Given symmetrical weights, the energy gap of a unit is the same as the net input to the unit. Thus if the net input exceeds 0, the energy gap is negative and the unit should be turned on. If the net input is less than 0, the energy gap is positive and the unit should be turned off. Thus, to minimize global energy we should turn a unit on only if the net input exceeds 0. This brings us back to the usual update rule for threshold units.

In fact Hopfield showed mathematically that if we continuously update unit states asynchronously in the described manner (i.e. put them in the 1 state if their energy gap is negative and the 0 state otherwise) we will locally minimize the global energy of the network, i.e. we will reach a situation in which the unit states are (locally) maximally compatible. He also showed that in normal circumstances it is advisable to update the unit states in a random fashion, but demonstrated that the actual order in which updates are carried out does not matter provided that no unit is ignored for more than a finite time.

This network mechanism is, of course, a gradient descent method. And like all gradient descent methods it is liable to get stuck in local minima. However, Hopfield has shown how the problem of local minima can be alleviated to some degree by modifying the mechanism so as to deal with units with graded (i.e. real-valued) activation levels. This ensures that the energy surface has a potentially infinite number of points and the chances of encountering a local minimum are somewhat reduced.

19.8. Using Hopfield nets as content-addressable memories

As mentioned above, Hopfield was interested in the way in which networks can behave as content-addressable memories. He wanted to know how to configure the weights of a network of binary threshold units so as to make the network store a given set of binary vectors. The sort of network that he wanted to construct was one that would store vectors in such a way as to be able to reproduce a complete vector given only some portion of it as input. A network that behaves this way has to be able to 'fill in the gaps' in the input vector. That is to say, if some of its units are set into states representing relevant components of the input vector, the network must move towards a situation in which the states of the remaining units represent the remaining components.

Hopfield showed that to achieve maximum storage performance the weights of the network have to be arranged so as to ensure that the relevant vectors correspond to minimum energy states of the network. Moreover, he showed that in order to achieve this we have to set each weight to a specific value. This is derived from an inspection of the components of the relevant vectors. The weight between the ith and the jth unit must be set equal to:

$$\sum_{ij} (2 V_i - 1)(2 V_j - 1)$$

This effectively sets the weights so as to reflect the cross-correlation between the vector components. Unfortunately, the maximum storage performance of the Hopfield net is relatively poor. It is capable of storing no more than about $0.14n$ vectors where n is the number of units in the network.

19.8.1. Example

Let us finish by looking at a simple application of a Hopfield net. Imagine that we would like to construct a network that stores the following five binary vectors in such a fashion that we can retrieve one of the vectors by specifying some of its components:

```
[1 1 1 0 1 0 1 0 0 0 1 0 0 1 1 1 1 0 0 0 1 1 1 0 0 1 1 1 0 1 1 1 1]
[0 0 1 1 1 0 0 1 0 1 0 0 0 1 0 1 1 1 1 0 0 1 0 1 1 1 1 1 1 1 1 1 0]
[0 0 1 0 1 1 1 0 0 0 1 1 0 1 0 0 0 0 1 1 1 0 0 1 0 1 1 1 1 1 0 0 1]
[1 1 1 0 0 1 1 1 0 1 0 1 0 0 1 1 0 1 0 1 1 1 1 1 1 1 1 0 1 0 1 0 0]
[0 1 1 1 0 1 1 0 0 0 0 1 0 1 1 1 0 0 0 0 0 1 0 0 0 0 0 1 1 1 1 0 0]
```

Each vector has 33 components so we need to construct a fully connected network of 33 binary threshold units. Once we have done this we should set the weights using the formula above. We now present a highly incomplete version of input vector number 4. This vector has 1s in positions 1, 2 and 6 and 0s everywhere else. As we can see from the state vectors shown below, the network moves, in just a few iterations, towards a state that reconstitutes vector 4. The vectors show the state of the network over a sequence of five iterations.

Initial input vector:

```
[1 1 0 0 0 1 0 0 0 0 0 0 0 0 0 0 0 0 0 0 0 0 0 0 0 0 0 0 0 0 0 0 0]
```

Example 265

Sequence of states:

```
1: [1 1 1 0 0 1 1 0 0 0 0 1 0 0 1 1 0 0 0 1 1 1 1 0 0 0 0 0 0 0 1 0 0]
2: [1 1 1 0 0 1 1 0 0 0 0 1 0 0 1 1 0 0 0 1 1 1 1 0 0 1 1 0 1 0 1 0 0]
3: [1 1 1 0 0 1 1 0 0 0 0 1 0 0 1 1 0 0 0 1 1 1 1 1 0 1 1 0 1 0 1 0 0]
4: [1 1 1 0 0 1 1 1 0 1 0 1 0 0 1 1 0 1 0 1 1 1 1 1 1 1 1 0 1 0 1 0 0]
5: [1 1 1 0 0 1 1 1 0 1 0 1 0 0 1 1 0 1 0 1 1 1 1 1 1 1 1 0 1 0 1 0 0]
```

Note that the final state of the network is identical to input vector 4.

19.9. Comments

By using the relevant weight-derivation procedure we can obtain Hopfield nets that exhibit arbitrary patterns of activity (provided that we are working within the storage limitations of the network). This means that we can divide the network up into input and output units and use the storage procedure to obtain a set of weights that gives us an implementation of a target mapping. Of course, this is to treat the Hopfield net and its weight-derivation procedure as a learning mechanism. But we have to remember that it is conventionally viewed as a memory or constraint-optimization device.

Hopfield and Tank, for example, have used the Hopfield net as a way of looking for optimal solutions to the travelling salesman problem. In this problem the aim is to find the shortest possible tour that visits every one of n cities once. In the Hopfield and Tank method, the units in the network represent a particular city being visited at a particular point in the tour (first, second, third, etc.) and the energy of the network rises not only as a function of the average distance between adjacent cities on the tour but also if (1) a city is visited more than once and (2) two cities are visited at the same time. Low-energy states should therefore correspond to tours that are (1) feasible and (2) optimal. Unfortunately, the complexity of the energy function has an impact on the prevalence of local minima in the energy surface. This means that the Hopfield and Tank method is capable of producing non-optimal solutions.

19.10. Further reading

The original reference for Hopfield nets is Hopfield (1982) while the generalization that broadens the framework to cover real-valued activation values is Hopfield (1984). McClelland and Rumelhart (1988, Chapter 3) contains some excellent material on the Hopfield net, as does the textbook by Wasserman (1989). Wasserman also introduces Hopfield and Tank's method for using a Hopfield-like approach for solving the travelling salesman problem; see also Dayhoff (1990, pp. 52-55). Hinton

(1989, p. 192). discusses the convergence proof for Hopfield nets in more detail. For a classic introduction to the role of schemas in information processing see Minsky (1981). For the connectionist perspective on schemas see Rumelhart *et al.* (1986c). This latter reference also introduces the visualization technique used above.

19.11. Problems

(1)   What do weight values typically represent in the case where unit states represent hypotheses?

(2)   Invent an example where one would need to use a *structured* Hopfield net.

(3)   In what cases do the units in a Hopfield net work like grandmother cells?

(4)   In the case where units represent hypotheses and the weight between two units represents the degree to which the corresponding hypotheses support each other, we can derive the compatibility of two unit states by taking the product of their activation levels and the weight between them, e.g., by computing L_i $L_j W_{ij}$. Justify this strategy in the case where both units have negative levels of activation.

(5)   How would you go about hand-coding a Hopfield net to represent a set of schemas for a particular domain? Use an example to illustrate your answer.

(6)   How can we measure the compatibility of a set of unit states in a Hopfield net? How many formulae do we need to apply and why?

(7)   What is the relationship between compatibility, energy and goodness?

(8)   Why does Hopfield measure the mean state of a network in terms of *energy*?

(9)   What is the energy gap of a unit and how is it derived? What is the significance of the energy gap?

(10) What is the argument in favour of using graded activation values in Hopfield nets?

(11) What problems might arise if the units in a Hopfield net update their states syn-
chronously?

20

The Boltzmann machine

20.1. Introduction: a learning method for Hopfield nets

In the previous chapter we looked at Hopfield's technique for storing and accessing memories in networks and we noted how this technique could be used to handle ordinary learning problems. One of the main disadvantages of Hopfield's technique is the fact that, because of the way the weight-derivation (i.e. storage) procedure works, it cannot make use of hidden units. Hinton and Sejnowski have described an architecture called the *Boltzmann machine* with an associated learning procedure (the *Boltzmann learning procedure*) that overcomes this limitation. The Boltzmann machine takes its name from Ludvig Boltzmann who articulated some of the statistical principles upon which the machine is based. It is essentially a trainable generalization of the Hopfield net.

The learning procedure for the Boltzmann machine is a supervised method although it can be used for unsupervised learning, too. It involves training the network to produce behaviour by providing it with examples. As usual, the network is assumed to have been configured with some units allocated as input units, some units allocated as output units and possibly some units allocated as hidden units as well. The presentation of an example involves clamping an input vector on to the input units and the desired output vector for that input on to the output units. The learning is obtained by reinforcing those patterns of activity in the network that are likely to assist the network in producing the desired output when only the *input* is presented, i.e. in *re*producing the desired behaviour.

In practice, the training regime involves reinforcing the weights on links between units that tend to be active simultaneously. It is therefore a descendant of the *Hebbian* learning procedure.[1] Unfortunately, the implementation of this simple idea (in the Boltzmann machine) turns out to be a fairly complicated procedure involving the computation of simultaneity statistics while the network is running at an energy level known as *thermal equilibrium*. On the other hand, there exists a formal proof that the learning procedure is guaranteed to produce a satisfactory set of weights, provided that one exists.

20.2. Escaping local minima by annealing

Before describing the learning procedure we should introduce a method that is employed in the Boltzmann machine for avoiding local minima. The approach used relies on the idea that Hopfield-type networks get stuck in local minima for the simple reason that they always try to move downhill! To escape from a local minimum it is essential to move *uphill*. Therefore, in order to avoid the problem of local minima within a gradient descent process, it is essential for the process to make occasional uphill jumps. The problem is, when should the process make the uphill jump? If its uphill jumps are made very infrequently then it is unlikely to jump out of a local minimum. On the other hand, if it makes frequent uphill jumps then it is likely to jump out of the global minimum back into a local minimum.

To gain an insight into this problem, imagine that you are holding up a surface with various bumps (maxima) and holes (minima). A small ball-bearing is placed on the surface and your goal is to get it into the deepest hole (global minimum). The ball-bearing tends to roll down into the nearest hole (local minimum) rather than the deepest hole. A simple way to counteract this is to shake the tray up and down. Initially, of course, you must shake the tray quite strongly but then, as the ball-bearing draws nearer to the global minimum, you should shake it more gently so as to tease the ball-bearing into the desired position (see Figure 20.1).

This idea of applying decreasing amounts of shaking to a bumpy surface leads directly to a method for escaping local minima in gradient descent processes. Obviously, we cannot easily arrange for an energy surface to shake up and down. However, we can arrange for this process to exhibit a decreasing tendency to make an arbitrary, uphill jump. And this achieves exactly the same effect. The approach is, in fact, a computational analogue of an industrial process called *annealing*. It is there-

---

[1] As we have noted, Hebb proposed the idea that learning in biological neural networks was achieved through the modification of synaptic junctions in accordance with the degree of correspondence between pre- and post-synaptic activations.

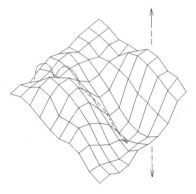

Figure 20.1. Visual representation of annealing.

fore called *simulated annealing* (Kirkpatrick *et al.*, 1983).[2]

In order to see how simulated annealing is used in the Boltzmann machine we have to think about the way in which units are set into new states. Normally, units in the Boltzmann machine behave like units in the Hopfield net. This means that their states are updated so as to reduce the global energy. A reduction in global energy corresponds to a downhill jump in the gradient descent. Thus, in order to obtain an uphill jump we need to be able to set units into the wrong state, i.e. a state with a higher global energy. Furthermore, in order to be able to vary the tendency to make uphill jumps, we have to be able to vary the probability of putting a unit into the wrong state.

In the Boltzmann machine, unit states are set by applying the squashing function to the net input to the unit. However, instead of treating the value of the squashing function as the next activation level of the unit, we treat the value as a probability that the unit should be turned on (i.e. set to have an activation level of 1). The great advantage of this is that it makes it easy to modulate the probability of setting the unit into the correct state.

---

[2] Annealing is used in the manufacture of some solid materials with the aim of minimizing the introduction of flaws. Basically, it involves applying a slow cooling schedule to the material during casting. This slow-cooling enables the atoms in the material to settle down into a stable configuration.

If the net input to a unit is greater than 0, the value of the squashing function will be greater than 0.5. A simple threshold unit would respond to a net input greater than 0.5 by turning on. But, under the Boltzmann arrangement, the unit responds by turning on with a probability that is related to the size of the net input.[3] A large net input will ensure that the probability of turning on is very close to 1. A small net input will ensure that the probability of turning on is close to 0.

Since the unit is only turned on (or off) with a certain probability there is always a non-zero probability of setting it into the wrong state. Other things being equal, the chances of setting a unit into the wrong state depend on the shape of the squashing function. If the function has a shape that is very close to a step function, then net inputs that are above threshold will evoke probabilities (for turning on) very close to 1. If the function is nearly linear then net inputs that are above threshold will not necessarily evoke a strong probability for turning on. The general conclusion is that we can vary the probability of putting a unit into the wrong state by varying the shape of the squashing function. And, it turns out, we can do this by introducing a single parameter into the formula. This parameter is normally called the *temperature* parameter in reference to the physical analogy being exploited. The modified formula is as follows:

$$\frac{1}{1 + e^{-n/t}}$$

where n is the net input, t is the temperature, and e is the exponential constant. Values of the temperature parameter are positive real numbers. By making the temperature value larger we make the behaviour of the function increasingly linear. This effect is demonstrated in Figure 20.2.

The general effect is that, with high temperatures, the probability of doing the right thing tends to be relatively low and thus the probability of making an uphill move in energy is relatively high. With low temperatures we have the opposite situation. The probability of making an uphill move is very small. Thus, to implement simulated annealing all we must do is arrange for the temperature parameter to be gradually reduced as the gradient descent process proceeds.

---

[3] This effect is most easily implemented by comparing a random number in the range 0-1 against the probability value. The probability of the random number being less than or equal to the probability value is just the probability value itself. Thus, if the probability is equal to or exceeds the value the unit should be turned on. Otherwise it should be turned off.

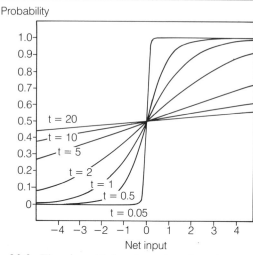

Figure 20.2. The sigmoid function at various temperatures.

20.3. Thermal equilibrium

The fact that the activation function is stochastic means that even at a mean energy minimum, the network will not be static. Units will change their states as a result of purely random influences. However, if the *probability* of finding a unit in a particular state remains fixed then the network is in a stable state. This situation is called *thermal equilibrium*.

At thermal equilibrium, the chances of the network being in a particular state (i.e. of the units having particular levels of activation) is related to that state's energy. If we look at two particular states called i and j, then we find that the ratio between the probability of the network being in state i and the probability of it being in state j depends solely on their energy difference. The formula that gives the probability ratio is as follows:

$$P_i / P_j = e^{-(E_i - E_j)/t}$$

P_i is the probability of the state i, P_j is the probability of state j, E_i is the energy of state i and E_j is the energy of state j,[4] and t is the temperature. The distribution that we obtain if we map out the probabilities of a given state (holding other values constant) is the *Boltzmann distribution*.

20.4. The Boltzmann machine learning procedure

Recall that in the simplest form of Hebbian learning we systematically increase weights between units that are frequently simultaneously active, and decrease weights between all other pairs. The result is that units that are often simultaneously active will tend to turn each other on. The general consequence is that the network will tend to exhibit certain characteristic patterns of activation.

This simple Hebbian notion is the basis of what is known as the *Boltzmann machine learning procedure*. This assumes that the network is made up of a set of input units and a set of output units and an optional set of hidden units. It makes no assumptions about connectivity but most commonly the network is fully interconnected. The basic steps in the learning procedure are as follows:

Boltzmann learning procedure

Repeatedly apply the following four steps to each pair in the training set.

(1)   Clamp the input vector on to the input units, i.e. fix the activations of the input units according to the components of the input vector.

(2)   Clamp the target vector on to the output units, i.e. fix the activations of the output units according to the components of the target vector.

(3)   Let the network run to thermal equilibrium.

(4)   Update weights using the Hebbian strategy (see below).

Note the essential difference between this procedure and the more familiar error-reduction strategy. In error-reduction learning we compare the actual outputs against the target outputs. In this procedure we fix the activation levels of the output units according to the target vector.

---

[4] The definition of global energy here is the same as for the Hopfield net (see Chapter 19) except for the addition of a bias term.

In order to ensure that the Hebbian learning will be effective, we have to apply it in a certain way. In particular, when working out by how much to change a weight, it is not enough to merely observe how often the two connected units are simultaneously active. We have to work out what the difference is between

- the probability that the two units are active when clamping is in effect, and

- the probability that the two units are both active when only the input units are clamped.

The phase in which clamping at both ends is in effect is called phase$^+$. The phase in which only the input units are clamped is called phase$^-$. The weight between the two units should then be incremented by a small proportion (given by the learning rate) of the difference between the two probabilities. In effect, the weight between the two units is increased only if they tend to be simultaneously active more often when clamping is in effect than otherwise.

It is important to note that although the presentation of training pairs is done in a way that makes a clean distinction between input and output, the learning algorithm itself makes no such distinction. It simply faces a situation in which some units are clamped and some units are unclamped. Its effective aim is to change weights so that, in normal running, the network will tend to exhibit the clamped pattern of activation. Once it has achieved this, clamping some subset of units into a particular pattern will tend to cause the network to exhibit the complete pattern. Thus, if a target output is 'presented' then the network should reproduce the corresponding input vector.

To summarize, when we train a network using the Boltzmann learning procedure, we are teaching the network to produce certain characteristic patterns of activation. Technically, since units behave stochastically, we are training the network to exhibit a particular probability distribution of states given fixed activations for certain units. If we are operating an ordinary supervised learning procedure, then we will construe the network as learning to implement an input/output mapping. But this is simply a conceptual convenience.

20.5. Asymmetric divergence

Can we be sure that the Hebbian learning regime will work? In fact there is a way of measuring how well the mechanism has learned to implement a particular probability distribution and, more importantly, a way of using the measure to demonstrate that a broadly Hebbian learning procedure will necessarily improve the network's performance. The measure in question quantifies the degree to which the probability distribution of the states of the visible units (i.e. the ones that can be clamped) implemented by the network differs from the desired one; i.e. the one achieved with clamping in effect. It is therefore something like a measure of how badly the network is doing, i.e. an error measure. The measure is called the *asymmetric divergence*, *information gain* or just G. The formula for G is as follows:

$$G = \sum_i P(V_i) \ln \left(P(V_i) / P'(V_i) \right)$$

where $P(V_i)$ is the probability of the *i*th state of the visible units when they are clamped and $P'(V_i)$ is the probability of the *i*th state of the visible units when they are not clamped.

Provided that (1) probability statistics are collected with the network running at thermal equilibrium, and (2) the learning rate is sufficiently small, updating weights using the Boltzmann learning procedure performs gradient descent in G, i.e. it ensures that the network gradually moves towards a configuration in which it produces the desired behaviour.

As in the case of back-propagation, the fact that the learning procedure performs gradient descent means that it can get stuck in local minima. Of course, simulated annealing is also a gradient descent process. So this means that the Boltzmann machine performs two different types of gradient descent and can therefore get stuck in two different types of local minima. During normal running it performs gradient descent in mean energy and can get stuck in energy minimum.[5] During learning it performs gradient descent in G and can therefore get stuck in information-gain minima.

20.6. Solving the 4-2-4 encoder problem

A simple example that is often used to demonstrate the learning capabilities of the Boltzmann machine is the so-called *4-2-4 encoder problem*. This is a supervised learning problem that, on the face of it, looks quite straightforward. The training set is as follows:

---

[5] Simulated annealing provably eliminates this risk provided that it is slow enough.

```
<[1 0 0 0]   [1 0 0 0]>
<[0 1 0 0]   [0 1 0 0]>
<[0 0 1 0]   [0 0 1 0]>
<[0 0 0 1]   [0 0 0 1]>
```

The problem is to implement an identity mapping involving 4-dimensional binary vectors (i.e. it involves mapping vectors on to themselves). Each vector has a single 1 and three zeros. Furthermore, the 1 appears in a different position in each case.

The problem seems quite easy; but we can make it harder by forcing the learning mechanism to implement the mapping in a certain way. We can do this by configuring the network so that a layer of four input units that are all connected together connect with a layer of two hidden units, that in turn connects with a layer of four output units, again all connected together. A network of this form is shown in Figure 20.3. For clarity we have omitted the within-layer connections.

This way of configuring the network makes the problem harder. Any network that implements the mapping must be able to tell the output units which of the four different output vectors to produce. But since the only information that arrives at the output units is derived from the two units in the middle layer we know that this information has to be encoded using a two-component activation vector.

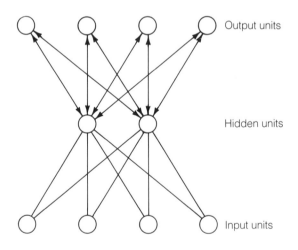

Figure 20.3. A 4-2-4 network.

Now in the case of the Boltzmann machine units can only take one of two different activation values. This means that there are only four possible activation vectors for the middle layer ([0 0], [1 0], [0 1] and [1 1]). Since there are four distinct output vectors we can see that there is exactly one possible code for each. To implement this mapping the machine must necessarily learn to use these particular hidden-vector encodings. The Boltzmann machine can, in fact, solve this problem quite reliably, although it can take a surprisingly large number of training epochs to do so.

20.7. Noisy clamping and weight decay

To get the Boltzmann machine to solve this learning problem we have to add an extra wrinkle to the learning procedure. Note that the mapping only involves four of the 16 possible input/output vectors one could have. This means that in solving the problem, the Boltzmann machine has to try to prevent 12 distinct output vectors from being exhibited by the output units. Now because the activation function is probabilistic, the only way it can do this is by making the probabilities of these vectors 0. And this involves producing weights that are infinitely large (and negative).

Clearly, the mechanism cannot produce infinitely large weights so we somehow have to stop it from *trying* to do so. There are various possibilities. We could, for example, introduce what is known as *weight decay*. This simply involves reducing each weight by some small amount in each iteration. Another possibility is to use what is known as *noisy clamping*. In this approach we make deliberate mistakes when clamping input and output vectors — sometimes clamping on a unit that should be clamped off, sometimes clamping off a unit that should be on. This way the probability of any vector that does not appear in the training set is very low but not zero, and therefore the tendency for the weights to grow infinitely large is reduced.

20.7.1. Epoch 1

Let us now look at the way in which the mechanism tries to solve the 4-2-4 encoder problem, i.e. tries to implement the mapping (training set) shown above in a network containing four input units, four output units, and a communication channel of two hidden units. The groups of input and output units are connected among themselves, i.e. each input (output) unit has a connection to every other input (output) unit; see the Hinton diagram shown in Figure 20.4.

If we run the network we find that at the end of epoch 1 all the weights have been set to negative values. This is due to the fact that the input/output vectors mainly contain 0s. When the network is running free, the states of the units are randomly initialized.

This means that an arbitrary input/output unit has a better chance of being on when the network is running free than when units are clamped. This, in turn, means that co-occurrence probabilities will typically be higher in phase⁻ than in phase⁺ and that weights will therefore tend to be decreased.

20.7.2. Epoch 7

By epoch 7 the mechanism has 'discovered' that since input/output vectors only ever have one non-zero component, quite good results (i.e. quite low-energy states) can be achieved simply by making all the input/output units inhibit each other strongly. This way, if one input unit comes on (in phase⁻) it will tend to turn all the other input units off, thus producing a pattern of activation identical to one of the input vectors. (Similar remarks apply to output vectors and units.)

A Hinton diagram of the weights observed at epoch 7 appears in Figure 20.4. Note the strong negative weights between the input units. Unfortunately, the results obtained this way are good only in the sense that they lead to the network being in

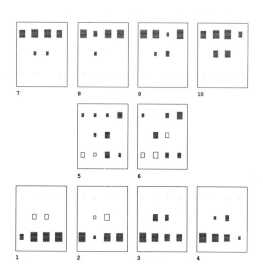

Figure 20.4. Early receptive fields in 4-2-4 encoder network.

low-energy states. They are not good in the sense that they enable the network to implement the target mapping. The behaviour of the network tends to produce the wrong output vector in most cases, as the following listing shows. This shows the input, target, and actual output vectors for each training pair:

```
input  [1 0 0 0]
target [1 0 0 0]
output [0 1 0 0]

input  [0 1 0 0]
target [0 1 0 0]
output [0 0 0 0]

input  [0 0 1 0]
target [0 0 1 0]
output [0 0 1 1]

input  [0 0 0 1]
target [0 0 0 1]
output [0 0 0 0]
```

20.7.3. Epoch 200

By epoch 200 the mechanism has produced the required pattern of weight values for the production of sensible hidden-vector encodings. This can be seen in the Hinton diagram shown in Figure 20.5.[6] Note that in the state shown, each input unit has a distinct pattern of weights on the links to the middle layer. These patterns form codes. Unit 1's weights represent the code <+,->, unit 2's represent the code <-,+>, unit 3's represent the code <+,+> and unit 4's the code <-,->. Each of these four codes corresponds to one of the four possible hidden vectors: [1 0], [0 1], [1 1] and [0 0]. Since, in the training set, only one input unit gets turned on in any iteration, there is always only one input unit that has any activation to encode! Therefore we get a single, hidden-vector encoding for each distinct input vector. The weights to the output units from the middle units are symmetrical and therefore 'decode' the hidden-vector encoding in the appropriate way.

Unfortunately, although the network has already discovered the required pattern of weight signs, the *sizes* of the weights are still insufficient to produce perfect encoding/decoding. The intra-layer weights and the randomness inherent in the activation function are — in combination — still having too great an influence on unit states. Thus the network still produces poor performance on the target mapping. We can see this in the listing below (which shows the network's performance at

---

[6] The sizes of the boxes are logarithmically related to weights in this diagram.

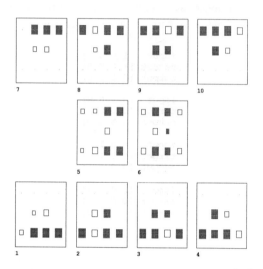

Figure 20.5. Satisfactory receptive fields in 4-2-4 encoder network.

epoch 200). The network produces the desired output in only one case out of four; therefore the error rate at this point is 75%: In order to get good performance the mechanism not only has to discover the right encoding, it also has to make the relevant weights large enough to outweight all other relevant factors. In the state shown above, the weights are too small to do this. However, with a sufficient amount of training, perfect performance can be achieved.[7]

---

[7] Ackley *et al.* (1985) report that in one case it took 1810 epochs to obtain perfect performance on this problem.

```
input   [1 0 0 0]
target  [1 0 0 0]
output  [0 0 0 1]

input   [0 1 0 0]
target  [0 1 0 0]
output  [0 1 0 0]

input   [0 0 1 0]
target  [0 0 1 0]
output  [0 1 0 0]

input   [0 0 0 1]
target  [0 0 0 1]
output  [1 0 0 0]
```

20.8. Comments

One of the advantages of the Boltzmann machine is the fact that the learning algorithm only uses locally available information. Each connection weight is updated from data derived from the activations of the units at either end of the connection. The update procedure does not require the provision of a mean error signal. Nor does it involve structured propagation of error signals throughout the network. This means that it forms a more plausible model for learning in biological neural networks. It also means that the algorithm may be well suited to a hardware implementation.

Against these advantages we have to set the fact that the Boltzmann machine is excessively slow in learning even on quite trivial problems. This speed problem is less of an issue now that more efficient variants of the Boltzmann machine learning procedure are available (see Section 20.9) but unfortunately it has not disappeared completely.

20.9. Further reading

The most accessible account of the Boltzmann machine is Hinton and Sejnowski (1986). An early exposition is Ackley *et al.* (1985). This also provides further details on the question of why probabilities of mean states are related to energy differences and discusses the derivation of the information gain measure. Smolensky (1986) presents a scheme that is very closely related to the Boltzmann machine, while Hinton *et al.* (1984) provide a more detailed account of the encoder experiments. A textbook providing a mathematical treatment of Boltzmann machines is Aarts and Korst (1989).

Recently, Peterson and Anderson have described a *Mean Field Theory Learning Algorithm* for neural networks that provides what is, in effect, a deterministic learning algorithm for the Boltzmann machine. The algorithm is substantially faster than the Boltzmann learning algorithm (Hinton, 1989) but still too slow for many purposes. See Peterson and Hartman (1989) for further information on the general performance of this algorithm.

20.10. Problems

(1)   What is Hebbian learning and how is it implemented in the Boltzmann machine?

(2)   What is the relationship between the Boltzmann machine and the Hopfield net?

(3)   What is physical annealing used for?

(4)   What is simulated annealing, what problem is it intended to reduce and how is it implemented in the Boltzmann machine?

(5)   What role does the temperature parameter play in the implementation of the Boltzmann machine?

(6)   How is temperature used to implement the stochastic activation function?

(7)   How should one change the temperature parameter to make the squashing function behave more like a threshold function?

(8)   What does it mean to say that a network is in a state of 'thermal equilibrium'?

(9)   What are the main differences between the Boltzmann learning procedure and the error-reduction learning procedure?

(10)   Why is it not possible to use error-reduction learning in a network where the units are totally interconnected?

(11)   How can we use the Boltzmann learning procedure to train a network to implement an input/output mapping and how can we train it so that when given part of a pattern as input, it completes the pattern?

(12) In what situation would we want to compute the asymmetric divergence of two probability distributions?

(13) How would one configure a Boltzmann machine for the problem of learning to form a binary encoding of the integers in the range 1-5? What would the training set be and how would one initialize links and weight values?

(14) Why might one use weight decay with the Boltzmann machine? In what circumstances might it be better to use noisy clamping?

(15) What is the initial behaviour of the Boltzmann machine learning procedure when applied to the 4-2-4 encoder problem and why?

(16) Continuing with the 4-2-4 encoder scenario: in the case where two input units form the same codes (i.e. the same pattern of weights to the units in the middle layer) the weight on the link between the units is likely to change in a particular way. How will it change and why?

(17) As we noted in Chapter 9, Karl Lashley (1929, p. 3) thought that his equipotentiality results were incompatible with 'theories of learning by changes in synaptic structure'. Do you think it is possible to accommodate this conclusion within the model of learning provided by the Boltzmann machine learning algorithm?

21

Discussion

21.1. Introduction: family likenesses among learning algorithms

One thing that should have become abundantly clear during the course of the book is the fact that the variety of learning procedures is extremely wide. The existence of this variety reminds us that, as yet, there is no 'grand unified' model of computational learning. Rather there are several species and subspecies. So what should we make of this diversity? Does it indicate that we are still tentatively exploring our way around the fringes of a satisfactory theory of learning or does it simply mean that there are many different ways of learning things and therefore many different computational implementations of the process?

The latter position is attractively neutral but perhaps not completely viable. To begin with it raises several worries; e.g., how do we know whether we have discovered all, some, or just a very few of the possible methods of learning? And how should we decide which particular learning goes best with which particular type of learning problem? But more importantly, it doesn't seem to take proper account of the very strong commonalities that exist between the various different learning algorithms.

We noted early on that many of the learning mechanisms we would look at were related in the sense that they all tried to exploit similarity in the input data. This common thread — which was particularly noticeable when we were looking at the *empirical*, symbolic methods such as focussing, ID3 and conceptual clustering — became slightly lost when we turned to connectionist methods such as back-propagation and the Hopfield net. However, it was still there lurking just under the surface.

To get a feel for the commonality between symbolic and connectionist methods we need to jump up a level and talk about the exploitation of *statistical probabilities* rather than the exploitation of similarities. Let us begin by looking at the behaviour of a fairly standard symbolic method such as ID3. Recall that ID3 looks at the input data and attempts to build a decision tree on the basis of attribute-value patterns. For example, if ID3 comes across an attribute value v which is exhibited by every member of class X but no member of any other class then ID3 realises that v is an excellent basis on which to differentiate class X from other classes.

In statistical terms, what ID3 is doing here is picking up on the fact that the *conditional probability* that an input which exhibits v is in class X is 1 whereas the conditional probability that an input which does not exhibit v is in class X is 0. In broader terms, ID3 is discovering statistical regularities in the training set, i.e. probability relationships between particular configurations of inputs values and particular target output values. [1]

Seeing the behaviour of ID3 in these statistical terms makes it much easier to grasp the relationship it has with connectionist methods such as the perceptron learning algorithm. Recall that in the PLA the aim of the learning is to modify the weights between the input units and the output unit so that the output unit only comes on for inputs in one of exactly two classes. Continuing to let X stand for the class we are interested in, we note that if all the inputs in X have a 1 in a particular position but none of the other inputs do, then the PLA will continually increase the weight to the input unit in that position. Moreover, assuming that all weights are started at 0, we know that the weight in question will be at least as large as any other weight in the network.

Once again, the learning is exploiting the fact that there is a strong statistical relationship between the presence of a 1 in a particular position of the input vector and the likelihood of the input being in class X. Thus, in a sense, PLA learning seems to be doing the same thing as ID3 learning. Of course, the way in which ID3 captures statistical regularities is quite different from the way in which the PLA captures it. But nevertheless, the essential similarity of the two methods is plain to see.

What about other learning methods? The Hopfield net and Boltzmann machine would not seem to be very closely related with symbolic algorithms such as ID3. And yet if we focus on the learning rule used in the Boltzmann machine we see that its essential aim is to set the weight between any two units so as to reflect the probability that they will be in the same state.[2] If, for simplicity, we consider a Boltzmann machine with no hidden units, then we see that the learning functions solely to try to capture statistical relationships between input components and output components (i.e. input-unit activations and output-unit activations) in the form of weights. Very similar

---

[1] The specified conditional probabilities only hold under the closed-world assumption.

[2] This, of course, is precisely the idea behind the mean-field theory approximation for Boltzmann machine learning.

arguments can be applied to any form of Hebbian learning rule.

On the symbolic side of the coin we might be quite happy to accept that ID3 learning is essentially a statistics-exploiting method but we may be worried about making a similar assumption for focussing or explanation-based generalization. But consider the way in which focussing works. In deriving a version-space representation by manipulating upper and lower marks in generalization hierarchies, it is essentially using the information encapsulated in the hypothesis space to make sensible assumptions about which attribute values are likely to be shared by members of the same input class (e.g., 'bike', 'moped' and 'car' are more likely to be shared than 'bike', 'moped' and 'jet'.) Thus the ultimate aim in focussing is the same as in ID3: to discover a representation of the ways in which attribute values predict class membership, i.e. to discover informative probabilities between input values and output values.

With explanation-based generalization the story becomes a little more tortuous. And yet it still goes through. An EBG learner's basic aim is to discover how an instance can be explained by a particular domain theory. By looking at the particular attribute values which are involved in the explanation, the learner is able to form a new definition of the goal concept which *emphasizes* those attribute values. Here the detection of an informative statistical relationship between configurations of attribute values and outputs is indirect. The domain theory effectively encapsulates knowledge about attribute salience. Thus in deriving an explanation in terms of the domain theory, the learner is able to discover which attributes are salient (as predictors of the output) and which are not. The learner does not discover these statistical properties directly. Rather it reifies the statistical information which is embedded in the domain theory.

We see, then, that the harder we look at the 'guts' of the various learning mechanisms, the more it seems that they all use roughly the same strategy. They try to discover which aspects of the inputs can serve to predict the target output, i.e. where the input/output conditional probability relationships are most informative. At first sight this may seem a somewhat startling conclusion. It seems to suggest that the whole gamut of learning algorithms reduces to a single computational model of induction. And — even more unpalatable! — that that model is a *statistical* one. It also raises the difficult question of why — if all learners are following essentially the same strategy — we have so many learning mechanisms.

In fact the latter question at least can be answered satisfactorily. We simply have to think about the way in which different learners are suited to different types of learning problem. It seems fairly clear that symbolic learners are best suited to problems which are stated in terms of symbolic input values, while connectionist learners are better suited to problems which are stated in terms of numeric input values. Similarly, at a more fine-grained level of description, we would say that the Kohonen net is well suited to problems which involve the formation of topographic maps, while ID3 is better suited to problems which can be solved by detecting common attribute values. And so on. As for the question of how many fundamental models of induction can be derived from the current plethora of learning algorithms, there is very little to say at present. We simply do not yet have a sufficiently rich theoretical comprehension of the process to enable a rational answer.

21.2. Higher-order learning problems

Despite everything that has been said in the previous section, it seems rather clear from the intuitive point of view that learning cannot *simply* be a matter of discovering statistical regularities (i.e. informative conditional probabilities). But if this is true, it should be possible to find examples of learning tasks which cannot be satisfactorily performed by statistically oriented algorithms. Can we find any such problems?

Let us look at a learning problem which seems as if it should be quite easily solved by any reasonably powerful learning algorithm. The task is to learn to discriminate between rectangular and non-rectangular configurations of points in a visual array. Positive and negative examples of the concept of 'rectangular-configuration' are shown as images in Figure 21.1. Positive examples appear in the top half of the figure. Negative examples appear in the bottom half.

We will look at the way in which three different connectionist algorithms deal with this problem, namely the *back-propagation* algorithm Rumelhart *et al.* (1986b); a powerful 'second-order' variant of back-propagation called *quickprop* (Fahlman and Lebiere, 1990); and the constructive algorithm *cascade-correlation* (Fahlman and Lebiere, 1990). We will present the algorithms with input images represented as vectors of eight coordinate values (i.e. four pairs of coordinate values representing four distinct points). This means that the networks will have eight input units and a single output unit. To rule out the possibility of using an inappropriate internal architecture we examine the performance obtained with a whole range of architectures and a range of different settings for the learning parameters.

The general form of the behaviour obtained from the algorithms is shown in the graphs in Figure 21.2. These were produced using parameter settings (and in the case of quickprop and back-propagation, a number of hidden units) which the trial-and-error experiments had shown to be optimal. Both graphs show training runs over 100000 epochs with back-propagation (bp), quickprop (qp) and cascade-correlation (cc). The upper graph shows mean error rates on the testing set at each epoch, while the lower graph shows mean error rates on the training set.

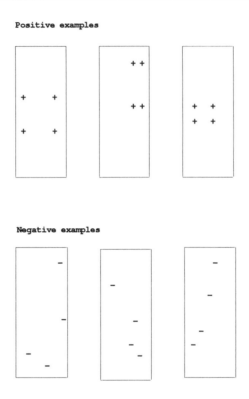

Figure 21.1. Training examples for the 'rectangles' problem.

One can see immediately that although all three algorithms (and particularly cascade-correlation) achieve good performance on the training set, none of them achieve satisfactory generalization on the testing set. In fact, the generalization performance of quickprop and cascade-correlation is maximally bad in this example. One way to explain the very bad performance of these network algorithms on this particular problem is by showing that the target mapping (as represented by the training set) exhibits very little statistical regularity. The statistics of the training set are effectively 'neutral' in this example: the training pairs yield up no informative conditional probabilities.

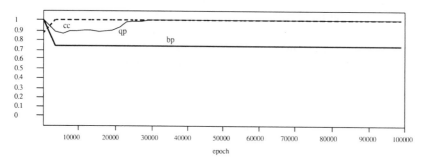

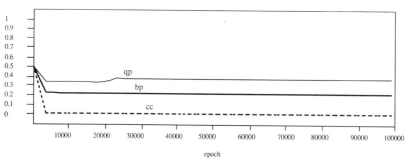

Figure 21.2. Error profiles for the 'rectangles' problem.

We can show this formally by looking at the various different orders of statistics associated with the training set. The first-order statistical properties of a target mapping between n-dimensional input vectors and m-dimensional output vectors can be derived from the relative frequencies with which certain input values are associated with certain output values. For example, if an input vector which has a 0.5 in its first position is always mapped on to an output vector with a 0 in its first position then we have a conditional probability of 1 (with respect to the mapping) of seeing a 0 as first output value given an input with 0.5 in the first position. The second- (nth-) order statistical properties of the mapping are just the relative frequencies (expressed as conditional probabilities) of seeing certain output values given combinations of 2 (n) input values.

Now clearly, in the rectangles mapping we should not expect to find any significant statistical properties of any order less than n (where n is the length of the input vectors). A particular input value or a proper subset of input values from a given input vector tells us nothing whatsoever about what the output should be. A given input vector represents a rectangle of points only if all the relationships between all the input values have a particular form. Putting it another way, whether or not an image contains a rectangular configuration of points depends on *relative* input values, not on absolute input values. Since the statistical properties of the mapping depend largely on absolute input values we can see that the mapping itself is unlikely to have any informative statistical properties.[3]

The conditional probabilities derived from a mapping which exhibits no statistical properties will *ceteris paribus* all be close to the chance level. We describe this situation by saying that the statistics of the training set are *neutral*. Other things being equal, a training set exhibiting neutral statistics will be very hard for any statistically-oriented learner to deal with.

21.3. ID3 failure

It is important to see that statistical neutrality is not just a problem for connectionist learners. We can show, for example, that it is also a problem for ID3 using the following example. Consider this training set:

```
<[diesel      car]    [yes]>
<[parafin     train]  [no]>
<[petrol      plane]  [yes]>
<[two-stroke  moped]  [no]>
<[parafin     moped]  [yes]>
<[petrol      bike]   [no]>
<[elec        train]  [yes]>
<[diesel      plane]  [no]>
```

Here, the instances are made up of a fuel attribute and a vehicle-type attribute. We can think of them as simple descriptions for imaginary vehicles. If we apply ID3 to this problem we obtain the decision tree and rules shown in Figure 21.3. The rules

---

[3] In fact there may be spurious statistical properties as a result of the fact that rectangular configurations can only appear in the image in certain ways, e.g., the upper points of a rectangle cannot appear in the lowest pixels of the image.

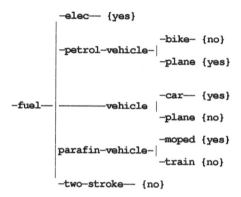

Figure 21.3. Decision tree produced by ID3 for 'vehicles' problem.

derived from the decision tree are as follows:

IF `fuel` = `two–stroke` THEN [no]
IF `fuel` = `elec` THEN [yes]
IF `fuel` = `parafin` AND `vehicle` = `train` THEN [no]
IF `fuel` = `parafin` AND `vehicle` = `moped` THEN [yes]
IF `fuel` = `diesel` AND `vehicle` = `plane` THEN [no]
IF `fuel` = `diesel` AND `vehicle` = `car` THEN [yes]
IF `fuel` = `petrol` AND `vehicle` = `plane` THEN [yes]
IF `fuel` = `petrol` AND `vehicle` = `bike` THEN [no]

The performance here is very poor: the list of decision rules effectively reproduces the entire training set. It is essentially a lookup table. If we draw out the training set geometrically we can see that we have a kind of worst-case scenario for ID3. In Figure 21.4 we have concatenated the usual positive and negative signs with the index number of the relevant training pair. Note that no positive shares any attribute value with any other positive. This means that ID3 cannot form a representation for the positive class in terms of shared attribute values.

One might argue that there is no plausible rule underlying the training set and that therefore the learning problem is unsolvable. However, this is not the case. The concept underlying the training set can be summarized by saying that positive instances are cases which describe an efficient but infrequently observed fuel-usage. [diesel

car	bike	moped	plane	train	
	6–		3+		petrol
1+			8–		diesel
		4–			two-stroke
		5+		2–	parafin
				7+	elec.

Figure 21.4. Distribution of instances in 'vehicles' problem.

car] is a case in point: one comes across cars running on diesel fairly infrequently even though diesel fuel can be a very efficient source of power for small motor vehicles.

The reason why ID3 has no hope of discovering this particular regularity is that it is not reflected in the first-order statistics of the training set. Once again, isolated absolute values are worthless as predictors of output. Therefore the first-order conditional probabilities are effectively neutral. ID3 is affected by this situation just as badly as our connectionist learners in the previous example.

21.4. Statistics, statistics and statistics

We seem to be arriving at a kind of paradox. Training sets such as the ones we have looked at above which have neutral first-order statistics would appear to be necessarily unlearnable. And yet, in both the cases that we looked at there is a clear and easily understood regularity underlying the target mapping. It seems that there are forms of regularity which are not statistically comprehensible in the ordinary sense.

We can make this point clearer by modifying the previous learning problem a little. Imagine that we redescribe the instances in terms of two functions. The first function takes an instance and returns a real number between 0 and 1 indicating the likeliness of the fuel for the given vehicle, and the second function takes an instance and returns a number indicating the potential efficiency of the fuel usage. If we draw out the feature space defined by these functions and superimpose points corresponding to the various positive and negative instances in the training set (using the usual conventions) we obtain the diagram shown in Figure 21.5. Note how all the positives are clustered together in a particular region of this feature space. What the clustering tells us is that the positive instances are all rather similar when viewed from this perspective even though they are very dissimilar when viewed as basic instances.

Similarities of this sort mean informative conditional probabilities. If we apply a coarse-grained discretization to the space it is quite likely that all the positives are going to share a single value of the potential-efficiency function and a single value of the frequency-of-fuel-usage function. Thus the conditional probabilities of the target output being positive given an input that has one (or both) of these two values will be high.

Of course being able to exploit these higher-level statistics means being able to construct the right feature space in the first place. And all the signs are this is a very hard problem. Let us think about the simplest case where we have a small set of candidate features and our aim is to find that subset which, when used to redescribe the instances, produces a tractable learning problem, i.e. one with non-neutral statistical properties. If we have n candidate features then we will have to search through all 2^n possible subsets of, them testing our learning algorithm against each one. If n is large this may be a very costly operation, especially since testing a particular subset involves first redescribing the instances in terms of the selected features and then running the learning algorithm.

But this is just the beginning of the complexity. In the case we looked at above, our

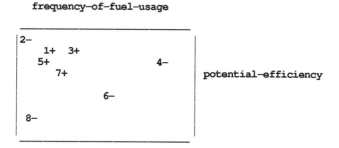

Figure 21.5. Clustering of instances in higher-level feature space.

features corresponded to functions that took complete instances and returned a particular 'feature value'. This is a simple case, but we might easily be dealing with functions that can be applied to instances in different ways. For example, if we have inputs such as

$$[0.3\ 0.4\ 0.2\ 0.8\ 0.7\ 0.8\ 0.1]$$

then we might have a function that computes the difference between two components. This function takes two arguments, i.e. it has to be applied to just two components of an input. If our inputs have n components then there are n^2 ways of applying the function. In considering all possibilities we really have to search through all ways of applying each potential feature as well as all possible ways of selecting a subset of features.

Just in case the complexity of this approach does not already appear to be completely unacceptable, consider the following. In the example described above we discovered that to find the required intra-class similarities we had to redescribe the instances in terms of a feature space based on the original attribute space. But in another example we might well find that we need to redescribe the instances in terms of a feature space based on the feature space based on the original attribute space. In fact we might find that we have to build an arbitrary number of feature spaces on top of the original attribute space before we arrive at a representation of the instances that yields up the required intra-class similarities in an exploitable form. Of course, when we come to consider the complexity of searching for the relevant feature constructions, we quickly obtain very large numbers indeed.[4]

We find, then, that searching naively for higher-level representations for a given input space is likely to be a costly operation — most probably too expensive to contemplate. The constructive induction methods such as cascade-correlation discussed in Chapter 16 seem to offer a solution to the problem, but much more research is needed to ascertain this for sure.

21.5. Concluding comments

The present chapter has been an attempt to pour a little cold water on the generally up beat approach taken in the rest of the book. The fact that we have concentrated heavily on *techniques* and *solutions* may have given the impression that computational learning is a magic trick with unbounded power. The lesson to be drawn from

---

[4] A complexity formula is given in Thornton (1990).

the present chapter is that this is categorically not the case.

As we have seen, computational learning involves the derivation of a representation of a target mapping. The complexity of the required representation depends on the distribution of inputs in input space. With some mappings — in particular, mappings where significant similarities are only visible at some higher level of description — this distribution is effectively random and the statistical properties of the training set are indistinguishable from noise.[5]

In this case, the representation required is likely to be very complex, to yield very little effective generalization and/or be extremely hard to derive. Attempting to bypass the problem by explicitly deriving new features (i.e. higher levels of description) is a highly combinatoric and usually intractable process. Thus, the general conclusion has to be that there is a fundamental limit to what *conventional* computational learning can achieve, and, in particular, that it may not be effective if the rule underlying the target mapping relates to similarities between features at a higher level of description, i.e. ones not explicitly evidenced in input vectors.

We may be able to finesse the problem in practice by *insisting* that input components describe the appropriate (i.e. similarity-bearing) properties of the underlying objects. But we can only push this so far. Sooner or later we will find ourselves in a situation where we cannot 'legislate' on the composition of our input data. Thus, whatever cheats we employ in the short term, in the long term we need a genuine theoretical solution to the problem of difficult target mappings. Given the amount of research currently taking place in computational learning and related topics, progress towards this goal may be relatively rapid. Or it may be infuriatingly slow. Only time will tell. In the meantime our best bet is — to keep on learning.

21.6. Further reading

Hinton and Sejnowski's (1986, pp. 290-292) chapter on the Boltzmann machine has a section on 'easy and hard learning' that discusses the significance of statistical order.

---

[5] Rendell and Cho (1990) describe this situation as being indicative of minimal *concentration*.

21.7. Problems

(1)   To what extent are real-world learning problems likely to involve learning to represent higher-order statistical properties? Justify your answer.

(2)   Try using back-propagation to learn a representation which maps any 20-dimensional binary vector containing two 1s separated by two 0s on to 1, and any other vector on to 0. Some examples of this input/output mapping are as follows:

```
<[0 0 0 0 0 0 0 1 0 0 1 0 0 0 0 0 0 0 0] [1]>
<[0 0 0 0 0 1 0 0 0 0 0 1 0 0 0 0 0 0 0] [0]>
<[0 0 0 0 0 0 0 0 0 0 0 0 0 0 0 1 0 0 1] [1]>
<[0 0 0 0 0 1 0 0 0 0 0 1 0 0 0 0 0 0 0] [0]>
<[0 1 0 0 0 0 0 0 0 0 0 1 0 0 0 0 0 0 0] [0]>
<[0 0 0 0 0 0 0 0 0 0 0 0 0 1 1 0 0 0 0] [0]>
<[0 1 0 0 0 0 0 0 0 0 0 0 0 0 0 0 0 1 0] [0]>
<[1 0 1 0 0 0 0 0 0 0 0 0 0 0 0 0 0 0 0] [0]>
<[0 1 0 0 1 0 0 0 0 0 0 0 0 0 0 0 0 0 0] [1]>
<[0 0 0 0 0 0 0 0 0 1 0 0 1 0 0 0 0 0 0] [1]>
```

Construct a Hinton diagram of the weights in the network and use this to analyse the representation. Is the representation an efficient one? Does it constitute a lookup table? Justify your answers.

REFERENCES

Aarts, E. and Korst, J. (1989). *Simulated Annealing and Boltzmann Machines*. Wiley.

Ackley, D., Hinton, G. and Sejnowski, T. (1985). A Learning Algorithm for Boltzmann Machines. *Cognitive Science*, *9*, 147-68.

Aleksander, I. and Burnett, P. (1987). *Thinking Machines: the Search for Artificial Intelligence*. Oxford: Oxford University Press.

Anderberg, M. (1973). *Cluster Analysis for Applications*. New York: Academic Press.

Anderson, J. and Hinton, G. (1981). Models of Information Processing in the Brain. In G. Hinton and J. Anderson (eds), *Parallel Models of Associative Memory*. Hillsdale, N.J.: Lawrence Erlbaum Associates.

Angluin, D. and Smith, C. (1983). Inductive Inference: Theory and Methods. *ACM Computing Surveys*, *15*, 3, 237-69.

Barrow, H. (1989). AI, Neural Networks and Early Vision. *AISB Quarterly*, 69, 6-25.

Beale, R. and Jackson, T. (1990). *Neural Computing: an Introduction*. Adam Hilger.

Bratko, I. and Lavrac, N. (eds) (1987). *Progress in Machine Learning*. Wilmslow: Sigma Press.

Bullock, A. and Woodings, R. (eds) (1983). *The Fontana Biographical Companion to Modern Thought fontana dictionary of modern thinkers)*. Fontana.

Bundy, A., Silver, B. and Plummer, D. (1985). An Analytical Comparison of Some Rule-Learning Programs. *Artificial Intelligence*, *27*, 2, 137-81.

Campbell, J. (1984). *Grammatical Man*. Harmondsworth: Penguin.

Chatfield, C. and Collins, A. (1980). *Introduction to Multivariate Analysis*. London: Chapman and Hall.

Clocksin, W. and Mellish, C. (1984). *Programming in Prolog edn)*. Berlin: Springer-Verlag.

Crick, F. and Asanuma, C. (1986). Certain Aspects of the Anatomy and Physiology of the Cerebral Cortex. In D. Rumelhart, J. McClelland and the PDP Research Group (eds), *Parallel Distributed Processing: Explorations in the Microstructures of Cognition. Vols I and II*. MIT Press.

Dayhoff, J. (1990). *Neural Network Architectures: an Introduction*. New York: Van Nostrand Reinhold.

DeJong, G. and Mooney, R. (1986). Explanation-based learning: An Alternative View. *Machine Learning*, *1*, 145-76.

Diamond, M., Scheibel, A. and Elson, L. (1985). *The Human Brain Coloring Book*.

New York: Barnes and Noble Books.

Dietterich, T., London, B., Clarkson, K. and Dromey, G. (1982). Learning and Inductive Inference. In P. Cohen and E. Feigenbaum (eds), *The Handbook of Artificial Intelligence: Vol III*. Los Altos: Kaufmann.

Dietterich, T. and Michalski, R. (1986). Learning to Predict Sequences. In R. Michalski, J. Carbonell and T. Mitchell (eds), *Machine Learning: an Artificial Intelligence Approach: Vol II*. Los Altos: Morgan Kaufmann.

Dretske, F. (1981). *Knowledge and the Flow of Information*. Oxford: Basil Blackwood.

Elman, J. (1989). Representation and Structure in Connectionist Models. CRL Technical Report 8903, San Diego: Center for Research in Language.

Everitt, B. (1974). *Cluster Analysis*. London: Heinemann.

Fahlman, S. and Lebiere, C. (1990). *The Cascade-Correlation Learning Architecture*. CMU-CS-90-100, School of Computer Science, Carnegie-Mellon University, Pittsburgh, PA 15213.

Fisher, D. (1987a). Knowledge Acquisition Via Incremental Conceptual Clustering. *Machine Learning*, 2, 2, 139-72, Boston: Kluwer Academic.

Fisher, D. (1987b). Conceptual Clustering, Learning from Examples and Inference. *Proceedings of the Fourth International Workshop on Machine Learning 22-25 university of california, irvine)*. Los Altos: Morgan Kaufmann.

Fisher, D. and Langley, P. (1985). Approaches to Conceptual Clustering. *Proceedings of the Ninth International Joint Conference on Artificial Intelligence: Vol II*. Los Altos: Morgan Kaufmann.

Fodor, J. and Pylyshyn, Z. (1988). Connectionism and Cognitive Architecture: A Critical Analysis. *Cognition, 28*, 3-71.

Forsyth, R. (1989). The Logic of Induction. In R. Forsyth (ed), *Machine Learning: Principles and Techniques*. London: Chapman and Hall.

Forsyth, R. and Rada, R. (1986). *Machine Learning: Applications in Expert Systems and Information Retrieval*. Chichester: Ellis Horwood.

Frean, M. (1989). *The Upstart Algorithm: a Method for Constructing and Training Feed-Forward Neural Networks*. Edinburgh Physics Preprint 89/479, Dept. of Physics, University of Edinburgh.

Gallant, S. (1986). Optimal Linear Discriminants. *Proceedings of the Eighth Conference on Pattern Recognition*.

Gardner, H. (1985). *The Mind's New Science*. New York: Basic Books.

Gennari, J., Langley, P. and Fisher, D. (1989). Models of Incremental Concept Formation. *Artificial Intelligence, 40*, 11-61.

Gold, E. (1967). Language Identification in the Limit. *Information and Control, 10*, 447-74.

Goldberg, D. (1989). *Genetic Algorithms in Search, Optimization, and Machine Learning*. Addison-Wesley.

Good, I. (1977). The Botryology of Botryology. In J. Van Ryzin (ed), *Classification and Clustering*. London: Academic Press.

Grossberg, S. (1976). Adaptive Pattern Classification and Universal Recoding: I. Parallel Development and Coding of Neural Feature Detectors. *Biological Cybernetics*, *23*, 121-34.

Hartley, R. (1928). Transmission of Information. *Bell System Technical Journal*, 535.

Haussler, D. (1988). Quantifying Inductive Bias: AI Learning and Valiant's Learning Framework. *Artificial Intelligence*, *36*, 177-221.

Hebb, D. (1949). *The Organization of Behavior*. New York: Wiley.

Hecht-Nielsen, R. (1990). *Neurocomputing*. Addison-Wesley.

Hertz, J., Krogh, A. and Palmer, R. (1991). *Introduction to the Theory of Neural Computation*. Lecture Notes Volume 1: Santa Fe Institute Studies in the Sciences of Complexity, Addison-Wesley.

Hilgard, E. and Bower, G. (1975). *Theories of Learning*. Englewood Cliffs, N.J.: Prentice Hall.

Hinton, G. (1977). Relaxation and its Role in Vision. Ph.D Thesis, University of Edinburgh.

Hinton, G. (1986). Learning Distributed Representations of Concepts. *Proceedings of the Eighth Annual Conference of the Cognitive Science Society*. Amherst, Mass.: Lawrence Erlbaum Associates.

Hinton, G. (1989). Connectionist Learning Procedures. *Artificial Intelligence*, *40*, 185-234.

Hinton, G. and Anderson, J. (eds) (1981). *Parallel Models of Associative Memory*. Hillsdale, N.J.: Lawrence Erlbaum Associates.

Hinton, G., Sejnowski, T. and Ackley, D. (1984). *Boltzmann Machines: Constraint Satisfaction Networks that Learn*. Technical Report CMU-CS-84-119, Carnegie-Mellon University.

Hinton, G., McClelland, J. and Rumelhaft, D. (1986). Distributed Representation. In D. Rumelhart, J. McClelland and the PDP Research Group (eds), *Parallel Distributed Processing: Explorations in the Microstructures of Cognition. Vols I and II*. Cambridge, Mass.: MIT Press.

Hinton, G. and Sejnowski, T. (1986). Learning and Relearning in Boltzmann Machines. In D. Rumelhart, J. McClelland and the PDP Research Group (eds), *Parallel Distributed Processing: Explorations in the Microstructures of Cognition. Vols I and II*. Cambridge, Mass.: MIT Press.

Holland, J., Holyoak, K., Nisbett, R. and Thagard, P. (1986). *Induction: Processes of Inference, Learning, and Discovery*. Cambridge, Mass.: MIT Press.

Hopfield, J. (1984). Neurons with Graded Response have Collective Computational Properties like those of Two-state Neurons. *Proceedings of the National Academy of Sciences*, *81*, 3088-3092.

Hopfield, J. (1982). Neural Networks and Physical Systems with Emergent Collective Computational Abilities. *Proceedings of the National Academy of Sciences*, *79*, 2554-8.

Hubel, D. (1979). The Brain. *Scientific American*, *241*, 44-53.

Hubel, D. and Wiesel, T. (1962). Receptive Fields, Binocular Interaction and

Functional Interaction and Functional Architecture of the Cat's Visual Cortex. *Journal of Physiology, 106.*

Hunt, E., Marin, J. and Stone, P. (1966). *Experiments in Induction.* New York: Academic Press.

Johnson, R. and Brown, C. (1988). *Cognizers: Neural Networks and Machines that Think.* New York: Wiley.

Jordan, M. (1986). An Introduction to Linear Algebra in Parallel Distributed Processing. In D. Rumelhart, J. McClelland and the PDP Research Group (eds), *Parallel Distributed Processing: Explorations in the Microstructures of Cognition. Vols I and II.* Cambridge, Mass.: MIT Press.

Judd, J. (1990). *Neural Network Design and the Complexity of Learning.* Cambridge, Mass.: The MIT Press.

Kirkpatrick, S., Gelatt, C. and Vecchi, M. (1983). Optimization by Simulated Annealing. *Science, 220,* 671-80.

Kohonen, T. (1989). Speech Recognition based on Topology-Preserving Neural Maps. In I. Aleksander (ed), *Neural Computing Architectures.* Cambridge, Mass.: MIT Press.

Kohonen, T. (1988a). The 'Neural' Phonetic Typewriter. *Computer, 21,* 3, 11-22.

Kohonen, T. (1988b). *Self-organization and Associative Memory edition).* New York: Springer-Verlag.

Kohonen, T. (1984). *Self-organization and Associative Memory.* Berlin: Springer-Verlag.

Kohonen, T. (1977). *Associative Memory: a System Theoretical Approach.* New York: Springer-Verlag.

Kohonen, T., Ojon, E. and Lehtio, D. (1981). Storage and Processing of Information in Distributed Associative Memory Systems. In G. Hinton and J. Anderson (eds), *Parallel Models of Associative Memory.* Hillsdale, N.J.: Lawrence Erlbaum Associates.

Kolmogorov, A.N. (1957). On the Representation of Continuous Functions of Many Variables by Superposition of Continuous Functions of One Variable and Additions. *Dokl. Akad. Nauk, 114,* 953.

Langley, P. and Carbonell, J. (1986). Machine Learning: Techniques and Foundations. Tutorial on Learning and Knowledge Acquisition at ECAI-86.

Langley, P., Simon, H., Bradshaw, G. and Zytkow, J. (1987). *Scientific Discovery: Computational Explorations of the Creative Processes.* Cambridge, Mass.: MIT Press.

Lashley, K. (1950). In Search of the Engram. *Society of Experimental Biology Symposium No. 4: Psychological Mechanisms in Animal Behaviour.* London: Cambridge University Press.

Lashley, K. (1929). *Brain Mechanisms and Intelligence.* Chicago: University of Chicago Press.

Le Cun, Y. (1985). A Learning Scheme for Assymetric Threshold Networks. *Proceedings Cognitiva.* Vol. 85, Paris.

Lebowitz, M. (1987). Experiments with Incremental Concept Formation: UNIMEM. *Machine Learning*, 2, 2, 103-38.

Lincoff, G. (1981). *The Audubon Society Field Guide to North American Mushrooms*. New York: Alfred A. Knopf.

Llewellyn, J. (1987). *Information and Coding*. Chartwell-Bratt.

Luria, A. (1973). *The Working Brain: an Introduction to Neuropsychology*. Penguin.

McClelland, J., Rumelhart, D. and Hinton, G. (1986). The Appeal of Parallel Distributed Processing. In D. Rumelhart, J. McClelland and the PDP Research Group (eds), *Parallel Distributed Processing: Explorations in the Microstructures of Cognition. Vols I and II*. Cambridge, Mass.: MIT Press.

McClelland, J. and Rumelhart, D. (1988). *Explorations in Parallel Distributed Processing: a Handbook of Models, Programs, and Exercises*. Cambridge, Mass.: MIT Press.

McCorduck, P. (1979). *Machines who Think: a Personal Inquiry into the History and Prospects of Artificial Intelligence*. New York: Freeman.

McCulloch, W. and Pitts, W. (1943). A Logical Calculus of the Ideas Immanent in Nervous Activity. *Bulletin of Mathematical Biophysics*, 5, 115-33.

McInerney, J., Haines, J., Biafore, K. and Hecht-Nielsen, R. (1989). Can Backpropagation Error Surfaces have Non-global Minima?. *Proceedings of the International Joint Conference on Neural Networks*. Vol. II, New York: IEEE Press.

Mezard, M. and Nadal, J. (1989). Learning in Feedforward Layered Networks: The Tiling Algorithm. *J. Phys. A: Math. Gen.*, 22, 2191-2203.

Michalski, R. (1986). Understanding the Nature of Learning: Issues and Research Directions. In R. Michalski, J. Carbonell and T. Mitchell (eds), *Machine Learning: an Artificial Intelligence Approach: Vol II*. Los Altos: Morgan Kaufmann.

Michalski, R. and Chilausky, R. (1980). Knowledge Acquisition by Encoding Expert Rules versus Computer Induction from Examples: A Case Study involving Soybean Pathology. *Int. J. Man-Machine Studies*, 12, 63-87.

Michalski, R. and Stepp, R. (1983). Learning from Observation: Conceptual Clustering. In R. Michalski, J. Carbonell and T. Mitchell (eds), *Machine Learning: an Artificial Intelligence Approach*. Palo Alto: Tioga.

Minsky, M. (1981). A Framework for Representing Knowledge. In J. Haugeland (ed), *Mind Design*. Cambridge, Mass.: The MIT Press (Originally Memo 306, AI lab, MIT).

Minsky, M. (1988). *The Society of Mind*. London: Pan.

Minsky, M. and Papert, S. (1969). *Perceptrons*. Cambridge, Mass.: MIT Press.

Minsky, M. and Papert, S. (1988). *Perceptrons: an Introduction to Computational Geometry* (expanded edn). Cambridge, Mass.: MIT Press.

Minton, S. and Carbonell, J. (1987). Strategies for Learning Search Control Rules: An Explanation-based Approach. *Proceedings of the Tenth International Joint Conference on Artificial Intelligence*. Los Altos: Morgan Kaufmann.

Mitchell, T. (1977). Version Spaces: A Candidate Elimination Approach to Rule Learning. *Proceedings of the Fifth International Joint Conference on Artificial*

Intelligence.

Mitchell, T. (1980). The Need for Bias in Learning Generalizations. Technical Report CBM-TR-117, Dept. of Computer Science, Rutgers University.

Mitchell, T., Utgoff, P. and Banerji, R. (1983). Learning by Experimentation: Acquiring and Modifying Problem-Solving Heuristics. In R. Michalski, J. Carbonell and T. Mitchell (eds), *Machine Learning: an Artificial Intelligence Approach.* Palo Alto: Tioga.

Mitchell, T., Keller, R. and Kedar-Cabelli, S. (1986). Explanation-Based Generalization: A Unifying View. *Machine Learning, 1,* 1, 47-80, Boston: Kluwer Academic.

Muggleton, S. (1987). Duce, An Oracle Based Approach to Constructive Induction. *Proceedings of the Tenth International Joint Conference on Artificial Intelligence.* Los Altos: Morgan Kaufmann.

Murray, K. (1987). Multiple Convergence: An Approach to Disjunctive Concept Acquisition. *Proceedings of the Tenth International Joint Conference on Artificial Intelligence.* Los Altos: Morgan Kaufmann.

Nilsson, N. (1982). *Principles of Artificial Intelligence.* Berlin: Springer-Verlag.

Nyquist, H. (1924). Certain Factors Affecting Telegraph Speed. *Bell System Technical Journal,* 324.

Parker, D. (1982). Learning Logic. Invention Report S81-64, File 1, Stanford, CA: Office of Technology, Stanford University.

Penfield, W. and Jasper, H. (1954). *Epilepsy and the Functional Anatomy of the Human Brain.* Little.

Peterson, C. and Hartman, E. (1989). Explorations of the Mean Field Theory Learning Algorithm. *Neural Networks, 2,* 475-94.

Pinker, S. and Prince, A. (1988). On Language and Connectionism: Analysis of a Parallel Distributed Processing Model of Language Acquisition. *Cognition, 28,* 73-193.

Quinlan, J. (1983). Learning Efficient Classification Procedures and their Application to Chess End Games. In R. Michalski, J. Carbonell and T. Mitchell (eds), *Machine Learning: an Artificial Intelligence Approach.* Palo Alto: Tioga.

Quinlan, J. (1986). Induction of Decision Trees. *Machine Learning, 1,* 81-106.

Rendell, L. (1986). A General Framework for Induction and a Study of Selective Induction. *Machine Learning, 1,* 1, 177-226.

Rendell, L. and Cho, H. (1990). Empirical Learning as a Function of Concept Character. *Machine Learning, 5,* 267-98.

Romesburg, H. (1984). *Cluster Analysis for Researchers.* London: Wadsworth.

Rosenblatt, F. (1962). *Principles of Neurodynamics.* New York: Spartan Books.

Rumelhart, D., Hinton, G. and Williams, R. (1986a). Learning Representations by Back-propagating Errors. *Nature, 323,* 533-6.

Rumelhart, D., Hinton, G. and Williams, R. (1986b). Learning Internal Representations by Error Propagation. In D. Rumelhart, J. McClelland and the PDP Research Group (eds), *Parallel Distributed Processing: Explorations in the*

Microstructures of Cognition. Vols I and II. Cambridge, Mass.: MIT Press.

Rumelhart, D., Smolensky, P., McClelland, J. and Hinton, G. (1986c). Schemata and Sequential Thought Processes in PDP Models. In D. Rumelhart, J. McClelland and the PDP Research Group (eds), *Parallel Distributed Processing: Explorations in the Microstructures of Cognition. Vols I and II.* Cambridge, Mass.: MIT Press.

Rumelhart, D. and McClelland, J. (1986). On Learning the Past Tenses of English Verbs. In D. Rumelhart, J. McClelland and the PDP Research Group (eds), *Parallel Distributed Processing: Explorations in the Microstructures of Cognition. Vols I and II.* Cambridge, Mass.: MIT Press.

Rumelhart, D. and Zipser, D. (1986). Feature Discovery by Competitive Learning. In D. Rumelhart, J. McClelland and the PDP Research Group (eds), *Parallel Distributed Processing: Explorations in the Microstructures of Cognition. Vol I.* Cambridge, Mass.: MIT Press.

Russell, B. (1946). *History of Western Philosophy.* London: George Allen & Unwin.

Samuel, A. (1967). Some Studies of Machine Learning Using the Game of Checkers: Part II. *IBM Journal of Research and Development, 11*, 601-17.

Samuel, A. (1959). Some Studies of Machine Learning Using the Game of Checkers. *IBM Journal of Research and Development, 3.*

Searle, J. (1984). *Minds, Brains and Science: the 1984 Reith Lectures.* London: BBC Publications.

Searle, J. (1980). Minds, Brains and Programs [with Peer Commentaries]. *Behavioural and Brain Sciences*, 3, 417-57.

Sejnowski, T. and Rosenberg, C. (1987). Parallel Networks that Learn to Pronounce English Text. *Complex Systems, 1*, 145-68.

Shannon, C. and Weaver, W. (1949). *The Mathematical Theory of Information.* Urbana: University of Illinois Press.

Simon, H. (1983). Why Should Machines Learn?. In R. Michalski, J. Carbonell and T. Mitchell (eds), *Machine Learning: an Artificial Intelligence Approach.* Palo Alto: Tioga.

Smith, E. and Medin, D. (1981). *Categories and Concepts.* Cambridge, Mass.: Harvard University Press.

Smolensky, P. (1986). Information Processing in Dynamical Systems: Foundations of Harmony Theory. In D. Rumelhart, J. McClelland and the PDP Research Group (eds), *Parallel Distributed Processing: Explorations in the Microstructures of Cognition. Vol I.* Cambridge, Mass.: MIT Press.

Sokal, R. (1977). Clustering and Classification: Background and Current Directions. In J. Van Ryzin (ed), *Classification and Clustering.* London: Academic Press.

Sowa, J. (1984). *Conceptual Structures: Information in Mind and Machine.* Reading, Mass.: Addison-Wesley.

Stepp, R. and Michalski, R. (1986). Conceptual Clustering: Inventing Goal-Oriented Classifications of Structured Objects. In R. Michalski, J. Carbonell and T. Mitchell (eds), *Machine Learning: an Artificial Intelligence Approach: Vol II.*

Los Altos: Morgan Kaufmann.

Stonham, T., Wilkie, B. and Aleksander, I. (1982). Computer Vision Systems for Industry: WISARD and the Like. *Digital Systems for Industrial Automation, 1*, 4.

Sutton, R. (1986). Two Problems with Back-Propagation and other Steepest-Descent Learning Procedures for Networks. *Proceedings of the Eighth Annual Conference of the Cognitive Science Society*. Lawrence Erlbaum Associates.

Thompson, B. and Thompson, W. (1986). Finding Rules in Data. *Byte, 11*, 12, 149-58.

Thornton, C. (1990). The Complexity of Constructive Induction. DAI Research Paper No. 463, University of Edinburgh, Dept. of Artificial Intelligence.

Thornton, C. (1989). Learning Mechanisms Which Construct Neighbourhood Representations. *Connection Science, 1*, 1, 69-85.

Utgoff, P. (1986a). Shift of Bias for Inductive Concept Learning. In R. Michalski, J. Carbonell and T. Mitchell (eds), *Machine Learning: an Artificial Intelligence Approach: Vol II*. Los Altos: Morgan Kaufmann.

Utgoff, P. (1986b). *Machine Learning of Inductive Bias*. Kluwer International Series in Engineering and Computer Science, Vol. 15, Kluwer Academic.

Utgoff, P. and Mitchell, T. (1982). Acquisition of appropriate bias for inductive concept learning. *Proceedings of the Second National Conference on Artificial Intelligence*.

Valiant, L. (1985). Learning Disjunctions of Conjunctions. *Proceedings of the Ninth International Joint Conference on Artificial Intelligence*. Los Altos: Morgan Kaufmann.

Valiant, L. (1984). A Theory of the Learnable. *Communications of the ACM, 27*, 1134-42.

Vogt, W., Nagel, D. and Sator, H. (1987). *Cluster Analysis in Clinical Chemistry: a Model*. Chichester: Wiley.

von der Malsburg, C. (1973). Self-Organization of Orientation Sensitive Cells in the Striate Cortex. *Kybernetik, 14*, 85-100.

Wasserman, P. (1989). *Neural Computing: Theory and Practice*. New York: Van Nostrand Reinhold.

Werbos, P. (1974). Beyond Regression: New Tools for Prediction and Analysis in the Behavioural Sciences. Master's Thesis, Harvard University.

Wielemaker, J. and Bundy, A. (1985). *Altering the Description Space for Focussing*. DAI Research Paper 262, University of Edinburgh.

Willshaw, D. (1981). Holography, Associative Memory, and Inductive Generalization. In G. Hinton and J. Anderson (eds), *Parallel Models of Associative Memory*. Hillsdale, N.J.: Lawrence Erlbaum Associates.

Winograd, T. (1972). *Understanding Natural Language*. New York: Academic Press.

Winston, P. (1970). Learning Structural Descriptions from Examples. AI-TR-231, Ph.D Thesis, Cambridge, Mass.: MIT AI Lab.

Winston, P. (1984). *Artificial Intelligence* (second edn). Reading, Mass.: Addison-Wesley.

Winston, P. (1975). Learning Structural Descriptions from Examples. In P. Winston (ed), *The Psychology of Computer Vision*. Mcgraw-Hill.

Wirth, J. and Catlett, J. (1988). Experiments on the Costs and Benefits of Windowing in ID3. In J. Laird (ed), *Proceedings of the Fifth International Conference on Machine Learning*. Los Altos: Morgan Kaufmann.

Young, R., Plotkin, G. and Linz, R. (1977). Analysis of an extended concept-learning task. In R. Eddy (ed), *Proceedings of the Fifth International Joint Conference on Artificial Intelligence*.

Index